SAUNDERS BOOKS IN PSYCHOLOGY

LEWIS F. PETRINOVICH and ROBERT D. SINGER, *Consulting Editors*

CURTIS D. HARDYCK

Associate Professor of Educational Psychology
University of California
Berkeley, California

LEWIS F. PETRINOVICH

Chairman and Professor of Psychology
University of California
Riverside, California

W. B. SAUNDERS COMPANY

Introduction to
STATISTICS for the
BEHAVIORAL SCIENCES

Philadelphia London Toronto 1969

W. B. Saunders Company; West Washington Square
Philadelphia, Pa. 19105

12 Dyott Street
London, W.C. 1

1835 Yonge Street
Toronto 7, Ontario

Introduction to Statistics for the Behavioral Sciences

PREFACE:
TO THE STUDENT

This book is designed for the student with a limited background in mathematics. The student with a mathematics background has been given the opportunity to explore the concepts and techniques of inferential statistics in more detail than is allowed in most texts written for individuals with no mathematical background.

The book evolves from the authors' experience in teaching introductory courses in statistics and from a dissatisfaction with current texts. In our experience most textbooks tend either to emphasize the mathematical aspects of statistical theory at the expense of application or to require that the student learn formulas without understanding the underlying logic on which the formulas are based.

We have some strong preconceptions regarding how statistics should be taught at the introductory level. We think it especially important to communicate the basic logic underlying the statistical methods to be used. We believe the student should understand the logic on which statistical theory is based before he attempts to understand the mathematical proofs underlying statistical inference. Ideally, of course, the student should understand the basic mathematics of statistical theory. However, we believe that a grasp of the mathematical bases on which statistics is based is not necessary to understand adequately the basic concepts of statistics.

The organization of this book differs considerably from the organization of most statistics texts. Its opening chapters are customarily encountered in the middle of elementary statistics texts—at least texts in the behavioral sciences. In addition, much of the material concerning descriptive statistics which is usually included has been omitted entirely, or else has been relegated to an appendix. Our reasons for placing such material in an appendix, or for omitting it altogether, stem from our experience in teaching introductory statistics courses. We have had the experience of spending hours explaining the calculation of such things as percentiles and percentile ranks only to find that the students have become confused with a mass of concrete details—and have lost sight of the important reasons for learning statistics. Since such things as the computation of percentiles and percentile ranks play relatively little part in inferential statistics, we have chosen not to present this material in order to more effectively develop the logic of statistical inference.

The specialized topics included in this book represent our bias about the most essential concepts for the student to know. The text emphasizes the use of statistics in experimentation. In our opinion, statistics should not be taught either as pure theory or as a calculating routine. It should be taught, rather, as a branch of applied mathematics used to solve problems in the real world. The purpose of a course in applied statistics is to assist an individual to perform and to understand scientific investigations. We have tried to emphasize this (to the exclusion of other topics) in the belief that the student and his academic discipline will be better served if there is a clear use and an immediate purpose for the statistics which he is learning. Computational problems have been keyed to the text throughout, and they will aid in developing an understanding of the material presented. They will also serve as an indicator of whether or not the material has been comprehended adequately enough to be used in a meaningful context.

We are indebted to the Literary Executor of the late Sir Ronald Fisher, F.R.S., to Dr. Frank Yates, F.R.S., and to Oliver and Boyd Ltd., Edinburgh, for permission to reprint Table A-9 from their book *Statistical Tables for Biological, Agricultural and Medical Research*.

The preparation of this book could not have been done without the assistance of many people. We are particularly grateful to Jane Rose, Judith Walter, and Gail Hicks, who typed and corrected innumerable drafts and revisions, to Katherine Eardley, who drew the illustrations for the final copy, and to Dr. Robert Singer, who read portions of a preliminary version.

CURTIS D. HARDYCK AND LEWIS F. PETRINOVICH

CONTENTS

Chapter 1

INTRODUCTION 1

Chapter 2

FUNDAMENTAL CONCEPTS 5

Chapter 3

THE ESTIMATION OF CENTRAL TENDENCY 25

Chapter 4

ESTIMATION OF VARIABILITY 43

Chapter 5

PROBABILITY AND THE NORMAL CURVE 67

Chapter 6

NORMAL CURVE MODELS: PRECISION OF ESTIMATE 89

Chapter 7

DIFFERENCES BETWEEN TWO GROUPS 107

Chapter 8

ANALYSIS OF VARIANCE 135

Chapter 9

CHI-SQUARE AND PROPORTIONS 155

Chapter 10

DISTRIBUTION-FREE METHODS 173

Chapter 11

REGRESSION 189

Chapter 12

CORRELATION 203

Chapter 13

SOME APPLICATIONS TO EXPERIMENTAL PSYCHOLOGY 227

Appendices

APPENDIX I—*Coding Scores for Hand Calculation* 247

APPENDIX II—*Statistical Tables* 255

APPENDIX III—*Answers to Odd-numbered Exercises* 291

SUMMARY OF ARITHMETICAL RULES 295

INDEX 299

1

INTRODUCTION

Statistics in Everyday Life

Today, statistics permeate the atmosphere in which we live. National political figures concern themselves with the statistics of public opinion to the extent that they retain full-time pollsters to maintain a constant check on the ebb and flow of public opinion. Daily news reports are filled with comments about "Dow-Jones Averages," average gross national product, and so forth. The weather report in many sections of the country is given in terms of crude probability figures: "The chances are eight out of ten that it will rain tomorrow." Anyone living in contemporary society is surrounded by statistics, and the advantages gained from at least an elementary understanding of the bases of these calculations is justification enough for learning statistics and for understanding statistical concepts.

In modern society a knowledge of statistical concepts and an ability to think in statistical terms are, perhaps, the best safeguards against being tricked into making foolish decisions on the basis of impressive advertising slogans calculated to mislead a prospective buyer. Perhaps the most cogent presentation of these uses (and abuses) of statistics is given by Darrell Huff in his book *How to Lie with Statistics.** Huff's book is recommended for any student who is interested in discovering the extent to which such misuses of statistics exist in our everyday life.

---

* Huff, D.: *How to Lie with Statistics*; New York: Norton, 1954.

In these days, when an impressive set of statistics is often used as an argument for purchasing a given commodity, a knowledge of some of the basic concepts involved in deriving simple statistical measures is one of the best safeguards against being sold the contemporary equivalent of the medicine man's snake oil cure-all.

Uses of Statistics in the Behavioral Sciences

Anyone preparing for a career in the behavioral sciences must understand statistical methods in order to comprehend the basic research literature in his field. Almost all conclusions concerning experimental data or survey results are based on statistical tests. If one is to understand how these conclusions are reached and is to be able to critically evaluate them, then it is essential that the logical steps involved in arriving at these conclusions be understood. Individuals in applied fields must have a knowledge of statistical principles to enable them to understand and to evaluate the research reports relevant to their interests. The research worker must have a thorough knowledge of statistics if he is to design experiments and to evaluate the results of such experiments.

In the behavioral sciences data are gathered to resolve questions regarding substantive issues. The experimenter who gathers such data must begin with a careful consideration of the types of statistical methods he is going to apply to the data in order that the measurements he makes are in the proper form to permit the intended analysis. On the basis of these statistical analyses the experimenter usually decides whether or not his observed outcomes could reasonably be expected on the basis of chance variability. If he decides that the differences, or the relationships, could have been due to chance he will conclude, essentially, that his experimental manipulations did not result in an effect that could be detected with his procedures and measuring instruments.

Methods of Teaching Statistics

There have been two primary approaches to teaching statistics. One approach is to present the material in a cook book form. The formulas and the statistics are interpreted for the student much as a recipe in a cook book is interpreted. The student is shown how to take various ingredients (defined by a set of symbols) and how to mix them into a recipe (the formula). If the recipe is followed closely enough a successful dish (calculation) will be the outcome. This approach has the advantage that almost any student can master at least the basic computational rules. However, even the good student is prepared by this teaching method only to plug a set of numbers into formulas and to mechanically solve those problems with which he has had some prior experience and instruction. The ability to apply the logic of statistical techniques to problems not previously encountered tends to be lacking in students taught by this approach.

The other conventional approach produces a much better trained individual and certainly improves the student's level of comprehension of statistical methods. At the same time, however, it demands much more of him. Here, the underlying logic of statistical method is presented by means of mathematical proofs, algebraic demonstrations, and extended abstract accounts. The student is usually assumed to have the mathematical background sufficient to understand such material (a situation which greatly limits the audience to which such a text can be addressed). Alternatively, an attempt can be made to present both the underlying logic and the mathematical bases of statistics in such a way that only the simplest knowledge of algebra is required. In our opinion this is a difficult if not impossible task.

We believe that still another approach can be fruitful. Modern computing methods and the availability of digital computers have made it possible to demonstrate by concrete examples what earlier could only be shown mathematically. In this text we will demonstrate basic principles using computer techniques and will relate these principles to mathematical statistical theory. This approach will result in a minimum of mathematical explanation and algebraic derivation, and, at the same time, make it possible to present the logic of statistical inference in a comprehensible manner.

Suggestions to the Student

At this point, we would like to make two suggestions to the student who will be using this text. First, we suggest that you keep in mind that statistical theory is a well integrated set of principles and postulates. At times you will be asked to accept certain statements without proof until explanation can proceed to a point where the logic of the statements can be demonstrated. We have adopted this approach rather than attempt to present the entire basis of statistical theory in the initial stages. We will warn you of situations where you are asked to accept something temporarily without proof. Similarly, you will be warned when the relationships among certain concepts might not yet be clear. You should understand the basic principles of statistical theory and the logic involved in making inferences by the time you finish this book. If you are unwilling to take some things on faith and wish to know the nature of the relationships that are presented to you, the necessary references to obtain a more complete understanding are provided in the text, but this will demand a great deal of effort on your part.

The second consideration involves the differentiation of statistics and pure mathematics. If your experience is similar to that of the majority of students taking a statistics course for the first time, your expectations are probably determined by the courses you have taken in mathematics—whether high school algebra, college algebra, or introductory mathematics. In short, you may expect a simple, exact, and straightforward solution to a problem once you understand the mechanics and rationale by which the solution can be obtained. Unfortunately, statistics is not this simple. Statistical methods require the application of mathematical techniques to problems in the real world (such as the interpretation of data collected in a scientific experiment), and require both the elements of mathematical procedure and of human judgment. Consequently, you must accept the idea that, after finishing a set of statistical calculations according to a set of prescribed rules, you must exercise a degree of subjective judgment and make reference to arbitrary conventions agreed upon by statisticians in order to interpret your results. This sequence of events will occur over and over again in the material you will encounter in this course. We cannot emphasize too strongly that statistics is a branch of mathematics applied to problems of the real world. If you limit your statistical work to events in which you can be guided by rules or equations, you will find that you are limiting yourself to a clerical, or at the most, to a primitive descriptive function.

The primary use of statistical methods in the behavioral sciences is to evaluate the results of experiments and to provide guidelines for the experimenter to interpret the results. Accordingly, a heavy emphasis has been placed on experimentation and data collection, as well as on the process of interpreting statistics and making inferences on the basis of these statistics.

2

FUNDAMENTAL
CONCEPTS

In this chapter some of the basic concepts and assumptions of statistical theory will be presented and briefly developed. The sequence of topics to be presented follows a logical sequence, although the student must temporarily accept some basic premises on faith, rather than learning the underlying justification at this time. The material to be presented in this chapter is basic to the understanding of statistical methods and will be referred to time and time again. Consequently, effort spent in understanding the material in this chapter will be well repaid in terms of time and effort saved in later chapters. Three fundamental concepts will be introduced: *random sampling*, the *normal curve*, and *probability*. In addition, some aspects of their interrelationships will be presented.

Measurements and Observations

Assume that we have a set of *observations* represented by numbers. These *observations* (the term we will use throughout the text to refer to any numerical measurement or score) could represent a variety of things: the heights or weights of people of a certain age and sex; the incomes earned by people in a given profession; or the test scores in a scholarship examination. Suppose that we have 1000 observations. If we were to take these 1000 numbers and place them

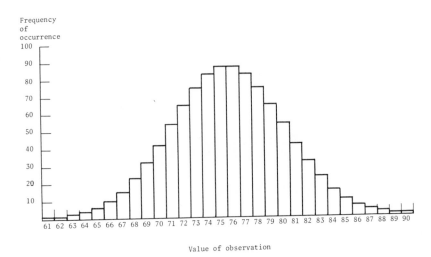

Figure 2–1. Normal distribution of 1000 observations.

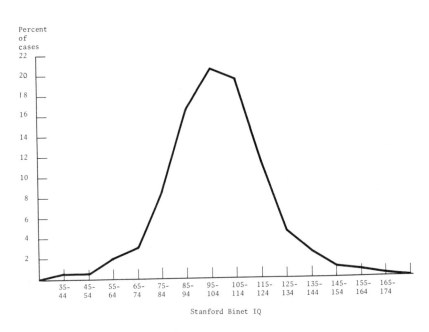

Figure 2–2. Stanford-Binet IQ's of 2904 unselected children between the ages of two and eighteen. (From *Measuring Intelligence* by L. M. Terman and M. A. Merrill. Copyright 1937, by Houghton Mifflin Company and reprinted with their permission.)

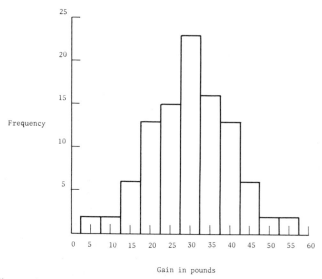

Frequency

Gain in pounds

Figure 2–3. Graphical representation of array of 100 normally distributed gains in weight of pigs. (Reproduced by permission from *Statistical Methods*, 5th edition, by George W. Snedecor, © 1956 by The Iowa State University Press.)

on a graph with the values of the numbers arranged from the lowest to the highest along the horizontal axis and the frequency with which they occur along the vertical axis, we would construct a graph such as is shown in Figure 2–1. As a matter of fact if these numbers represented any of a variety of observations in the real world, we would expect them to be distributed in a shape similar to the observations in Figure 2–1.

There may well be some skepticism as to whether real observations do look anything like those in Figure 2–1. Figure 2–2 represents scores on one of the standard tests of intelligence, the Stanford-Binet, and Figure 2–3 represents the weight gain of 100 pigs over a period of 20 days. These rather different examples are presented to emphasize the point that a wide variety of observations in the real world may look very similar to the demonstration set of 1000 numbers.

Populations

Examination of Figure 2–1 reveals, first of all, that there is a considerable range of values (from 61 to 90) and that some of these numbers occur much more frequently than do others. If these 1000

GRAPHICAL METHODS

The conventional method of graphing observations is to represent the values of the observations along the horizontal axis or *abscissa*, and the frequency with which observations occur along the vertical axis or *ordinate*. Figures 2–1, 2–2, and 2–3 represent three possible variations in graphical representation.

Figures 2–1 and 2–3 are *histograms*—a type of graphical representation in which the height of a bar is used to represent the frequency with which a given value occurs. Figure 2–2 is a *frequency polygon*. In this type of graphical representation points are placed to indicate the frequency of occurrence of given values and these points are then connected by lines. Such a method provides a continuous line enclosing the observations. The basic principle underlying all methods is the same—a change in area or size is used to represent the frequency with which a given value occurs.

Note that Figures 2–1, 2–2, and 2–3 also differ in the arrangement of the values along the horizontal axis. These units are known as class intervals. In Figure 2–1, the size of the class interval is 1, for Figure 2–2, the class interval is 10, and for Figure 2–3, the class interval is 5.

What determines the number of class intervals? This is largely arbitrary, since the nature of the scores to be grouped must be taken into consideration. Too fine a grouping destroys the purpose of grouping scores and too coarse a grouping will tend to lose information. In general, 10 to 15 intervals are usually satisfactory. As far as the question of where to start class limits can be answered, one approach is to have the lower limit of each class interval divisible by the class interval, *i*. However, this is a suggestion, not a rule. Note that Figures 2–2 and 2–3 do not use this approach.

In statistical terminology, the class intervals we have used are in terms of working limits. The theoretical limits for the lowest interval of Figure 2–1 are 60.5 to 61.5. This means that the interval theoretically encompasses all values within the range 60.5 to 61.5. Keep in mind that these are the limits in the mathematical sense and that the working limits run from 61 to 62.

numbers represented all the scores of students in a small college on a scholarship examination, we would have what is known in statistics as a *population*. A population, in statistical terminology, is the total number of all possible observations of the same type. For example, the United States census figures define certain characteristics of the entire population of the United States. Within this population another population can exist, say of all 36 year-old bald-headed men with one artificial leg. Similarly, all the students at a college at a certain time constitute the population of that college at that time.

What are the essential characteristics of the population of numerical observations (which we will now consider to be scholarship examination scores) shown in Figure 2–1? One essential characteristic is the shape of the distribution of the scores when they are graphed as in Figure 2–1.

For this set of scores, the *distribution* (which is the statistical term for the arrangement of the observations along the scale of measurement) is symmetrical about a central point, tapering off gradually with fewer and fewer observations at the extremes. In appearance, the shape of this distribution somewhat resembles a bell, being very similar in appearance to a distribution known as the *normal curve* (about which much will be said later). Another important characteristic of this distribution is the most representative score—the one number used to represent the value of all the observations. One such representative score is the *arithmetic mean*, which is obtained by summing the numerical values of all of the observations and then dividing that sum by the number of observations. For our example, the arithmetic mean would be equal to $\dfrac{75,500}{1000} = 75.5$. Still another essential characteristic is the degree of variability—the extent to which the scores scatter or disperse around this most representative score.

Representativeness of Information: Samples

One of the principal concerns of statistics is the representativeness of the information at hand concerning characteristics of the population. If you are fortunate enough to be able to collect information on all the members of a population, then you need have no fear about the representativeness of your information; every possible case is represented in the study. For example, the Bureau of the Census does not need to worry whether its statements about the average number of children per family in the population of the United States are correct, since this information is based on the entire U.S. population; in other words, there is no estimation required. To take another example, if you wish to know how students at a certain college perform on a certain type of national scholarship examination and if you are able to give the test to every student in the college, then you need not be concerned about estimating how well students can do since you have collected all the information possible. However, in all but a very few types of statistical investigations, measurement of the entire population is not possible. Usually you must settle for some estimate based on testing a few classes or sets of students selected along such lines as academic major, and then you must estimate from their scores how well all the students in the college would be expected to do. In all but a few situations you must settle for some very small estimate of the total population and must make an inference about the characteristics of the total population from the small number of cases actually studied. Those members of the population which are actually tested and on whose results the characteristics of the population can be estimated are known in statistics as a *sample*.

RANDOM SELECTION

There are certain requirements or rules in statistics which should be observed when obtaining a sample. These requirements serve the same basic function as the rules in certain types of games; they must be followed if you are to be able to complete the game satisfactorily. The first rule to be considered is that of *random selection. Random selection requires that every member of a population have an equal chance of being selected in a sample.*

At this point we have defined what is meant in statistics by a population and by a sample. We have also indicated that samples are used to estimate the characteristics of a population under conditions where not everyone in the population can be measured. If a sample is to accurately represent a population, every member of that population should have an equal chance of being chosen in the sample.

An example of this procedure can be demonstrated with Figure 2–1. Assume that the distribution of 1000 observations represents the scores of college students on a scholarship examination. In order to draw a random sample from this population, we will arbitrarily assign identification numbers to each student. We will assign the student who received the lowest score (a value of 61) the identification number of 0001. The student with the next higher score (62) would have an identifying number of 0002. Since two students received scores of 63, it does not matter to which one we assign identification number 0003 and to which we assign 0004. The rest of the identification numbers are assigned such that succeeding numbers are assigned to students with increasingly higher test scores. Table 2–1 is a list of identification numbers and test scores for our entire population of 1000 scores.

When all the subjects in the population have been identified in this fashion, we can draw a random sample. To do this we use the table of random numbers (see Table A–1, p. 256). To select a sample of ten students we enter the table at any point we wish. Since our identification numbers run from 0001 to 1000, we can either read four numbers or let 000 stand for 1000 and read three numbers. Since the time needed to draw a random sample by selecting three digits will be considerably less, we will use this option. We will begin at the top of page 260 and read the first three numbers— 976, and thus select subject 0976 as our first observation for sample 1. Moving down the column to the next three digits, we find the value of 116 and select subject 0116. Since all of our subject identification numbers have at least one leading zero, it does no harm to the principle of random selection to drop the first zero and say that the value of 000, should it appear in the table, will be used to select subject number 1000. The primary consideration in random selection is to make sure that every subject in the population has an equal chance of being selected.

Five samples of ten observations each which have been sampled from the population of 1000 observations are shown in Table 2–2. The identification numbers of the subjects drawn in each of five samples are listed. Note that subject 0143 appears both in sample 1 and in sample 2. This is not an error; in true random sampling each observation is returned to the population as soon as it is selected. Thus it is theoretically possible for the same observation to appear in more than one sample or even to appear more than once in the same sample. This method of sampling is called random sampling

Table 2-1. Identification Numbers and Test Scores for 1000 Students.

0001	61	0256		0939	
		↓	73	↓	83
0002	62	0330		0961	
0003	63	0331		0692	
		↓	74	↓	84
0004	63	0413		0976	
0005*		0414		0977	
↓	64	↓	75	↓	85
0008		0500		0986	
0009		0501		0987	
↓	65	↓	76	↓	86
0014		0587		0992	
0015		0588		0993	
↓	66	↓	77	↓	87
0024		0670		0996	
0025		0671		0997	88
↓	67	↓	78		
0039		0745		0998	88
0040		0746		0999	89
↓	68	↓	79		
0062		0810		1000	90
0063		0811			
↓	69	↓	80		
0094		0864			
0095		0865			
↓	70	↓	81		
0136		0906			
0137		0907			
↓	71	↓	82		
0190		0938			
0191					
↓	72				
0255					

* Subjects 0005 through 0008 all have scores of 64. The same convention applies to all ↓ groupings.

with replacement. Usually in actual experimentation this requirement is not observed since each subject is allowed to appear in only one condition. Therefore, the usual sampling procedure is not truly random, but is, rather, random sampling without replacement. This violation of the truly random procedure does affect the chances of subsequent cases being drawn, but if the number of cases in the

Table 2–2. IDENTIFICATION NUMBERS AND SCORES FOR FIVE RANDOM SAMPLES, DRAWN FROM TABLE 2–1.

					Sample				
1		2		3		4		5	
ID#	Score	ID#	Score	ID#	Score	ID#	Score	ID#	Score
0143	71	0590	77	0033	67	0719	78	0326	73
0942	83	0781	79	0216	72	0869	81	0749	79
0071	69	0323	73	0029	67	0515	76	0947	83
0416	75	0949	83	0493	75	0117	70	0631	77
0234	72	0085	69	0024	67	0904	81	0936	82
0421	75	0143	71	0947	83	0969	84	0887	81
0420	75	0359	74	0783	79	0854	80	0801	79
0967	84	0001	61	0790	79	0244	72	0444	75
0238	72	0091	69	0855	80	0763	79	0524	76
0580	76	0046	68	0727	78	0982	85	0356	74

population is quite large (as is usually true) the effect of non-replacement is so small that it is of no practical significance.

The locations of the observations sampled are shown in Figure 2–4 for the first two samples. The numbers along the baseline indicate the scale values. The dotted rectangles indicate the locations of the observations for sample 1. The black rectangles indicate the locations of the observations for sample 2. As can be seen, the observations are spread throughout the entire population. As is evident from Figure 2–4, a sample is *not* a miniature replica of a population. Therefore, when decisions about a population are based on a sample it is necessary to make allowance for the role of chance.

Arithmetic Mean

As was mentioned earlier, we draw samples in order to make the best possible decision about the characteristics of a population. The average value (or central location) of a set of observations is one of the things we frequently want to know. For example, one average, the *arithmetic mean*, is calculated by adding up all the observations and dividing that sum by the total number of

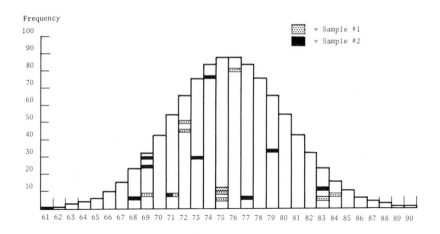

Figure 2–4. Location of two sets of sample observations within a population drawn by random selection.

observations. To determine the arithmetic mean, for our total population of 1000 scores, we would add up all the observations and divide this sum by 1000. The sum of our 1000 observations is 75,500. When this sum is divided by 1000 the mean value of 75.5 is obtained. If we could follow this procedure every time we wanted to know the average of a population, sampling would not be necessary. However, in most circumstances we have only samples and must infer from these sample values what the values are for the the total population. If we now take the two samples drawn earlier (Table 2–1 and Figure 2–4) and calculate the mean for each set of ten observations, we can compare these values with the population value and observe how close we come to the actual population mean using samples of only ten observations.

For sample 1, the sum of the scores is 752 and the mean is 75.2. For sample 2, the sum is 724 and the mean is 72.4. When we compare these values to the actual population mean of 75.5, we can see that although neither sample estimates it precisely we have come quite close using only ten observations. In Figure 2–5 this is depicted graphically.

If we look closely at sample 2 we can readily understand why its mean is so low. By chance the lowest observation in the population, 61, was one of the values selected randomly. This value was

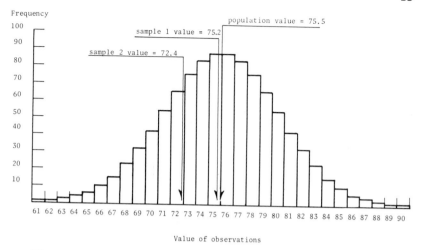

Figure 2–5. Accuracy of two sample means based on ten observations estimating the mean of a population of 1000 observations.

not balanced by a correspondingly high observation (which would be a value of 90). Therefore, the mean for this sample (72.4) is quite a bit lower than the population mean of 75.5.

Statistical Inference

When we are drawing different samples from the same population we should be aware that samples vary by chance. On some occasions (as with sample 2) an extremely infrequent value in one tail of the distribution will be drawn and will not be balanced by a comparably infrequent value in the other tail. This will result in the sample mean being located away from the population mean and toward the tail from which the infrequent score is drawn. It is possible, under conditions of random sampling, to have many of the observations drawn from only one side of the distribution. For example, all the cases selected could be above the population mean. Such a sample would not provide an accurate estimate of the population mean.

Using estimates of the characteristics of a population to infer the actual characteristics of the population is the process of statistical inference. If we do not know the value of the population arithmetic mean, the best estimate we can make is the mean of a sample drawn from the population by random methods. Similarly, the best estimate of the degree of variability of the population scores around the arithmetic mean is the variability of the sample observations around the arithmetic mean of the sample.

The extent to which we can accurately estimate a population *parameter* (the term used to define a statistic calculated on an entire population), such as the arithmetic mean, on the basis of a sample statistic is a function both of random variation and of sample size. *The larger the sample size the more accurate will be the estimation of the population parameters.*

Standard Deviation

The index of variability that is most often used in connection with statistical methods based on the normal curve is called the *standard deviation*. The standard deviation is an expression of the average degree of variability of observations around their arithmetic mean and is one of the essential characteristics of a set of observations. The methods for the computation of the standard deviation will be presented in Chapter 4. At this point it is sufficient to note that it is a quantity which reflects the amount of variability of the observations around the arithmetic mean and that it has certain invariant relationships to the normal distribution, which makes it a valuable tool in statistical inference.

The process of estimating population values and of determining the amount by which these estimates may be in error will be dealt with at considerable length in the remainder of this book. However, before proceeding with the methods of making statistical inferences, some additional basic material must be presented. If the material to be presented is neither intuitively nor logically obvious, you are asked to accept the sequence of events to follow. Hopefully, the logic will be reasonably clear by the end of this chapter.

NORMAL CURVE

To begin, let us review some basic characteristics of the population of 1000 observations we have been using. Note that the observations are symmetrical about the mean of 75.5 and that the frequency with which the observations occur decreases as they are

Frequency
of
occurrence

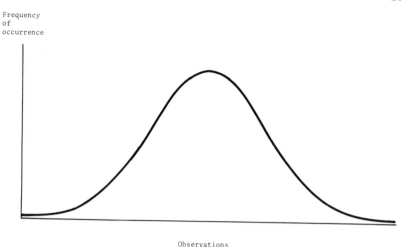

Observations

Figure 2–6. Theoretical normal curve.

located away from the mean. For example, an observation of 75 occurs 87 times out of 1000, while an observation of 89 occurs only once, and an observation of 65 only six times. As you may suspect, these observations were deliberately arranged to have this shape so they would resemble a mathematical entity that is fundamental to statistical inference. This entity is known as the normal curve. Figure 2–6 is an illustration of a theoretical normal curve and Figure 2–7 is our population of 1000 observations with the normal curve shown superimposed on it. The equation for the normal curve (which requires a knowledge of calculus to understand) need not concern us here. What is important is that the distribution of many events in the real world, if examined in large amounts, are found to have the same basic shape as the normal curve. Our earlier examples (pp. 6 and 7) were offered as evidence for this point.

Certainly not all things are normally distributed. We would not, for example, expect to give 20 students in a class an exam and find that the scores resembled the normal curve when graphed. However, if 1000 students were tested, the distribution of the scores might well resemble the normal curve. However, the fact that large numbers of observations tend to look like the normal curve when graphed is not the most important consideration. Many types of observations never distribute normally. For example, Figure 2–8 is the distribution of the times people arrive for work in the morning. Most people arrive exactly at the scheduled time for work to begin.

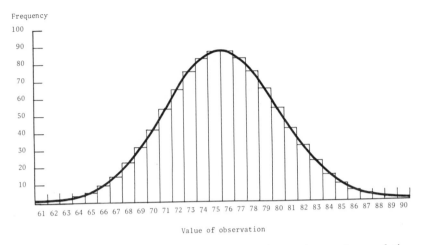

Figure 2–7. A theoretical normal curve superimposed upon the population of 1000 observations.

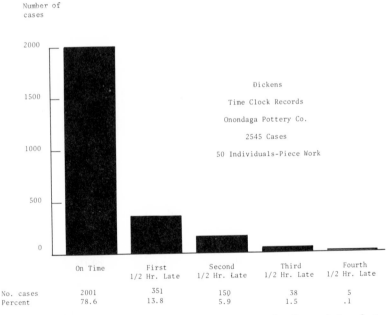

Figure 2–8. A distribution of the times people arrive for work in a factory (From "The J-Curve Hypothesis of Conforming Behavior" by F. H. Allport in *Readings in Social Psychology*. Copyright 1947 by Henry Holt Co. and reproduced with their permission.)

In this example no one arrives early, and as the minutes go by fewer and fewer people arrive. Observations such as these would never distribute normally, no matter how many thousands of them we accumulate, since the underlying reality is not normally distributed. However, if we drew small samples of 30 or more observations from this set of measurements and then calculated the arithmetic mean for each of these samples we would find that the distribution of sample means would assume a shape very similar to the distribution of the normal curve if we carried the process on long enough. This is one of the fundamental laws of statistical inference: *Statistics (such as means) calculated on samples of 30 or more observations will distribute normally even when the population from which they are taken is not distributed normally*. Consequently, the properties of the normal curve can be used in problems of statistical inference even when the underlying measurements are not distributed normally.

This can easily be illustrated as in Figure 2–9, which contains two sets of scores. The scores in Figure 2–9 *A* were obtained by drawing 100 samples of 30 observations each from our population of 1000 normally distributed observations and calculating the mean for each sample. The resulting 100 means are graphed on the distribution of the population of scores. These means tend to distribute in a "normal curve" fashion. The mean of these sample means is 75.36, which is quite close to the true population mean of 75.5. The observations in Figure 2–9 *B* were obtained in the same manner, but the population from which they were drawn resembles the distribution based on the times at which people arrive for work, as shown in Figure 2–8. (This is called an exponential distribution.) However, the distribution of means calculated from samples of 30 observations drawn randomly from this population has much the same shape as the distribution of means calculated from the population of normally distributed observations. The mean of these sample means is 4.9. The true population mean is 4.8. Again, the estimate is quite close to the population mean.

Uses of the Normal Curve. It might seem reasonable to question just why the normal curve is so important in statistics. The answer is straightforward: the normal curve can serve as a mathematical model for the frequency with which observations in the real world would be expected to occur and, therefore, may be used to estimate the probability of an event occurring or not occurring. For example, look at Figure 2–1 again. Note that certain

A

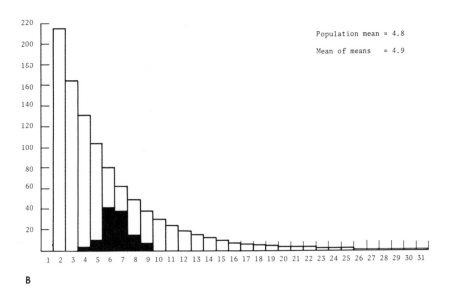

B

Figure 2–9. *A* and *B*, see text for explanation.

observations such as 74 or 76 occur many more times than do observations of 62 or 90. Suppose we write these observations on slips of paper and then shake them in a bag until they are completely mixed. (This is essentially what is done when we use a random number table to select a sample.) Suppose you now reach in and draw out one slip of paper. What are your chances of drawing an observation of 74? An observation of 90? Given the circumstances that any observation in the total of 1000 has an equal chance of being selected, the chances of drawing an observation with the value of 74 are better than those of drawing an observation with the value of 90 simply because the value of 74 occurs more often. In statistics the likelihood of selecting a value is referred to as the probability of the occurrence of the value.

PROBABILITY

The probability of an event occurring is the likelihood the event will occur compared to the likelihood that it will not occur. The probability of an event occurring is defined as follows: if something can happen in A ways and not happen in B ways, then the probability of A occurring is equal to $\dfrac{A}{A + B}$. This ratio can vary from values such as .000000001 or less (extremely low probability) to 1.00 (the event *always* happens). If your local weather report stated that the chances of rain in the next 24 hours were three out of ten, then the probability of rain is $\dfrac{3}{3 + 7}$ (three chances it will rain; seven chances it will not) $= 3/10 = .30$. This will be a sufficient definition of probability for the time being.

To return to a consideration of our population of 1000 observations, we can ask what the probability is of obtaining an observation with the value of 75. Since there are 1000 observations and the value of 75 occurs 87 times, the probability of drawing a value of 75 from this population is equal to 87/1000, which is equal to .087. Similarly, if we wished to know what the probability is of drawing a value of 64, we would divide 4 (the frequency of occurrence of the value of 64) by 1000 to obtain the probability of .004. Thus the probability of drawing a value of 64 is considerably less than the probability of drawing a value of 75.

The probability of an event occurring or not occurring is directly related to the frequency with which it does occur relative to the number of ways it does not occur. In our example of 1000 observations a value of 90 occurs only once, whereas a value of 74 occurs 84 times. If something can happen only one way out of 1000 and cannot happen 999 ways out of 1000, the probability of its occurring will certainly be less than for an event that can occur in 84 ways and cannot occur in 916 ways.

How does the normal curve enter into the estimation of probability? This will be dealt with in detail in Chapter 5. The calculation of probabilities is not possible unless something is known about the underlying distribution of the observations in the population. The characteristics of the normal curve distribution can be completely specified, and can provide a model for reality which will allow us to determine probabilities. Keep in mind also that the normal curve is suitable as a model of reality because statistics tend to distribute normally if a large number of values are collected.

SUMMARY

1. The characteristics of a population can be inferred from a sample drawn under true random conditions. In our illustration, we used a sample of ten observations to estimate the arithmetic mean of a population of 1000 observations.

2. The larger the sample the more precise the estimate of the population values.

3. Many sets of observations in the real world will distribute in a symmetrical, bell-shaped manner if they include a large enough number of observations.

4. Statistics, such as the arithmetic mean, when calculated from random samples, will distribute in a symmetrical, bell-shaped manner even if the population from which they are drawn does not have this distribution.

5. The normal curve is a theoretical mathematical equation which has the same symmetrical bell-shape as do the statistics calculated from random samples.

6. The probability with which an event will occur is defined as the frequency with which it does occur relative to the total number of possible outcomes.

7. The theoretical normal curve can be used as a model of the

frequency with which events occur and can be used to estimate the probability with which events occur.

The field of statistics has been defined as a body of methods used to make wise decisions in the face of uncertainty. Usually, we are faced with the circumstance that we do not know the characteristics of a population, and on the basis of the evidence available from the sample we want to make an inference regarding the characteristics of the population. We have discussed the fact that if a population is normally distributed we know a great deal about the distribution of its observations relative to one another since we can use the mathematical normal distribution to describe the characteristics of the population in the real world.

In this chapter we have identified the essential elements which characterize a distribution: the number of observations, type (or shape) of a distribution, location of the distribution, and variability of the distribution. Since in the real world we usually do not know anything about the "true" population values, the best estimate we can make of these values is on the basis of the sample values we have obtained. The best estimate we can make of the population mean is the obtained sample mean. The best estimate we can make of the population variability is the obtained sample variability. If we can also assume that the population is normally distributed (as many things are) and that the number of cases is extremely large, then we have all of the information we need to estimate the population parameters completely.

The exact nature of the processes by which we estimate population parameters, and the use of statistical procedures to evaluate the result of experiments is the major concern of the remaining sections of this book.

EPILOGUE

By now you should understand some of the steps involved in statistical inference. If you are confused at all, you are urged to reread the chapter. Some of the basic principles of statistical methods are developed in more detail later and reference will frequently be made to the introduction given in this chapter.

3

THE ESTIMATION OF CENTRAL TENDENCY

In the last chapter, the concept of random sampling was introduced and illustrated. Samples of ten observations were drawn randomly from a population of 1000 observations and the distribution of the samples in the population was shown. If we draw a sample from a population it is because we want to know something about that population. Consequently, we must carry out calculations that will provide us with summary information about the characteristics of that sample.

What we would like is a single number which can be used to represent all the observations in the sample. If this number is to be the sole representative of all of the values of the observations, then it should be a value which is near the middle of the sample values or where the sample values are most numerous.

Statistical Notation

Before we discuss the specific measures of central tendency we should introduce some conventions concerning statistical notation which will be observed throughout this book. Statistical symbols basically are no different than the conventional shorthand expressions used in many branches of life. For example, college students abbreviate references to their courses by saying that they are taking

"Econ 104" or "Psych 32." This is basically a shorthand language understood by anyone who has learned what the symbols stand for. The symbols used in statistics are basically the same, and are no more difficult to learn (although it may seem so at first).

The symbol X is used to stand for any observation in a distribution (this is called an observation or "raw score"). Let us use one of our samples of ten observations as an illustration. X can stand for any of those ten observations. X_1 is used to symbolize the first observation in the sample, X_2 to symbolize the second observation, X_3 to symbolize the third observation, and so on through X_{10} which symbolizes the tenth observation. If we want to indicate to someone that the ten observations should be added together to obtain the sum we can, then, write the following: $X_1 + X_2 + X_3 + X_4 + X_5 + X_6 + X_7 + X_8 + X_9 + X_{10}$. For sample 3, Table 2–2, this indicates that the following procedure should be followed: $67 + 72 + 67 + 75 + 67 + 83 + 79 + 79 + 80 + 78$. Since this is a very cumbersome notation, especially with a large number of observations, a simpler way of indicating this is to write $X_1 + X_2 + \cdots + X_{10}$. This notational method is still cumbersome. Therefore, another statistical symbol, the Greek capital letter *sigma* ($\sum$), is used to stand for the words "the sum of." Now, we can write the instruction to add all the observations as $\sum X$. This instructs us to add together all the observations represented by the letter X. In our example this would mean adding the ten observations of the sample together. If we symbolize the observations in a second sample by the letter Y we can give instructions to add all the observations symbolized by Y by writing $\sum Y$. If the observations in sample 4 are symbolized by Y, then $\sum Y$ equals $78 + 81 + 76 + 70 + 81 + 84 + 80 + 72 + 79 + 85 = 786$. It should be emphasized that any arbitrary symbol can be used to stand for observations. If only one set of observations is involved we prefer the symbol X, however.

Another conventional symbol is the letter N which stands for the number of observations. If we wished to instruct someone to take the simple arithmetic average (or mean) of some numbers we could write: $\dfrac{\sum X}{N}$. This indicates that all the observations symbolized by X are to be added together and this sum is to be divided by the number of observations. The result of this computation is the arithmetic mean. Since the arithmetic mean is used so often it has its own symbolic representation, $\overline{X}$.

As you become more familiar with the symbols used, they will look less strange and will begin to take on meanings of their own. They will become intelligible immediately on perceiving them as are such shorthand abbreviations as "Econ 104," "Psych 32," and similar ones which are immediately understandable without your having to think about the meanings expressed.

ARITHMETIC MEAN

The arithmetic mean, which was introduced in Chapter 2, is one of the most frequently used measures of central tendency. It takes every observation into account, and is (with certain exceptions) a value which is near the middle of the sample values. It is one of the most common and most useful summary measures in statistics.

The arithmetic mean is a quantity with which you are all familiar. You have all been concerned with whether your grades are above or below "average," with whether a test score was above or below "average" and so forth. To find the arithmetic mean you *sum all the observations and divide that sum by the number of observations.* We can express this statement using statistical notation as follows:

$$\bar{X} = \frac{\Sigma X}{N}. \tag{3.1}$$

For our population the sum of the 1000 observations is 75,500. When that sum is divided by the number of observation (1000) the arithmetic mean is found to be $75.5 \left(\bar{X} = \dfrac{75,500}{1000} = 75.5 \right).$

Sample Means as Estimates of the Population Mean

We are seldom able to calculate the arithmetic mean for an entire population since all the observations are not available. In the majority of situations we are limited to gathering samples and attempting to estimate the population mean on the basis of these samples. Often this must be done on the basis of one sample alone.

Table 3–1. The Sum of Observations and the Arithmetic Means for Each of the Five Samples of Ten Observations Each in Table 2–2.

	1	2	3	4	5
$\sum X$	752	724	747	786	779
N	10	10	10	10	10
$\overline{X}$	75.2	72.4	74.7	78.6	77.9

In Chapter 2 five samples of ten observations each were drawn on a random basis and Figure 2–4 was constructed to show the distribution of these observations through the population. We can now ask how accurately these small samples estimate the mean of the population. To do this we perform the same calculations we did to determine the population mean: the observations within each sample are summed and these sums are then divided by the number of observations in each sample. Table 3–1 is the result of these calculations for the five samples of Table 2–2.

In Figure 3–1 these five means are located in the distribution of the population values. Our ability to estimate accurately the population mean on the basis of relatively small samples drawn on a true random basis is really quite good; however, there are

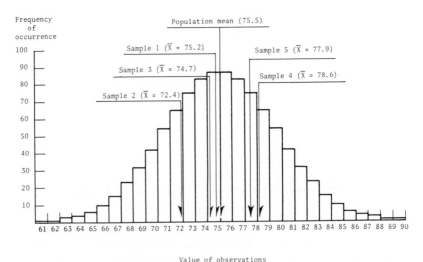

Figure 3–1. Relationship of sample means ($N = 10$) to the population mean.

occurrences (samples 2 and 4) in which the deviation from the actual population mean is considerable.

At this point it might seem reasonable to ask "if the samples had been larger, would the population mean be estimated more accurately?" The general rule that can be stated in answer to this question is as follows: *The larger the sample size in relation to the population size, the greater the precision of the estimate.* As an illustration of this, consider Table 3–2. This table contains the values for five samples of 20 observations each (exactly twice the size of our original samples). Note that the mean values calculated from these samples

Table 3–2. THE SUM OF OBSERVATIONS AND THE ARITHMETIC MEANS FOR EACH OF FIVE SAMPLES OF 20 OBSERVATIONS.

$\sum X$	1504	1518	1490	1500	1510
N	20	20	20	20	20
$\bar{X}$	75.2	75.9	74.5	75.0	75.5

deviate much less from the population value than is the case with samples of ten observations each. Whereas the range of sample means ($\bar{X}$'s) with $N = 10$ was from 72.4 to 78.6, the range of sample $\bar{X}$'s with $N = 20$ is only from 74.5 to 75.9, a range of 1.4 as compared to the range of 6.2 for the means based on ten observations. The values of these five means are located in the distribution of the population values in Figure 3–2. If the number of cases in each sample had been less than ten, the variability of the sample $\bar{X}$'s around the population mean would have been even greater.

The likelihood of an inaccurate estimate of the population mean based on a single sample is, thus, fairly high with a small sample N. Conversely, as the number of cases in each sample increases, the less the variability of the sample $\bar{X}$'s around the population mean, and the less the likelihood of a bad estimate of the population mean based on a single sample. The limiting case, of course, would be reached when the single sample N is so large that it includes all of the cases in the population. In this event, the estimate would *be* the population and there is *no* error.

Earlier, in discussing our original population of 1000 observations, we mentioned that they tended to follow a symmetrical, somewhat bell-shaped pattern. In Chapter 2 we discussed the relationship between sample means and the population mean. We will now draw randomly 100 samples of size 30 (remembering that under true random conditions each observation is returned to the original population as soon as it is selected, so that, theoretically, it is possible for one score to be selected over and over again) and will calculate the arithmetic mean for each of the 100 samples. We can graph these values in the same way we graphed the original 1000 population observations. The obtained distribution is shown in Figure 3–3. You can see from Figure 3–3 that our set of 100 $\overline{X}$'s has a very definite relationship to the original population of observations. If we treat the $\overline{X}$'s as observations and average them in turn, we find that the average (or mean of means) is extremely close to the population average. Note also that the distribution of $\overline{X}$'s is very similar in shape to the original population distribution.

Observations occur with the greatest frequency near the mean and disperse symmetrically about it, with observations at some distance from the mean becoming increasingly less frequent. Note also that when the means are treated as observations the range is much less than in the original population of 1000 observations. The fact that a set of means distributes in this fashion, and that fairly accurate

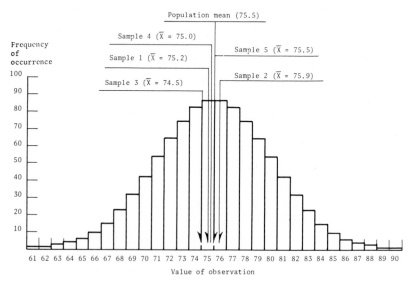

Figure 3–2. Relationship of sample means based on 20 observations to the population mean.

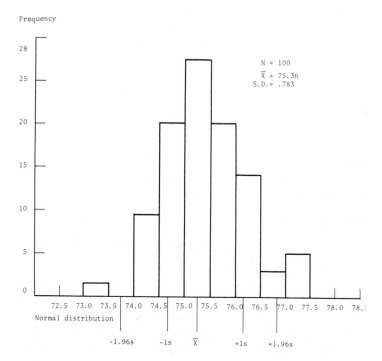

Figure 3–3. Distribution of 100 means calculated from samples of 30 observations each randomly selected from a normal population.

estimates of the population values are possible using sample values has considerable importance in statistical inference. This will be discussed in the next chapter.

ALGEBRAIC PROPERTIES OF THE MEAN

The value of the mean is one around which all the values of the observations are balanced according to their algebraic weight. The mean, then, is a point in a distribution of values at which the algebraic sum of the deviations from it is zero. Consider the following six values: 60, 61, 62, 64, 65, and 66. The $\sum X = 378$, and the $\bar{X} = \frac{378}{6} = 63$. We can set the $\bar{X}$ of the values to equal zero and express each of the values in terms of how far they deviate from the mean. (Since the use of numbers to represent quantities is arbitrary this does no violence to reality.) Expressed in this fashion 60 becomes a -3 $(60 - 63)$, 61 becomes a -2 $(60 - 62)$, 61 a -1, 64 a $+1$ $(64 - 63)$, 65 a $+2$, and 66 a $+3$. If we now add these values we have $(-3) + (-2) + (-1) + (+1) + (+2) + (+3) = 0$.

The deviation of a value from the mean is symbolized as x. Thus, $x = X - \bar{X}$, and the summation, $\sum x = 0$. If one of the six values changes $\bar{X}$ cannot remain the same. Assume that the value 66 becomes a 69. If we set $\bar{X} = 63$ as before, our $x = (-3) + (-2) + (-1) + (+1) + (+2) + (+6) = +3$. Since $\bar{X}$ must be the algebraic center of this distribution we must change the value of $\bar{X}$. For this new state of affairs $\sum X = 381$;

$$\frac{\sum X}{N} = 63.5;$$ and $x = (-3.5) + (-2.5) + (-1.5) + (+.5) +$

$(+1.5) + (+5.5) = 0$. Raising the value of 66 to 69 therefore increases $\bar{X}$ to 63.5 and, as it must, $\sum x = 0$.

Since each value influences the mean according to its algebraic weight the value of the mean is strongly influenced by extreme values in one direction which are not balanced by extreme values in the other direction. To return to our original six numbers, assume that the value 66 is changed to a value of

136. Now $\sum X = 448$ and $\dfrac{\sum X}{N} = 73.0$. The value of $\bar{X}$ now

exceeds the value of all but the one extreme value. Obviously, the mean would not be a good quantity to choose to represent the distribution of observations in this instance.

OTHER MEASURES OF CENTRAL TENDENCY

Median.   Another measure of central tendency which is often used is the median (Mdn). The median is defined as *a point above which 50 per cent of the observations fall and below which 50 per cent of the observations fall*. Notice that the median is based on the *number of observations* and not on the values of the observations as is the mean. The median is simple to determine since one merely has to rank the observations in order of their scale value and then to count the number of observations until the halfway point is reached. The ranking process does not take into account the size of the difference between one value and the next. It is simple to determine the median if the number of cases involved is an odd number. For example, consider the following five numbers: 7, 12, 1, 98, and 44. To determine the median the numbers should be arranged in order of magnitude: 1, 7, 12, 44, 98. The median, then, is 12: two observations (1 and 7) fall below the median and two observations (44 and 98) fall above the median. A difficulty arises when there is an even number of observations. Consider the following four values which are arranged in order of increasing magnitude: 14, 15, 17, and 18. The median of these four observations will be the value midway between the second value (value 15) and the third (value 17). There is no observation at that point so it will be necessary to split the difference between the two values. The total distance between 15 and 17 is two, and half of that distance is one. Therefore, the median is 15 + 1, or 16. This example is illustrated graphically below. Each observation can be considered to occupy an equal amount of space along a continuous scale of values as illustrated.

			Median		
Observation	1	2	↓	3	4

Value	14	15	16	17	18

The median, then, falls halfway between the two ends of the scale. What is the median of the following four values: 12, 13, 17, and 18? Again, let us diagram the observations on a continuous scale.

				Median			
Observation	1	2	–	↓	–	3	4

Value	13	14	15	16	17	18	19

Again, the median will be the scale value halfway between observation 2 (value 14) and observation 3 (value 18). The total distance between 14 and 18 is four, and half of that distance is two. Therefore, the median is 14 + 2 = 16. Even though the value of two of the observations has changed in the second example the median remains the same since the rank order of the values does not change, and each of the two observations was symmetrically displaced. Let us consider another set of four values: 12, 14, 17, and 18.

				Median			
Observation	1	–	2	– ↓ –		3	4

Value	12	13	14	15	16	17	18

The median will still fall half the distance between observation 2 (value 14) and observation 3 (value 17). Now, the distance between the two observations is three values; one-half of three is 1.5. Therefore, the median is $14 + 1.5 = 15.5$.

Consider one final set of four values: 13, 14, 15, and 16.

		Median		
Observation	1	2 ↓ 3		4

Value	13	14	15	16

The median will fall half the distance between observation 2 (value 14) and observation 3 (value 15, as before). This distance is one; one-half of one is 0.5. Therefore the median is 14.5.

In all four of these examples the median falls at a point where no observation occurs. In the last example the median occurred at a point halfway between two whole number values. This can occur even though the original measurements on which the scale of values are based are in terms of whole numbers, since the ranking procedure on which the determination of the median is based considers the number of observations and not the scale of values.

Since the median is based on the order of the observations rather than on their scale values it is less affected by extreme values in one direction which are not balanced by extreme values in the other direction.

Consider the effect of changing the value of the lowest observation from 13 to 10 in the last set of four values which was presented.

					$\bar{X}$ Median		
Observation	1	–	–	–	↓ 2 ↓	3	4

Value	10	11	12	13	14	15	16

The median is not affected; it is still 14.5. The mean, however, is now 13.75 (instead of the previous 14.5). If the lowest observation value was changed to 5, the median would still be unaffected, while the mean would now be 12.5. Notice that both of these latter mean values are below all but the lowest observation. Therefore, the mean is not a good measure to use in an instance such as this when we are interested in choosing one representative number to characterize the location of the distribution of values.

The median is also known as the *fiftieth percentile*. Percentiles and percentile ranks are specialized statistics used most frequently in test construction. Since they have little use in statistical inference, computational methods for these measures are not presented in this text.

Mode. One additional measure of central tendency is the mode, which is defined as the value which occurs most frequently. (More precisely, this is the value of the variable at which the concentration of the observations is densest.) In Figure 3–4 *A* the most frequently occurring observation, and hence the mode, is 15. This distribution has but one mode and would, therefore, be described as *unimodal*. It is possible, of course, to have more than one mode in a distribution.

Figure 3–4 *B* has two modes; one mode is 13 and the other is 16. It would be described as *bimodal*. This type of distribution often occurs when two samples, each with a different location, are combined into one distribution. (An example of this would be a combined height distribution made up of both men and women. The mean height of the men would be higher than would be the mean height of the women, and a bimodal distribution would probably be the result.) The mode has the advantage of being quick to determine and is a useful descriptive term to characterize the shape of a distribution.

Skewed Distributions

A distribution of observations is called a skewed distribution if there are cases occurring at the extreme of one tail of the distribution which are not balanced by cases in the other tail. Figure 3–5 *A* is a *negatively skewed distribution* and Figure 3–5 *B* is a *positively skewed distribution*. The term "skew" refers to the direction toward

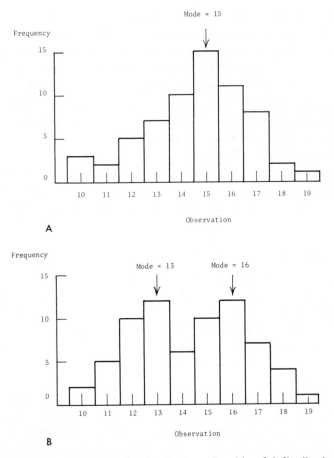

Figure 3–4. *A*, a unimodal distribution. *B*, a bimodal distribution.

which the tail of the distribution is extended (and not, it should be noted, to the portion of the distribution where the majority of observations are located). If the elongated tail of the distribution extends in the direction of higher values then the direction of the skew is *positive*; if the elongated tail extends in the direction of lower values the direction of the skew is *negative* (see page 37).

In a skewed distribution the three measures of central tendency always stand in the same relationship as illustrated in Figure 3–5. The mode will not be affected by the distribution of observations in the tails of the distribution at all. The median will be different since each observation in one tail which is not balanced by an observation in the other tail will change the median. The mean will be affected the most since each extreme observation influences the mean a great deal.

Therefore, in a positively skewed distribution the mean will be the highest of the three measures of central tendency, the median will be the next highest, and the mode will be the lowest. In a negatively skewed distribution this order will be reversed. Often, it is useful to report both a mean and a median if the distribution is markedly skewed. This gives the reader of these descriptive statistics an estimate of the degree to which the distribution is skewed. If the quantity $\overline{X} - Mdn$ is a positive number the distribution is positively skewed. If the quantity $\overline{X} - Mdn$ is a negative number the distribution is negatively skewed.

If the distribution is unimodal and symmetrical then the three measures of central tendency will all have the same location and only one of them need be reported. If this is the case the mean is usually the value reported.

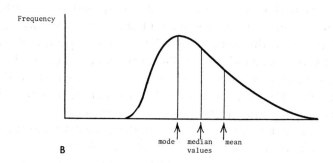

Figure 3–5. Skewed distributions. *A*, negative skew. *B*, positive skew.

Comparison of the Three Measures
of Central Tendency

Sampling Stability. One important requirement for any sample statistic used to estimate the value of a population parameter is that the value of the statistic be stable from sample to sample. If we obtain widely varying estimates from sample to sample the conclusions we can draw regarding the true population value must be quite tentative since we have no idea which of the different sample values we should accept as being closest to the population value. The most stable of the three measures of central tendency from the sampling standpoint is the mean. If successive samples are drawn from the same population the values of the mean will be found to show less variability than the values of either the median or the mode.

The mode is the least satisfactory measure of central tendency from the standpoint of sampling stability. Its location is determined by the observations at one scale value only. Therefore, if the number of observations are nearly equal at several points near the center of the distribution, the movement of only one or two in a distribution of several thousand observations can cause the mode to shift about. The mean would be affected hardly at all by such small shifts of observations in the center of the distribution, while the median would be moved only if the observations crossed from one side of the median to the other.

Usefulness. In general, the mean is the most useful measure of central tendency. It is used, in some form, in the sequence of computations involved in most methods of statistical inference. Most inferential methods require the computation of arithmetic sums and means. A few methods of statistical inference involve hypotheses about the median, but these methods are usually not as sensitive as the methods based on the mean, nor are they as adaptable to a wide variety of data. (This issue will be discussed further in Chapter 10.) The mode is practically useless in inferential statistics. Therefore, when the distributions of observations are relatively symmetrical the mean is preferred to both the median and the mode because of its greater usefulness in statistical inference.

The mean also permits a great deal of algebraic flexibility. The mean multiplied by N equals the total sum of the observations.

$[\overline{X}(N) = \sum X]$. This algebraic property permits us to perform many operations (and to simplify computational procedures) in ways which would not be possible using either the median or the mode.

Ease of Computation. If a frequency distribution is available the mode can be determined with no computation whatsoever. The median is easy to determine for a small number of observations since this determination is based on ranking and counting. With a large number of observations the median is difficult to determine since the procedure of ranking many numbers is quite laborious. The mean is probably easier to calculate with a large number of observations than is the median since running subtotals can be kept, and the accuracy of the computation thereby can be verified much more easily.

In summary, the method to be preferred depends on the importance of each of these three factors. If a rough, quick measure will suffice and no further inferences are to be made, the mode might be preferred. If a bit more stability is desired, the median might be used instead. If the most stable and useful measure is desired, then the mean should be computed, provided that the distribution is not extremely skewed.

Abuses of the Average. The average is one of the most frequently abused statistics. First, since there are three "averages" available it is not uncommon for someone desiring to give misleading information to report not the most representative measure of central tendency, but the one most advantageous to the position he wishes to support.

Second, most people have been taught in school to "average" numbers; that is, to calculate the arithmetic mean. Therefore, if one reports the median or the mode, most people untutored in the ways of statistics will assume that the arithmetic mean is being reported if the word "average" is used to identify the statistic.

Third, most people do not appreciate the fact that in badly skewed distributions the mean is inappropriate. For example, in reporting the average income of workers in a particular factory it is possible that of the 100 individuals, 99 of them earn between $5000 and $6000 while one of them (the president of the concern) earns $100,000. Basing an arithmetic average on this distribution could, then, result in an average income which is greater than the income of all but one person. Obviously, the mean is not a good index to use to represent the location of this type of distribution. In this example, either the mode or the median would be preferred. If the aim of the president of the concern is to avoid raising salaries, however, he might prefer to report the mean, since it bolsters his position.

Another frequent abuse of averages, especially prevalent in advertising, is the use of the phrase "up to." It is often reported that Brand X gives "up to" three times the wear of the average of the four leading competitors. This does *not* mean that Brand X is superior to the other four brands. In fact, it is possible that Brand X is the worst of the lot. The statement is usually interpreted by uncritical readers to mean that an average item of Brand X will be almost 3 times better than the average item of any of the other four brands. The statement does not say this, however. The statement says no more than that if the very best item produced by Brand X is selected, and if this best item is compared to the average item of the other four, the *best* of X will exceed the *average* of the others. The average of Brand X might be considerably below the average of the other four brands, and the best of Brand X might be far inferior to the best of the other four. This possibility would be enhanced if the quality control for Brand X was quite poor, in fact. Let us assume that the workmen producing Brand X are not trained or supervised adequately. The quality of the product, then, would depend on the workers' own diligence and conscientiousness. The result would probably be a product of considerable variability in quality. However, exceptionally good items would still be expected from Brand X. If these items from the extreme positive tail of the distribution are then compared to the center of the distribution for the other four, the cards are stacked in favor of Brand X.

In general one should always be wary when statistics are presented in order to convince one of the soundness of an advocate's position. Those skilled in misrepresenting reality usually understand that it is easier to convince people using arguments based on numerical bases than it is to convince them using arguments based on verbal reasoning alone. Many people uncritically accept false "facts" and inappropriate representations of reality if they are stated quantitatively (especially if they are expressed to four decimal places). The material presented in this chapter should make it possible for you both to accurately represent a distribution of numbers and to interpret such representations.

EXERCISES

1. Find the mean for the following sample: $X_1 = 15$; $X_2 = 27$; $X_3 = 12$; $X_4 = 14$; $X_5 = 20$; $X_6 = 18$.

2. a. Find the mean, median, and mode for the following distribution of scores: 2, 18, 9, 5, 5, 25, 4, 5.

   b. Is the distribution skewed? If so, in what direction?

3. a. Compute the mean and the median for the following distribution of scores: $X_1 = 10$; $X_2 = 25$; $X_3 = 9$; $X_4 = 11$; $X_5 = 32$; $X_6 = 12$; $X_7 = 13$; $X_8 = 34$; $X_9 = 14$; $X_{10} = 14$.

   b. For this distribution which of the two measures would be the best representation of central tendency? Why?

4. a. Which measure of central tendency is most affected by the degree of skewness in a frequency distribution? Why?

   b. Which measure of central tendency is least affected by the degree of skewness? Why?

5. One property of the mean is that the sum of the deviations of each observation from the mean must equal _____. Write the preceding statement in symbols.

6. The median is also known as the _____ percentile. Why?

7. In a negatively skewed distribution, rank the median, mode, and mean in terms of lowest to highest value.

8. For the following observations prove that $\bar{X}(N) = \sum X$: 10, 9, 11, 13, 15, 14, 12, 8.

9. Find the median for the following distribution of scores:

X	f
30–32	1
27–29	2
24–26	5
21–23	6
18–20	4
15–17	2
12–14	1
	$N = 21$

10. If you were told that the mean for five students was 80.0 and that the mean for the three (out of the total five) who were men was 82.3, what would be the mean for the two women?

4

ESTIMATION OF
VARIABILITY

In the last chapter it was stated that the best single descriptive number to characterize the location (or central tendency) of a population of observations is the arithmetic mean, providing that the distribution of observations is unimodal and symmetrical. The mean can be estimated fairly precisely on the basis of relatively small samples and is usually the best representative of the individual observations in a symmetrical distribution.

Although the mean conveys considerable information about a population it constitutes only a partial description of the population's characteristics. It is often as important to know something about the degree of variability of the individual values as it is to know the central location of these values.

An average, itself, tells us nothing about dispersion. In fact, we compute an average in order to see through the variability to the general location of the distribution. Obviously, if you cannot swim you should not decide to wade a stretch of river if you are told only that the average depth of the water is three feet. The average, indeed, might be only three feet, but sometimes you might be in shallow water of only a few inches while at other times you might be in 12 to 20 feet of water. It is important to know something, then, about the dispersion of values around the mean if the distribution is to be described adequately.

The distributions shown in Figure 4–1 all have the same mean,

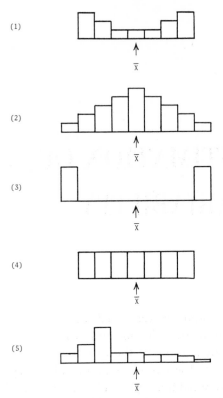

Figure 4–1. Representation of five sets of observations with the same mean and different variability.

but differ greatly in the manner in which the observations vary around that mean.

The same rules that we used to decide that the mean is the most useful average should apply to the choice of a measure of variability. This measure should summarize the characteristics of all the observations, as does the mean. Similarly, its value should reflect general tendencies for the entire distribution of observations and should not be radically affected by a few extreme values. Also, the measure should permit us to make inferences concerning the variability of the population distribution.

What is needed is another sort of average: an average whose value increases as the variability of the observations in the distribution increases. If the mean is the single most efficient description of the location of a set of observations, any estimate of variability

Table 4-1. DEMONSTRATION OF THE DEVIATIONS OF ALL OBSERVATIONS AROUND A MEAN SUMMING TO ZERO.

Score X	Mean $\bar{X}$	$X - \bar{X}$	$(X - \bar{X})^2$
71	75.2	−4.2	17.64
83	75.2	7.8	60.84
69	75.2	−6.2	38.44
75	75.2	−.2	.04
72	75.2	−3.2	10.24
75	75.2	−.2	.04
75	75.2	−.2	.04
84	75.2	8.8	77.44
72	75.2	−3.2	10.24
76	75.2	.8	.64
752			$\sum (X - \bar{X})^2 = 215.60$

$$\sum x = .0$$
$$\sum |x| = 34.8$$

we use would do well to use the mean as a base around which the variations in observations are expressed.

One possibility is to subtract the mean from each value and then determine the average of these differences. However, the very nature of the mean makes this impossible. The mean is the algebraic balance point around which all values vary, and it is affected by every observation. The sum of the deviations around the mean, by definition, is zero. This is demonstrated in Table 4–1 where the mean for sample one has been subtracted from every observation in the sample and these deviations have been summed. The deviations sum algebraically to zero. In fact, as discussed in Chapter 3, if these values do not equal zero the value of the mean is incorrect. Obviously, we cannot estimate variability in this manner.

AVERAGE DEVIATION

There are two solutions which we can use. One is to subtract the mean from each value and to sum the deviations, disregarding the algebraic signs, and then to divide this sum by the number of cases on which it is based. This gives us a value which is the average amount of deviation regardless of the direction of the deviation. This value is called the *average deviation*. For the scores in Table 4–1 the sum of the deviations when the algebraic signs are ignored (symbolized as $\sum |x|$) is 34.8. The average deviation, then, is 34.8/10 or 3.48.

SUM OF SQUARES

Another solution is to subtract the mean from each value and then to square each of these differences. When we do this all the squared differences are positive and as the differences between the mean and the observations increase the sum of these squared differences will increase. This computation is shown for the ten observations in the fourth column of Table 4–1. This quantity is called the *sum of squares* and is symbolized as $\sum x^2$. The $\sum x^2$ is 215.60 for these ten values. This procedure uses the mean as a reference point, and eliminates minus signs by squaring the deviations. Thus, we have a number whose size increases as the amount of variability increases.

This second solution is the preferred method of representing the degree of variability, although it is not the most intuitively appealing one. It is preferred to the average deviation method because of its usefulness when making inferences based on a normal distribution assumption. If observations are normally distributed, a number of inferences regarding variability can be made using a standard table of the normal distribution and a statistic based on the sum of squares. This provides us with some powerful inferential methods, as we shall see in the next few chapters.

In order to obtain this measure of the variability of observations we divide the sum of the squared deviation values ($\sum x^2$) by the number of observations (N). This gives us a quantity which is defined as the *variance* and which is symbolized by the square of the lower case Greek letter sigma (σ^2) when referring to population parameters. The formula for the population variance is

$$\sigma^2 = \frac{\sum x^2}{N}. \tag{4.1}$$

The variance is an average expressing the dispersion or scattering of observations around the arithmetic mean. The greater the dispersion of values around the mean, the larger the variance will be. This can be demonstrated by calculating the variance for some of the samples used in earlier examples. The formula for the variance of a sample is

$$\frac{\sum x^2}{N-1}. \tag{4.2}$$

We will see the reasons for using $N-1$ rather than N in a moment. The steps involved in calculating the variance of a sample are as follows:

(1) Calculate the mean. $\bar{X} = \sum X/N$.
(2) Subtract the mean from each observation. $x = (X - \bar{X})$.
(3) Square each of the terms obtained in step (2). $x^2 = (X - \bar{X})^2$.
(4) Sum the squared differences. $\sum x^2 = \sum (X - \bar{X})^2$.
(5) Divide the sum of the squared differences by the number of observations minus one. $\sum x^2/(N-1)$.
(5a) Alternatively, the sum of squared differences can be multiplied by the reciprocal of the number of observations minus one. Operations (5) and (5a) are exactly equivalent. However, operation (5a) is recommended since fewer calculating errors will be made during multiplication than division. Table A–12 provides the reciprocals of numbers.

The preceding steps are presented in detail in Table 4–2.

Calculation of the Sum of Squares for the Population of 1000 Observations

In the examples shown in Table 4–2, the sum of squares ($\sum x^2$) was calculated by subtracting the mean from each observation, squaring the resulting difference, and summing the differences. While this does not present a difficult calculation for small sets of numbers, the process of subtracting the mean from each of 1000 values, then squaring each of the 1000 differences, and, finally, summing the 1000 squared differences is a rather tedious process. There is also a strong likelihood that calculational errors will be made since the procedure requires such a large number of individual calculations. Fortunately, there are some computational short cuts to obtain the sum of squares which can be done in one operation

Table 4–2. CALCULATION OF THE VARIANCE.

	Observations
Step 1: Calculate the mean.	1
	2
$\bar{X} = \sum X/N = 15/5$	3
	4
$\bar{X} = 3$	5
	$\sum X = 15$

Step 2: Subtract the mean from each observation.

$$x$$
$$1 - 3 = -2$$
$$2 - 3 = -1$$
$$3 - 3 = 0$$
$$4 - 3 = +1$$
$$5 - 3 = +2$$
$$\sum x = 0$$

Step 3: Square each of the differences obtained in step 2.

$$x^2$$
$$(-2)^2 = 4$$
$$(-1)^2 = 1$$
$$(0)^2 = 0$$
$$(+1)^2 = 1$$
$$(+2)^2 = 4$$

Step 4: Sum the squared differences.

$$\sum x^2 = 10$$

Step 5: Divide the sum of the squared differences by $N - 1$.

$$s^2 = \frac{\sum x^2}{N - 1}$$
$$= 10/4$$
$$= 2.50$$

Step 5a: Alternate calculation: Multiply the sum of the squared differences by $1/(N - 1)$.

$$s^2 = \frac{1}{N - 1} \left(\sum x^2 \right)$$
$$= \tfrac{1}{4}(10)$$
$$= .25(10)$$
$$= 2.50$$

on an automatic calculator. The "raw score" computational method which we will use is algebraically equivalent to the basic formula presented. To obtain the $\sum x^2$ in one machine operation it is necessary to sum the values of the observations, to square each value, and to sum these squares. (See Chapter 1 of the Student Workbook for a description of the standard calculators which are available and for a brief description of the method of operation of each machine.) The square of the summed observations is symbolized by $(\sum X)^2$, which is read as "the sum of observations, quantity squared." The sum of the squared observations is symbolized by $\sum X^2$. The $\sum X^2$ for our original 1000 observations in Table 2–1 equals 5,720,980. To obtain the quantity $(\sum X)^2$ we take the original sum of the observations as given on p. 27 in Chapter 3 (75,500) and square it ($75,500^2 = 5,700,250,000$). We now take this $(\sum X)^2$ and divide it by the total number of observations (N). The general equation for obtaining the sum of squares is

$$\sum x^2 = \sum X^2 - (\sum X)^2/N. \qquad (4.3)$$

If we substitute our obtained values for the population into this formula we obtain the following:

$$\sum x^2 = 5,720,980 - \frac{5,700,250,000}{1000} = 5,720,980 - 5,700,250$$

$$= 20,730.$$

Formulas for Population Values and for Statistics

At this point an important notational distinction must be made between *population values* (or parameters) and *sample-based estimates* of these population parameters. When the values under consideration are population parameters, Greek letters are used to symbolize the values. Thus, when we are referring to the variance of a population we use the symbol σ^2 ("little sigma" squared) to represent it. When the values are obtained samples we usually use lower case English letters to symbolize them. The variance of a sample is represented by the symbol s^2. This convention is followed in most statistics texts and will be followed throughout in this text. The only exception to this rule is found when referring to the mean. The arithmetic mean of a population will be symbolized by the Greek letter μ (pronounced "mew"). The arithmetic mean of a sample will be symbolized by $\overline{X}$, however. This convention is highly useful since it will help to keep clear at all times whether we are referring to hypothetical population values or to the actual sample distributions we are using to estimate those population values.

Not only does the notational system differ when referring to population parameters as opposed to sample estimates, but the two kinds of values are computed differently in some cases. For the arithmetic mean, no difference is involved between the way the mean $(\overline{X})$ is calculated for a sample and the way the mean (μ) is calculated for a population. However, when calculating the variance for a sample we divide our sum of squares $(\sum x^2)$ by $N - 1$, rather than by N as we would when calculating the variance for a population.

The following definitional formulas have been presented already:

$$\sigma^2 = \sum x^2/N, \qquad \textit{population variance}$$

$$s^2 = \sum x^2/(N - 1), \qquad \textit{sample variance}$$

Substituting the necessary values into the equation for the population variance, we have:

$$\sum x^2 = 20{,}730.$$

Multiplying by the reciprocal of N, we obtain:

$$\sigma^2 = (20{,}730)\left(\frac{1}{1000}\right)$$

$$= (20{,}730)(.001)$$

$$= 20.73.$$

Alternatively, dividing 20,730 by 1000:

$$\sigma^2 = \frac{20{,}730}{1000}$$

$$= 20.73.$$

Obviously, the two methods produce the same result.

Why do we use a different formula to calculate the population variance and the sample variance? We have seen earlier that it is

Table 4–3. Accuracy of Estimate of the Population Variance from Small Samples ($N = 10$) Without and With an $N - 1$ Correction ($\sigma^2 = 20.73$).

Sample	1 $\sum x^2/N$	2 $\sum x^2/(N - 1)$
1	$142.68/10 = 14.27$	$142.68/9 = 15.85$
2	$177.63/10 = 17.76$	$177.63/9 = 19.73$
3	$191.23/10 = 19.12$	$191.23/9 = 21.24$

possible to estimate the mean of a population quite accurately even with relatively small samples. We have also seen that estimates of the mean are seldom extremely inaccurate even though the sample size may be quite small. Unfortunately, the same relationship does not hold for the variance. The variance will be underestimated systematically as the sample size becomes smaller and smaller. For example, if we estimate the population variance on the basis of three samples of $N = 10$ without dividing by $N - 1$ we would obtain the results shown in column 1 of Table 4–3.

If we compare the uncorrected variances for the samples with the population variance calculated previously, we can see that the sample variances tend to be systematically smaller than the population variance of 20.73. If we did not use the $N - 1$ correction, we would consistently underestimate the value of the population variance using these sample estimates.

However, if we now correct our estimates by dividing each $\sum x^2$ by $N - 1$, as in column 2 of Table 4–3, we can see that our accuracy of estimate is much better. How much would the accuracy of our estimate improve if we were to increase our sample size? In column 1 of Table 4–4 the estimates of the population variance obtained without the $N - 1$ correction for three samples of $N = 50$ are shown. Column 2 contains the same estimate with the $N - 1$ correction. The accuracy of estimate obtained (even without the $N - 1$ correction) is considerably improved over the estimate obtained with samples of only ten observations.

The use of the $N - 1$ correction adjusts the systematic error introduced when small samples are used to estimate the population variance. If we draw a sample of 750 observations and our population is only 1000, the difference in the variance obtained by dividing by 749 instead of 750 is so small that it is not even observable until

Table 4-4. Accuracy of Estimate of the Population Variance from Samples of 50 Observations Without and With an $N - 1$ Correction ($\sigma^2 = 20.73$).

Sample	1 $\sum x^2/N$	2 $\sum x^2/(N - 1)$
1	1295.39/50 = 25.91	1295.39/49 = 26.44
2	996.76/50 = 19.94	996.76/49 = 20.34
3	889.79/50 = 17.80	889.79/49 = 18.16

several decimal places are reached. However, if our sample size is ten the difference in the values obtained by dividing the sum of squares by 10 in one case and by 9 in the other will be much more substantial, and this difference increases as the number of observations decreases. Therefore, the usual practice is always to use the $N - 1$ correction when using sample values to estimate population parameters.

Calculation of Sample Variances

We have already calculated the sum of squares for sample 1 (Table 4–1) using formula (4.2) in which we subtract each score from the mean, square that difference, and sum those differences. Now let us use the raw score formula (4.3) to calculate the variance for sample 1.

$$\sum X^2 = 56{,}766$$

$$(\sum X)^2 = (752)^2 = 565{,}504$$

$$\sum x^2 = \sum X^2 - (\sum X)^2/N$$

$$= 56{,}766 - (752)^2/10$$

$$= 56{,}766 - 565{,}504/10$$

$$= 56{,}766 - 56{,}550.4$$

$$= 215.6$$

$$s^2 = \sum x^2/(N - 1)$$

$$= 215.6/9$$

$$= 23.96.$$

A

$\bar{X} = 75.2$

B

$\bar{X} = 72.4$

Figure 4–2. *A*, dispersion of observations for sample one. *B*, dispersion of observations for sample two.

Note that the calculation of the sum of squares with formula (4.3) results in exactly the same value as that obtained with formula (4.2).

The question now arises concerning the use of the variance to indicate the degree of dispersion of the distribution of observations. If we were to pictorially represent the values of sample 1 we would obtain the dispersion about the mean shown in Figure 4–2 *A*.

Let us compare sample 1 with another of the samples drawn earlier. If we calculate the variance of sample 2, we obtain the result shown in Table 4–5. The variance for sample 2 is larger than that for sample 1. If we graph sample 2 (Figure 4–2 *B*) in the same manner as we did sample 1 (Figure 4–2 *A*) and compare the two graphs, we see that the observations for sample 2 are more widely dispersed. This greater dispersion is reflected in the larger numerical value of the variance for sample 2 (39.38) as compared to that for sample 1 (23.96).

STANDARD DEVIATION

The variance, while accurately reflecting the degree of dispersion of a set of observations about the mean, is not stated in units along the baseline of a scale of measurement.

You will recall that we squared each value to eliminate negative numbers in order that the obtained measure of variability (the variance) would be a number which becomes larger as the variability of the observations about the mean becomes greater. In doing so we no longer are expressing the observations in their original units. However, if we now take the square root of the variance this will again transform the quantity we use to express variability to the original units. This gives us a number which allows us to specify how far above or below the mean a given value is, and this number is expressed in the same units as the original observations are expressed.

Table 4–5. CALCULATION OF THE VARIANCE FOR SAMPLE 2.

X	X^2	
77	5929	
79	6241	
73	5329	$\sum x^2 = \sum X^2 - (\sum X)^2/N$
83	6889	$= 52,772 - (724)^2/10$
69	4761	$= 52,772 - 52,417.60$
71	5041	$= 354.40$
74	5476	
61	3721	$s^2 = \sum x^2/(N-1)$
69	4761	$= 354.40/9$
68	4624	$= 39.38$
$\sum X = 724$	$\sum X^2 = 52,772$	

This quantity is known as the *standard deviation* (symbolized as σ for a population and as s for a sample) and has a number of uses in statistics. Its principal utility lies in the fact that it is a linear measure expressed in units of the original measurements and can be used to describe the position of any observation using a common reference point, the mean. The standard deviation is essentially a mean. It gives positive numbers that increase when variability increases. Since it is a measure of the average amount of variability, the standard deviation (and the variance, of course) can never be a negative number. You cannot have less than no variability. The basic formula for the variance, formula (4.1), indicates the average amount of variability, based on the squared deviations from the mean. This formula cannot result in a negative number. We obtain the population standard deviation by taking the square root of the population variance. The relationships are as follows:

$$\sigma^2 = \sum x^2/N$$
$$\sigma = \sqrt{\sum x^2/N}$$
$$= \sqrt{20.73}$$
$$= 4.55.$$

Table A–11 may be used to find the square root of 20.73.

Having calculated the standard deviation for the population, we can use the mean and the standard deviation to describe the relative position of any observation in the distribution. For example, since our population standard deviation is 4.55, we know that the value of an observation exactly one standard deviation above the mean is $75.50 + 4.55 = 80.05$. Similarly, we know that any observation two standard deviations above the mean is $75.50 + 9.10 = 84.60$ and an observation three standard deviations above the mean is $75.50 + 13.65 = 89.15$. The same rule applies for values below the mean; an observation two standard deviations below the mean is obtained by subtracting twice the value of the standard deviation from the mean. Therefore, the value of an observation two standard deviations below the mean is $75.50 - 9.10 = 66.40$. Similarly, it is quite possible to find out exactly what value lies 2.58 standard deviations below the mean. To do this we determine what .58 of one standard deviation is. For our present illustration this value is $.58(4.55) = 2.64$. Subtracting $2(4.55) + .58(4.55)$ from the mean will give us the value of the observation lying exactly 2.58 standard deviations below the mean $(75.50 - (9.10 + 2.64) = 75.50 - 11.74 = 63.76)$.

Certain relationships occur for all distributions with the general form of our set of 1000 observations. In all normal distributions 68.27 per cent of the values lie between plus or minus one standard deviation; 95.45 per cent lie between plus and minus two standard deviations; and 99.73 per cent lie between plus and minus three standard deviations. The frequency with which an observation is expected to occur in a normal distribution is directly related to how many standard deviations it is from the mean; observations greater than two standard deviations above or below the mean occur with much less frequency than do observations within plus and minus one standard deviation. These particular relationships are of considerable importance when we wish to determine the probability of obtaining a certain value, or of obtaining an observation within a certain range of values when selecting at random from a normally distributed population.

Standard Scores

Having considered the variance, and its square root (the standard deviation), as measures of variability, we can introduce a useful descriptive index based on the scale of standard deviations. It is possible to transform the scale of values in which measurements are expressed, and as long as the transformations are linear (that is, they do not alter the relative size of the intervals between individual values) no violence is done to the original scale of measurement. Instead of expressing our observations in raw score units, as we have been doing, we could express them in terms of units of the standard deviation. One convenient way to do this is to let the value of the mean equal zero and then to express each observation in terms of how many standard deviations it is from the mean. If the observation is above the mean it is expressed as a positive number; if it is below the mean it is expressed as a negative number. Observations expressed in this form are known as *standard scores*, symbolized by *z* and, hence, called *z-scores*.

The formula for transforming a set of observations into standard scores is

$$z = \frac{X - \bar{X}}{s} . \tag{4.5}$$

Thus, the mean is subtracted from each observation and each remainder is divided by the standard deviation. The mean of a set of standard scores will be zero, the standard deviation will be one, and, of course, the variance will be one.

Illustrated in Table 4–6 are the values of sample 1 (Table 2–2) and their transformations into standard scores. If we compute the mean and standard deviation of this set of transformed scores, we find that the mean is indeed zero, since the scores, positive and negative, sum to zero, and zero divided by anything is still zero. The standard deviation and the variance are equal to one because we

Table 4–6. THE CALCULATION OF STANDARD (z) SCORES.

	1	2	3
	Observations	x	z
	X	$X - \bar{X}$	$\dfrac{x}{s}$
Step 1: Calculate the mean and	69	−6.20	−1.2679
standard deviation for the	71	−4.20	−.8589
original observations. (If	72	−3.20	−.6544
calculators are not avaliable,	72	−3.20	−.6544
the squares of the observations	75	−.20	−.0409
may be found in Table A–11.)	75	−.20	−.0409
	75	−.20	−.0409
	76	+.80	+.1636
	83	+7.80	+1.5951
	84	+8.80	+1.7996
$\sum X = 752$			.0000
$N = 10$			10
$\bar{X} = 75.20$			.0000
$\sum X^2 = 56766$			9.0164
$(\sum X)^2 = 565504$			.0000

$$\frac{(\sum X)^2}{N} = \frac{(565504)}{10}$$

= 56550.40			.0000

$$\sum X^2 - (\sum X)^2/N = \sum x^2$$

Step 2: Subtract the mean	= 215.60		9.0164
from each value keeping	$s^2 = \sum x^2/(N-1)$		1.00
the sign (+ or −) of the	= 215.60/9		
numbers.	= 23.95		
Step 3: Divide each value in	$s = \sqrt{s^2}$		1.00
column 2 by the value of s.	= 4.89		

divided the difference between each score and the mean by the standard deviation of the original set of observations. Since the variance is the square of the standard deviation, it is also one since the square of one is still one.

Figure 4–3 is a graphical representation of these transformations. You can see that none of the basic relationships between the scores

Figure 4–3. Relationship of the original observations to the standard (z) scores.

is changed in any way. The only change under such linear transformation is that different numbers are used to represent the scores.

Transformations of Standard Scores. A set of standard
scores can have any desired value for the mean and the standard
deviation. It is only necessary to change the original equation as
follows:

$$ Z = \frac{X - \bar{X}}{s} s' + \bar{X}', \tag{4.6} $$

where s' is the value you want to establish for the new standard
deviation and $\bar{X}'$ is the value you want to establish for the new mean.
Table 4–7 illustrates the calculation for a small set of scores; the
new mean will be set at 50.00 and the new standard deviation will
be set at 10.00.

The new mean of the scores (referred to as Z scores to distinguish
them from z-scores with a mean of zero) is now 50 and the new
standard deviation is 10. How was this accomplished? First, we
multiplied each of the scores by a constant value (10) and then added
another constant value (50). Since the mean of our first set of
standard scores was zero, multiplying zero by ten does not affect the
mean. Adding 50 to zero does produce a change of 50 in the mean,

Table 4–7. CALCULATION OF STANDARD SCORES WITH MEAN EQUAL TO 50.00
AND STANDARD DEVIATION EQUAL TO 10.00.

1	2	3	4	5
Scores	$X - \bar{X}$	$(x)(1/5)$	$[(x)(1/5)]s' + \bar{X}'$	Z
1	−2	−1.26	$(-1.26)(10) + 50$	37.4
2	−1	−.63	$(-.63)(10) + 50$	43.7
3	0	.00	$(.00)(10) + 50$	50.0
4	+1	+.63	$(+.63)(10) + 50$	56.3
5	+2	+1.26	$(+1.26)(10) + 50$	62.6

$\sum X = 15$ 0.000 250.0

$N = 5$ 5   5

$\bar{X} = 3$ .000 $\bar{X} = 50.00$

$\sum X^2 = 55$ $\sum X^2 = 12{,}896.90$

$(\sum X)^2 = 225$ $(\sum X)^2 = 62{,}500.00$

$(\sum X)^2/N = 225/5 = 45.0$ $(\sum X)^2/N = 12{,}500.00$

$\sum x^2 = 55 - 45 = 10$ $\sum x^2 = 396.90$

$s^2 = 2.50$ $s^2 = 99.27$

$s = 1.58$ $s = 9.96$

The calculation is identical to that of Table 4–6, until column 4, where each value in column 3 is multiplied by 10 and added to 50. The new values in column 5 are known as Z scores and have a mean of 50 and a standard deviation of 10.

however. The standard deviation of 1, when multiplied by 10, becomes 10. A score one standard deviation above the mean becomes a 60 when the constant of 50 is then added. A score one standard deviation below the mean becomes a 40, since −1 multiplied by 10 is −10 and 50 added to this is +40. The general rule for transformations of this type can be stated as follows:

1. The addition ·(or subtraction) of a constant to every score increases (or decreases) the value of any measure of central tendency (mean, median, or mode) by the value of that constant. The addition or subtraction of a constant has no effect on any measure of variability, such as the standard deviation (or the variance).

2. Multiplying (or dividing) every score by a constant has the effect of multiplying (or dividing) every measure of central tendency

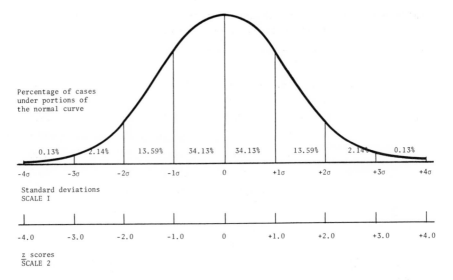

Figure 4–4. (From Berstein, A. L., *A Handbook of Statistics Solutions for the Behavioral Sciences*. Copyright 1964 by Holt, Rinehart and Winston, Inc. and reproduced with their permission.)

by the value of that constant. The standard deviation is multiplied (or divided) by that constant and the variance is multiplied (or divided) by the square of the constant.

Previously, standard score transformations were characterized as being *linear* transformations. This means that no basic characteristics are changed by the transformations except the scale values in which they are expressed: a score one standard deviation above the mean in the original set of observations is still one standard deviation above the mean in the standard score transformation. If we were to transform our population of 1000 observations into standard scores and plot the scores on a graph, this graph would look exactly like the original graph—each score stands in relation to other scores exactly as it did in the original. The only difference would be that the units expressed on the baseline of the graph would be changed.

Figure 4–4 illustrates two scales of measurement in relation to the normal curve. Scale 1 is in standard deviation units and illustrates the percentages of the total area under the normal curve at various standard deviation distances from the mean. Scale 2 illustrates the relationship of standard scores to the standard deviation units in scale 1.

Use of Standard Scores. When we use standard scores we are expressing each observation in terms of how far it deviates from the mean in units of the standard deviation. The advantage of this manner of expressing values is that it makes possible the comparison of an individual's standing on one distribution with his standing on another distribution. If we have the distribution of the heights of a group of people and the distribution of the weights of the same people, we can, by standard scoring, decide whether or not a given individual is heavier than he is tall, *relative to the appropriate comparison distributions*. Obviously, if an individual is at the mean in height and is one standard score above the mean in weight we know something about his body build, relative to the comparison distribution.

One can also express a value relative to a distribution of observations by using percentiles. However, the advantage of using standard scores is that it is possible to determine a person's standard score knowing only the mean of the distribution, its standard deviation, and the original observation in question. In order to determine a percentile it is necessary to have the entire distribution available.

One further advantage that standard scores have over percentiles is that it is possible to recover the original observation if we know the standard score, as long as the mean and the standard deviation of the distribution are also known. For example, if the mean of a distribution equals 100, the standard deviation equals 10, and a standard score is -2.5 we can determine the original value as follows:

$$z = \frac{X - \bar{X}}{s}$$

$$-2.5 = \frac{X - 100}{10}$$

$$-25 = X - 100$$

$$X = 100 - 25$$

$$X = 75.$$

This could also be expressed as follows:

$$X = zs + \bar{X}$$

$$X = -2.5(10) + 100 \qquad (4.7)$$

$$X = 75.$$

Other Measures of Variability

The two measures of variability we have discussed up to this point, the average deviation and the standard deviation, use the mean as a reference point around which the variability is expressed. The average deviation expresses the variability as the mean of the deviations from the mean, disregarding the algebraic sign of the deviations. The standard deviation expresses the variability as the mean of the squared deviations from the mean, and is preferred because of its relation to the normal curve. In some instances, such as when there are badly skewed distributions, a mean is a misleading statistic, and the median is preferred as a measure of central tendency. Similarly, if the distribution of scores is incomplete at either end because, for example, the extremes are reported as open categories, a mean cannot be determined and we must use a median. In such instances it will not be appropriate to use either the average deviation or the standard deviation, and some measure appropriate for use with medians is necessary.

Semi-interquartile Range.   The measure of variability used most frequently in instances in which a mean cannot be used, or, when we have only the median (the fiftieth percentile) available as a measure of central tendency, is the *semi-interquartile range*. The semi-interquartile range is defined as follows:

$$\frac{Q_3 - Q_1}{2},$$
$$(4.8)$$

where Q_3 is the third quartile (which is the seventy-fifth percentile, below which 75 per cent of the scores lie), and Q_1 is the first quartile (which is the twenty-fifth percentile, below which 25 per cent of the scores lie).

This measure tells us the range of the values which include one-half of the middle 50 per cent of the observations. This measure is purely descriptive since percentiles have little function in inferential statistics.

The semi-interquartile range is often used to indicate the direction and the amount of skew in a distribution. If $Q_3 - Q_2$ (the fiftieth percentile) is equal to $Q_2 - Q_1$, then the distribution is not

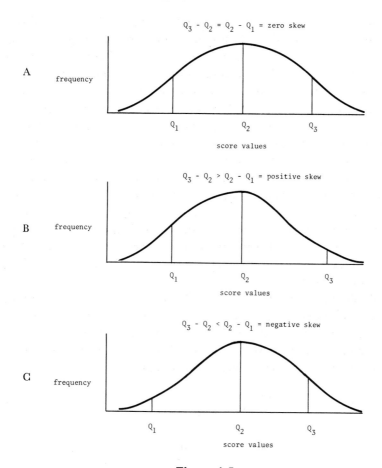

$Q_3 - Q_2 = Q_2 - Q_1 =$ zero skew

A   frequency

Q_1 Q_2 Q_3

score values

$Q_3 - Q_2 > Q_2 - Q_1 =$ positive skew

B   frequency

Q_1 Q_2 Q_3

score values

$Q_3 - Q_2 < Q_2 - Q_1 =$ negative skew

C   frequency

Q_1 Q_2 Q_3

score values

Figure 4-5.

skewed (Figure 4–5 *A*). If $Q_3 - Q_2$ is greater than $Q_2 - Q_1$ then the distribution is positively skewed. (The relation *greater than* can also be expressed by the symbol $>$. Therefore, the preceding statement can be written $Q_3 - Q_2 > Q_2 - Q_1$.) (Figure 4–5 *B*.) Similarly, if $Q_3 - Q_2$ is less than $Q_2 - Q_1$, then the distribution is negatively skewed. (The relation *less than* can be expressed by the symbol $<$. Therefore, this statement can be written $Q_3 - Q_2 < Q_2 - Q_1$.) (Figure 4–5 *C*.)

Range. One other measure of variability is the *range*. This is the difference between the highest and lowest value. While this measure is certainly easy to calculate since it involves only the subtraction of the lowest from the highest observation its disadvantages are numerous. The addition or subtraction of a single observation at either extreme can result in a substantial change in the value of the range and thereby can result in quite misleading estimates of variability. Since the change in only one observation can greatly change the range it is not a stable statistic from a sampling viewpoint. Also, its interpretation depends on the size of the sample on which it is based. If we have only two observations in the distribution the range would be determined by subtracting the lower value from the higher. If we now add a third observation we cannot decrease this range; the range will either stay the same or will increase. Since this will be true as we add observations it is misleading to compare ranges if samples are of unequal size. As N increases the range would be expected to increase since the probability of sampling one of the infrequently occurring observations from either tail of the distribution is increased.

While statistics such as the range and interquartile range can be used as estimates of the standard deviation in large samples (cf. Chapter 15, Dixon and Massey*), their efficiency is still much less than if the estimates were based on sums of squares, and such estimates should be used only under specialized circumstances.

---

* Dixon, W. J., and Massey, F. J., Jr.: *Introduction to Statistical Analysis*, 2nd ed.; New York: McGraw-Hill, 1957.

EXERCISES

1. a. Calculate the sample variance for the following distribution of scores: 25, 37, 28, 33, 47, 21, 27, 32, 31, 29.

   b. Using distribution C (Exercise 4), compute the sum of squares using the raw score formula. Compute the sample variance. Compute the sample standard deviation.

2. If you were told that two normal distributions had the same mean, would they be identical? Why?

3. A person's z-score on a test is -1.5. The mean on the test was 70, and the standard deviation was 6. What was the person's original score?

4. Find the semi-interquartile range for the following three distributions. Are any of the distributions skewed? In which directions?

A		B		C
Scores	f	Scores	f	Scores
52–53	1	95–99	6	12
50–51	0	90–94	11	28
48–49	5	85–89	16	19
46–47	10	80–84	7	15
44–45	9	75–79	9	15
42–43	14	70–74	8	35
40–41	7	65–69	2	14
38–39	8	60–64	3	15
36–37	6	55–59	2	
34–35	5	50–54	1	
32–33	3	$N = 65$		
$N = 68$				

5. Find the average deviation for distribution C.

6. What is the range in the following distribution: 7, 9, 13, 5, 12, 23, 54, 3, 5.

7. If you were told that the mean grade for a test in a class of 60 students was 74, the standard deviation was four and your grade is 2.3 standard deviations above the mean, what would your grade be?

8. If the mean for 60 students is 50, the median is 60, and s is 5, and 5 points are added to each score the mean will become _____, the median will become _____, and the variance will be _____. If we multiply each score by 2 the mean will become _____, the median will become _____, and the variance will be _____.

9. Assume a normal distribution of scores with a mean of 60 and a standard deviation of 8. What raw score corresponds to the z-scores of +1.28 and −1.28?

10. In a normal distribution with $\overline{X} = 50$ and $s = 10$, how many times out of 100 would you expect scores higher than 60 to occur?

5

PROBABILITY AND THE
NORMAL CURVE

Suppose, improbable though it may be, that you and a friend sitting next to you in class become bored by a lecture. To while away the time until the end of the hour, you try some inexpensive gambling. You cannot match pennies in the usual fashion since this amount of activity would attract the attention of the instructor and few instructors would tolerate such activity taking place during a lecture. However, your friend is sitting where he is not so easily seen when he flips a coin. You agree that he should flip a coin and if the coin comes up heads, he wins. If it comes up tails, you win.

Of course there are only two possible outcomes on each flip, and the odds are even; in the long run he should win half of the time and you should win half of the time. However, as gamblers, we know that sometimes we might get "lucky" and there will be a long run of, say, tails in our favor. If such a run is long enough then one player might be bankrupt before the odds correct themselves, and in this case the lucky gambler wins from his bankrupt opponent.

Suppose you begin playing and the coin comes up heads (he wins) on the first five flips. This would not seem too unreasonable on an intuitive basis. What if he wins the first ten flips; then the first 20; the first 50; the first 100? When would you decide that something was amiss and that it was unreasonable to continue on the assumption that the game was honest?

We know that, when gambling on outcomes of equally probable

events, it is possible to have a "run of luck" for one of the events. On what basis, then, do we decide that this "unlucky" run of events, say ten heads in a row, has exceeded what could reasonably be expected on the basis of luck alone? Essentially, we want to reason from a particular set of events (a sequence of coin tosses) to a general state of affairs (the "true" probability of each of the possible outcomes).

PROBABILITY AND INFERENCE

Probability is central to statistical inference. For example, the experimenter who takes a group of rats, divides them into two groups, administers a new drug to one group and an inert substance to the other, and then tests the ability of the rats to learn a maze, will end his experiment by analyzing his measure of learning in terms of probability statements. He will ask the question: "What is the probability that a difference between the groups in the rate of maze learning is more than would be expected by chance alone?"

Specifically, the experimenter is asking the question "Does the drug affect maze learning to the extent that I can conclude that there is a greater difference between the two groups of animals than would be expected by chance alone?"

In this chapter we will expand on the concept of probability (symbolized as P) introduced in Chapter 2, and will present the basic rules for computing probabilities. The uses of normal curve models to determine probabilities will be presented, and the relationship of probability to the normal curve, and to statistical inference, will be developed.

In Chapter 2 the concept of probability was introduced and defined as the ratio of the ways something can happen to the ways it both can and cannot happen. If an event can happen in X ways and not happen in Y ways, the probability of X occurring is equal to

$$X/(X + Y). \tag{5.1}$$

Let us now see how this formula can be applied to the example of coin tossing.

Determining "Runs of Luck." It will help us to decide whether or not the coin game is honest if we have some idea regarding the probability of obtaining a "run of luck" against us, rather than having to rely on our intuitive judgment alone. In order to determine the probability of a given outcome we must know the probability of each of the possible single events. When we call a coin unbiased we mean that the likelihood that it will come up heads is the same as that it will come up tails on any single toss of the coin. Since these are the only two acceptable outcomes we can say that the probability of heads on any toss of the coin is .50 (i.e., $P_H = .50$), and the probability of a tails on any toss of the coin is the same $(P_T = .50)$. The probability of an event occurring (say heads) plus the probability of the event not occurring (tails) must equal 1.00.

The probability of obtaining either heads or tails on the first toss is, as we have seen, .50. What is the probability of obtaining heads on each of two independent tosses? There are four possible outcomes in this instance: the first toss can be heads and the second heads (H, H); the first toss can be tails and the second heads (T, H); the first heads and the second tails (H, T); both the first and the second can be tails (T, T). Out of these four possible outcomes only one (H, H) is favorable to getting two heads. Therefore, the probability of obtaining two heads on two independent coin tosses is one out of four, or $P = .25$. The probability of obtaining two tails is the same: 1/4 or $P = .25$. One head and one tail can be obtained in two ways $(T, H$ and $H, T)$. Therefore the likelihood of obtaining this outcome is 2/4 or $P = .50$.

What is the probability of obtaining three heads in a row? The possible outcomes are shown below:

H, H, H; H, T, H; H, H, T; T, H, H;

T, H, T; T, T, H; H, T, T; T, T, T.

Of these eight possible outcomes only one is favorable to getting three heads (H, H, H). Therefore, the likelihood of obtaining three heads in a row is one out of eight, or $P = .125$.

Rules of Probability

We can state the general rule for determining the probability of obtaining *all* of an independent series of events as follows: If each of the specified events is independent of the outcome on the previous tosses, the probability that *all* of the set of independent events will occur is the product of the separate probabilities of each event.

Thus, the probability of obtaining two heads in a row is, as we have seen, $(1/2)(1/2) = (1/2)^2 = 1/4 = .25$. The probability of obtaining three heads in a row is $(1/2)(1/2)(1/2) = (1/2)^3 = 1/8 = .125$.

Now, we are able to answer our original question: what is the probability of flipping a coin ten times and getting ten successive heads: $P = (1/2)(1/2)(1/2)(1/2)(1/2)(1/2)(1/2)(1/2)(1/2)(1/2) = (1/2)^{10} = 1/1024 = .00098$. A run like this, while possible, is very improbable, and if it should continue you should suspect that the true probability of obtaining heads is *not* .5. This means that the game is not "honest" and you would be well advised to discontinue the coin tossing game.

PERMUTATIONS AND COMBINATIONS

Let us now explore a slightly different example using coins. Assume you toss six coins at a time and tally the frequency with which heads and tails appear: the chances are that you would have close to three heads and three tails. What is the probability that you would toss (given unbiased coins) four heads and two tails; five heads and one tails; six heads and no tails? To calculate the answers to such questions as these we need to make a distinction between *permutations* and *combinations*.

Permutations and combinations differ primarily in terms of the importance of order. Specifically, if the problem involves predicting the precise order of the outcome we are interested in permutations. If there is no concern for the order of outcomes we are interested in combinations. For example, given four objects labeled *A*, *B*, *C*, and *D*, what is the probability of picking object *A* followed by object *B*? If we begin by randomly choosing one object, our chances of picking object *A* are one in four. Assuming that we do obtain *A* on the first choice, there are now three alternatives remaining (assuming that we cannot pick *A* a second time). Thus we would have 4×3 or 12 permutations possible:

AB, AC, AD, BA, BC, BD, CA, CB, CD, DA, DB, DC.

Obviously only one of these permutations (*AB*) is the specified event: all 11 of the others will not meet our specifications. Therefore the probability of selecting object A followed by object B on a purely random basis is one out of 12, and $1/12 = .083$.

Now let us assume that the order of selecting the two objects is unimportant. This is the same thing as saying that outcome AB and outcome BA are to be considered equivalent. Therefore the number of arrangements shrinks to the following six combinations:

$$AB, \ AC, \ AD, \ BC, \ BD, \ CD.$$

Two of the 12 permutations are the specified event (AB and BA) and the probability, therefore, equals two out of 12, which equals one out of six. Therefore $P = .167$.

While it is possible to diagram all the permutations and combinations (as was done above) if the set of objects is fairly small, the process becomes extremely tedious when larger numbers become involved. Fortunately, there are formulas which will allow the calculation of permutations and combinations. However, to use the formulas it is necessary to become familiar with the concept of a *factorial*. The factorial of a number is obtained by multiplying the number times itself minus one, multiplying that product by the number minus two, and so forth, ending at one. (The factorial of zero is one.) The factorial of four (which is written as 4!) is calculated as follows:

$$4! = 4 \times 3 \times 2 \times 1.$$

Table 5–1 contains the factorial of the numbers from one to 15. To calculate the permutations of N objects taken K at a time, we substitute the necessary factorials into the following equation:

$$P^N_K = \frac{N!}{(N - K)!} \ .$$

Applying this formula to the earlier problem of the four objects A, B, C, and D to be arranged in groups of two and then substituting the necessary values from Table 5–1 into the preceding formula, we have

$$P^4_2 = \frac{4!}{(4 - 2)!} = \frac{24}{2} = 12.$$

This is the number of possible permutations which was arrived at by actually counting the number of permutations. Similarly, the

Table 5–1. FACTORIALS

n	$n!$
1	1
2	2
3	6
4	24
5	120
6	720
7	5,040
8	40,320
9	362,880
10	3,628,800
11	39,916,800
12	479,001,600
13	6,227,020,800
14	87,178,291,200
15	1,307,674,368,000

number of combinations of N objects taken K at a time can be calculated by the equation:

$$C_K^N = \frac{N!}{K!\,(N-K)!}. \qquad (5.3)$$

By substituting values from Table 5–1 into the preceding formula we have

$$C_2^4 = \frac{4!}{2!\,(4-2)!} = \frac{4 \times 3 \times 2 \times 1}{(2 \times 1)(2 \times 1)} = \frac{24}{4} = 6,$$

which, again, is the value obtained earlier by actually counting the number of combinations.

We will apply these procedures to the questions raised earlier in the chapter concerning coin flipping. We want to know the probability that of six unbiased coins flipped in the air, four would come up heads and two would come up tails. Since we do not care which specific coins come up heads and which come up tails, we use our combinations formula. The first question concerns the number of possible combinations of six things taken four at a time. This is calculated by substituting the appropriate values from Table 5–1 into the combinations formula:

$$C_4^6 = \frac{6!}{4!\,(6-4)!} = \frac{720}{24(2)} = \frac{720}{48} = 15.$$

Now from the result of this calculation we know that there are 15 ways that our six tossed coins can come up with four heads and two tails. We now know the number of ways the event can occur, but to calculate the probability we need to know all the other possibilities that can occur with six tossed coins. What about one head and five tails? Six heads and no tails, etc.? If we are to calculate the probability of a certain event we must know all the other possibilities to determine the number of possible outcomes. We can calculate these in the same manner in which we determined the number of ways the event we are interested in (four heads and two tails) could occur.

To begin, let us specify all the other ways the event can occur:

> 6 heads and 0 tails,
> 5 heads and 1 tails,
> 4 heads and 2 tails (calculated above),
> 3 heads and 3 tails,
> 2 heads and 4 tails,
> 1 heads and 5 tails,
> 0 heads and 6 tails.

To calculate the probability of these outcomes, all that is necessary is to work the combinations formula for each of the above events. The calculations follow.

$$C_6^6 = \frac{6!}{6! \, (0)!*} = \frac{720}{720} = 1$$

$$C_5^6 = \frac{6!}{5! \, (1)!} = \frac{720}{120} = 6$$

$$C_4^6 = \frac{6!}{4! \, (2)!} = \frac{720}{48} = 15$$

$$C_3^6 = \frac{6!}{3! \, (3)!} = \frac{720}{36} = 20$$

$$C_2^6 = \frac{6!}{2! \, (4)!} = \frac{720}{48} = 15$$

$$C_1^6 = \frac{6!}{1! \, (5)!} = \frac{720}{120} = 6$$

$$C_0^6 = \frac{6!}{0! \, (6)!} = \frac{720}{720} = 1$$

$$\overline{64}$$

* $0! = 1$

When we finish this tedious series of computations, the sum of all these possible events will equal 64. Thus, there are 64 possible outcomes when tossing six coins. Now we apply the probability formula of $X/(X + Y)$ to determine the probability of obtaining four heads and two tails. $X = 15$ (the number of ways four heads can be obtained). $X + Y = 64$ (the total number of ways that the coins may distribute). When we divide 15 by 64 the answer is .234; therefore, the probability of obtaining four heads and two tails when six coins are tossed is .234.

Table 5–2. PASCAL'S TRIANGLE.

N	Coefficients in Expansion of $(x + y)^2$											Sum
1						1	1					2
2					1	2	1					4
3				1	3	3	1					8
4			1	4	6	4	1					16
5		1	5	10	10	5	1					32
6	1	6	15	20	15	6	1					64
7	1	7	21	35	35	21	7	1				128
8	1	8	28	56	70	56	28	8	1			256
9	1	9	36	84	126	126	84	36	9	1		512
10	1	10	45	120	210	252	210	120	45	10	1	1024

The computation of probabilities by the method illustrated above can be a tedious process. Fortunately, there is an easier method to achieve the same end. The actual probabilities may be obtained from a table known as Pascal's triangle for the special case when $P_x = P_y = .5$. This table, which is printed as Table 5–2, provides the exact probabilities and totals for all combinations of events up to ten. Examine the values for $N = 6$ and note that they are identical to the values calculated earlier for our six coin tosses. Also, note that the values total to 64, the sum of all the possible combinations for six separate events. The construction of Pascal's triangle is quite easy: the first and last values of the series for any number are always 1; all other terms are obtained by adding together the two values just above the one to be calculated. For example, the second term for $N = 6$ is obtained by summing the two values immediately above it; $1 + 5 = 6$; the next value is $5 + 10 = 15$; and so forth.

What does the combinatorial formula and Pascal's triangle have to do with the normal curve? As we stated in Chapter 2, the normal curve can be used to evaluate the probabilities of events occurring in much the same manner that the probability of tossing eight heads and two tails can be determined. To understand the relationship between the determination of probabilities as presented in the first part of this chapter and probabilities as determined from normal curve distributions it must be understood that probability is a frequency ratio; it is the number of times an event happens divided by the number of times it can and cannot happen. The probability distribution when $P = .5$ (as in coin tossing) and when N is infinitely large is a normal distribution. When we consider the distribution of the outcomes that can occur when ten coins are tossed we find that there is only one way in which ten coins can be tossed and result in ten heads and no tails; there are nine ways in which there can be one head and nine tails; there are 45 ways in which there can be two heads and eight tails; and so on. These are exactly the values given in Pascal's triangle for $N = 10$. Using these values as frequencies and graphing them, we obtain a distribution similar in appearance to the normal curve. This figure is symmetrical about a central point, and the frequencies diminish as we move away from that central point. In fact, if we superimpose a normal curve on the graph the similarity between the results obtained on the basis of chance and the theoretical normal curve is quite striking.

In Figure 5–1 are distributions obtained by reading the values from Pascal's triangle for $N = 4, 6, 8,$ and 10 (taken from Table 5–1). The distributions begin to look more and more like the normal curve as N gets larger and larger.

NORMAL CURVE

The normal curve is a theoretical mathematical concept. The fact that it happens to describe the distribution of objects in the real world, such as the frequency with which things occur on the basis of chance alone, is one of those fortunate relationships between the world of mathematical equations and the world of observation. The normal curve can be used to determine the probability of specified events occurring.

This is done by representing the number of observations in the distribution in terms of the proportional area of the distribution.

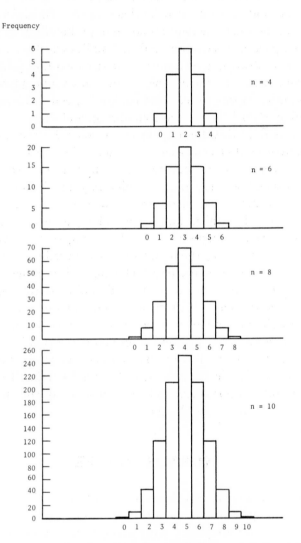

Figure 5–1. Values from Pascal's triangle for $n = 4, 6, 8$ and 10.

To do this we let the total number of observations, whether 30, 50, 1000, or 1,000,000 equal 1.00 of the total area under the curve defining the distribution. This procedure is similar to the method we use in plotting a bar diagram (also called a histogram). When plotting a bar diagram we represent each observation by a rectangle of a given size. If we knew the size of the rectangular unit we could determine the number of observations of any given value by measuring the height of a column of rectangles constructed for a given value. The theoretical distribution is a smooth curve. However, we are still representing the number of observations by proportional area. Therefore, if .20 of the total area under the curve falls between two values we know that .20 of the total number of observations lie between these two score values.

It is necessary that some common score unit be used in order to allow the normal distribution to be fitted to populations which are characterized by different numbers of observations, by different means, and by different variances. Just such a common score unit was presented in the last chapter—the standard score (z). A set of standard scores has a mean of zero and a standard deviation of one as a function of the way in which the scores are calculated. To transform the values from Table 2–1 into standard score form we use the equation $\dfrac{X - \bar{X}}{s}$. Figure 5–2 is the population of 1000 observations with both a scale of the original scores and of the standard scores corresponding to the original scores indicated along the horizontal axis. (If you have forgotten the section on standard scores you should go back and review pages 56 and 57 before proceeding further.)

The normal distribution, then, is constructed using proportions of the total area to represent frequencies. The total area under the curve equals 1.00 and standard scores are used as the score units. Let us examine some of the properties of the normal curve in more detail. The normal curve is smooth, and it is symmetrical about its standard score mean of zero. Its range extends to plus and minus about four standard deviations (cf. Figure 4–4). Theoretically, the normal curve never quite reaches the baseline. For most practical purposes however, $\pm 4s$ is quite sufficient to enclose all of the frequencies in the distribution.

The area under the curve is equal to the total number of observations in the population (by definition). Since there is an invariant relationship between the standard deviation and the point at which it occurs in any normal distribution there is, then, an invariant relationship between the standard deviation and the proportion of the total area occurring between the mean and one standard deviation. Indeed, it can be seen that there is an invariant relationship between the proportional area of the curve and any given standard deviation distance. Since the normal curve is a graph which represents each case by an equal area it follows that the proportion of the total area under the curve will equal the proportion of the total cases contained in any given region of the curve. Hence, proportional area is equal to the proportional frequency contained in any given region of the normal curve.

Table A–2 is used to find the area between the mean and any given standard score. The table is organized with the standard score values listed to the first decimal in the first column. The remaining columns list the values for the second decimal. In the body of the table is listed the proportion of the total area under the normal curve which falls between the mean and the particular standard score. A standard score value of 0.00 indicates that the score under consideration falls at the mean of the distribution. Since a standard score of 0.00 is at the mean no area falls between that score and the mean; indeed, the entry in the table for 0.00 (the first score in the second column of the table) is .0000. If the standard score is 0.01, then a small proportion of the total area falls between the mean and that standard score; the table indicates that .0040 of the total area falls between the mean and a z of .01. Inspection of the table reveals that between the mean and plus one standard deviation $(+1\sigma)$ .3413 of the total area under the curve is found. Again, since proportional area equals proportional frequency, .3413 of the total number of the scores occur between the mean and plus one standard deviation $(+1\sigma)$.

Thus, .6826 of the observations occur between plus and minus one standard deviation $(\pm1\sigma)$. Since .3413 of the observations occur between the mean (μ) and one standard deviation $(+1\sigma)$ and .4772 of the observations occur between μ and $+2\sigma$, then .4772 − .3413 = .1359 of the observations occur between $+1\sigma$ and $+2\sigma$. Thus, the probability of obtaining a score which is greater than 2σ away from μ is less (since there are fewer of them) than is the probability of obtaining a score greater than 1σ away from μ.

Since the normal curve is symmetrical and .4772 of the observations occur between μ and either $+2\sigma$ or -2σ, .4772 + .4772 = .9544 of the observations occur between $\pm2\sigma$. Since .4987 of the observations occur between μ and either $+3\sigma$ or -3σ, then .4987 + .4987 = .9974 of the observations occur between $\pm 3\sigma$.

If we have a table of the normal curve available, we can, by converting any observations to a standard score, determine the number of individuals who would be expected to obtain any given score value. To do this it is necessary to know μ, σ, and N. The method for making such determinations is presented in the next section.

Normal curve methods can be used providing that the number of observations is at least 30. This is an arbitrary lower limit which is used because the bias in using samples varying in N from size 30 to infinity (∞) is negligible. If fewer than 30 observations are available different methods of inference, referred to as small sample methods, are used. These small sample methods correct for the systematic bias introduced when small samples are used to infer normal curve parameters.

Use of the Normal Curve Table. We can use normal curve methods to determine the probability that a subject chosen at random from the 1000 subjects represented in Table 2–1, will have a score higher than 87 on the scholarship examination. (See pages 11 – 13.)

If the normal curve is to be used to determine the probability of obtaining any given value it is necessary to translate the value into standard scores. This sets the mean of the distribution at zero, and the standard deviation at one. A value of 87, then, would be converted to standard score form as follows:

$$z_{87} = \frac{X - \bar{X}}{s}$$
$$= \frac{87 - 75.5}{4.55}$$
$$= \frac{11.50}{4.55}$$
$$= 2.53.$$

The population of 1000 scores is shown in Figure 5–2 with the horizontal axis labeled both in raw score units and in standard score units. It is helpful, when solving problems of this type, to visualize the region of the normal curve in which we are interested.

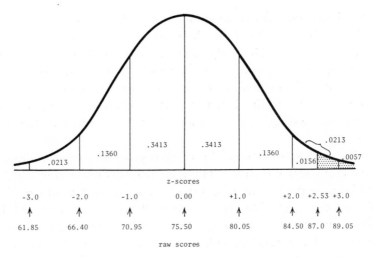

.3413   .3413

.1360   .1360

.0213   .0156   .0057

.0213   .0213

z-scores

-3.0   -2.0   -1.0   0.00   +1.0   +2.0 +2.53 +3.0

61.85   66.40   70.95   75.50   80.05   84.50 87.0 89.05

raw scores

Figure 5–2. Area of the normal curve (shaded) falling beyond a z-score of +2.53.

In Figure 5–2 we have shaded the area of the curve about which we are concerned.

From Table A–2 we find that .4943 of the area above the mean falls between the $\overline{X}$ and a z of +2.53. Therefore, only .5000 − .4943 = .0057 of the area remains above a z of +2.53. Since relative area and relative frequency (and hence probability) are the same, we know the probability that an individual picked at random from the population will have a score higher than 87 is .0057. Since there are 1000 cases in the population we would expect to have 1000 × .0057, or about six scores higher than 87.

We can ask a series of questions concerning the probability of scores occurring at any point or within any region of the distribution providing we know the $\overline{X}$ and s.

(a) What is the probability of obtaining a score lower than 87? In the previous example we found that a score of 87 is a standard score of +2.53. In this example, however, we are concerned with the shaded region of Figure 5–3. Since .0057 of the area falls above $z = 2.53$ then .4943 of the area falls between the mean and $z = 2.53$ and .5000 of the area falls below the mean: .5000 + .4943 = .9943. Therefore, the probability of selecting a case at random which would be lower than 87 is .9943. Therefore, we could expect about 994 of our 1000 scores to be lower than 87.

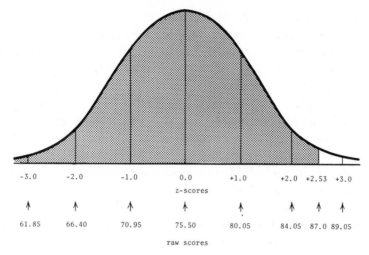

z-scores

raw scores

Figure 5–3.

(b) What is the probability of obtaining a score less than 72.5?
Here, we are concerned with the shaded portion of Figure 5–4.

$$z_{72.5} = \frac{72.5 - 75.5}{4.55}$$

$$= \frac{-3}{4.55}$$

$$= -0.66.$$

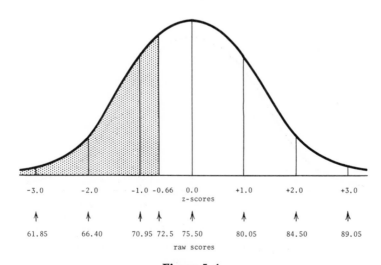

z-scores

raw scores

Figure 5–4.

Referring to the table we find that .2454 of the area falls between the mean and a z of $-.66$ (since the normal curve is symmetrical the proportional areas are the same for both plus and minus values). Since .5000 of the total area falls below the mean, and since .2454 of that .5000 falls between the mean and a z of -0.66 then $.5000 - .2454 = .2546$. The probability of obtaining a score lower than 72.5 when selecting at random from our population is .2546. Put another way, about 255 subjects would be expected to score lower than 72.5.

(c) What is the probability of selecting someone with a score in the range 78 through 85?

In this problem we are concerned with the shaded area of Figure 5–5. In order to answer this question we must find two different z scores as follows:

$$z_{78} = \frac{78 - 75.5}{4.55}$$

$$= \frac{2.5}{4.55}$$

$$= .55$$

$$z_{85} = \frac{85 - 75.5}{4.55}$$

$$= \frac{9.5}{4.55}$$

$$= 2.09.$$

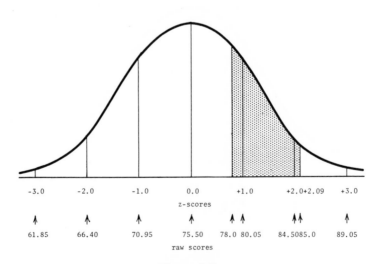

Figure 5–5.

Since we want to find the area between two z-scores above the mean it is necessary to find the area from the mean to the lower score, then from the mean to the higher score, and to find the remainder by subtracting the smaller area from the larger. Between the mean and a z of +2.09 is .4817 of the total area under the curve; between the mean and a z of +.55 is .2088 of the total area. Then .4817 of the area occurs between the mean and a score of 85 while .2088 of the area occurs between the mean and a score of 78. Thus, .4817 − .2088 = .2729, which is the proportion of the area in the shaded range defined by the scores 78 through 85. Therefore, about 273 scores would be expected between 78 and 85.

(d) What is the probability of selecting a score between the symmetrically placed scores of 71.50 and 79.50, as illustrated in Figure 5–6? Since these are symmetrically placed scores it is necessary to compute only one z-score:

$$z_{79.5} = \frac{79.50 - 75.50}{4.55}$$

$$= \frac{4.00}{4.55}$$

$$= .88.$$

Between the mean and a z of +.88 is .3106 of the total area. Since the same area will fall between the mean and a z of

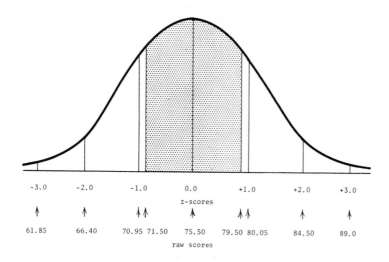

Figure 5–6.

−.88 we can find the total area by adding .3106 and .3106 to obtain .6212. Therefore, the probability of obtaining a score in the region bounded by the scores 71.50 and 79.50 is .6212.

(e) What is the probability of selecting a score between the asymmetrically placed scores of 72 and 76, as illustrated in Figure 5–7?

$$z_{76} = \frac{76 - 75.5}{4.55}$$

$$= \frac{.5}{4.55}$$

$$= .11.$$

Between the mean and a z of $+.11$ is .0438 of the total area.

$$z_{72} = \frac{72 - 75.5}{4.55}$$

$$= \frac{-3.5}{4.55}$$

$$= -.77.$$

Between the mean and a z of $-.77$ is .2794 of the total area. Therefore, the probability of obtaining a score within the region bounded by scores of 72 and 76 is $.0438 + .2794 = .3232$.

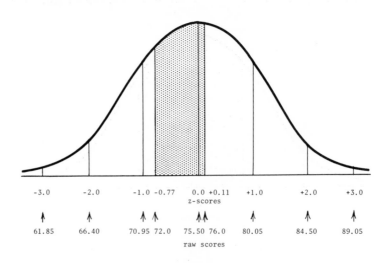

Figure 5–7.

It can be seen from the foregoing examples that the normal curve table can be used to solve a variety of problems if we can assume normality and if we know the mean and the standard deviation of the population. This fact provides us with some powerful inferential techniques, the development of which will be the subject of the next few chapters.

EXERCISES

1. What is the probability of flipping a coin and getting four tails in a row followed by two heads in a row?
2. If there are ten cans and five of them are filled with water in how many orders can the set of five water-filled cans be selected?
3. In how many ways can the five water-filled cans be selected from the ten cans when the order is ignored?
4. In a normal distribution the mean is 60 and the standard deviation is 4.3. If the acceptable scores are any scores within 1.56 of the mean, what is the range of acceptable scores?
5. In a normal distribution of 100 scores about how many scores would we expect to find between $z = 1.30$ and $z = 1.90$?
6. Explain the meaning of each of the entries in Pascal's triangle in the row to the right of $N = 5$.
7. In a normal distribution the mean is 50 and the standard deviation is 2.0.

    a. If an individual has a z-score of -2.74, what is his raw score?

    b. If his z-score is 1.34, what is his raw score?
8. In a normal distribution the mean is ten and the standard deviation is .5. What proportion of the scores would fall between a z-score of $+1.0$ and a z-score of -1.0?

6

NORMAL CURVE MODELS: PRECISION OF ESTIMATE

You are now able to draw a random sample, to calculate the mean, variance, and standard deviation, and to determine the probability of obtaining a particular case from a normally distributed population.

We, now, want to determine the *precision* with which it is possible to estimate a population parameter from a sample value. In other words, we want to determine the probability that the parameters we have estimated fall within some prescribed range of values. As shown in Figure 3–1, our ability to estimate the mean on the basis of small samples is really quite good since most of the time we are quite close to the true population mean. However, some samples do vary more than others (see samples 2 and 4 in Figure 3–1). We would now like to say something more precise than merely stating that the accuracy of estimating the population mean from a sample mean is really quite good most of the time. The only way in which we could be absolutely sure of the accuracy of our estimates would be to calculate the population mean. But, if we could accomplish this, we would not need to collect samples in the first place.

A satisfactory approach to this problem would be to determine the probability that our estimate of the population mean does not

A

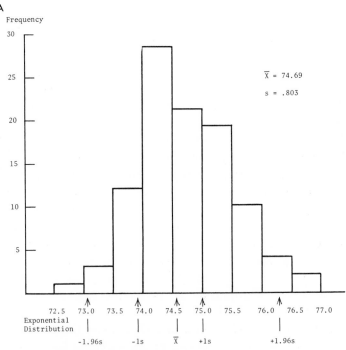

B

Figure 6–1. *A*, Distribution of 100 means calculated from samples of 30 observations each randomly selected from a normal population. *B*, Distribution of 100 means calculated from samples of 30 observations each randomly selected from an exponential population.

exceed some stated range of values. It is possible to do this (1) by utilizing some properties of the normal curve, and (2) by taking advantage of the fact that a large number of statistics calculated from random samples distribute normally.

Perhaps a brief review of some of the material in Chapter 5 will be helpful here. In Chapter 5, the characteristics of the normal curve were discussed and, from Table A–2, it can be seen that in a population distribution with the characteristics of the theoretical normal curve .68 of the observations will fall between plus and minus one standard deviation; .95 of all the observations will fall between plus and minus 1.96 standard deviations from the mean.

Now, let us review briefly some aspects of sampling as presented in Chapter 2. In Chapter 2 there is a graph of 100 means calculated from samples of $N = 30$ from our "normal" population of 1000 observations (Figure 2–9 A). Figure 2–9 B is a graph of 100 means calculated from samples of $N = 30$ drawn randomly from an exponential population. The distributions of both of these calculated values distribute in a normal curve fashion. If we were to calculate the percentage of observations falling within plus and minus one standard deviation and plus and minus 1.96 standard deviations, and then to compare these percentages to the values for the theoretical normal curve, we would find that the differences between the percentages for the two distributions are rather small. Figures 6–1 A and 6–1 B contain the results of these calculations.

With 100 normally distributed observations, we would expect five of them to lie outside the range of $\pm 1.96s$. For the 100 means calculated on samples drawn from a normal population (Figure 6–1 A), a total of six observations lie outside these ranges. For the means calculated on samples drawn from an exponential population (Figure 6–1 B), exactly five observations are outside this range. It is this remarkable correspondence of real events to mathematical expectations that makes the methods of statistical inference so valuable.

SAMPLING DISTRIBUTIONS

In order to follow the discussion to be presented it will be necessary both to make some assumptions and to take certain things on faith, since their proof is beyond the scope of this book. First of all keep in mind that we want to estimate the population mean from only one sample. If we have drawn the observations in our sample under random conditions, this sample mean can itself be considered to be a random sample from a population of *means*. In fact, a set of 100 means calculated from our normal population of observations can be considered to be a population of means (although a very limited one); however, each "observation" is a sample *mean* instead of an individual *observation*. We can assume that our sample mean is one of an infinite number of sample means that could be calculated from the population of 1000 observations. Remember, if each observation is replaced in the population as soon as it is selected, the population of 1000 is theoretically infinitely large. Consequently, means calculated from this population under these conditions represent samples from an infinitely large population of means. In statistics, populations such as these are called *sampling distributions*. The sampling distribution of means will have its own mean which is identical to the population mean.

Since we can assume that our sample mean is one of this population of means which are distributed in a normal curve fashion, we can rephrase our original question as follows: What is the probability that our obtained sample mean is between plus and minus one standard deviation of the mean of the distribution of means? To answer this we need to know the standard deviation of the distribution of means. But all we have is a single sample! However, we can estimate the population mean on the basis of a single sample if we assume that this single sample is randomly selected from a distribution of means which, as we know, will distribute in a normal curve fashion. The statistic used to make this estimate is the *standard error of the mean* ($\sigma_{\bar{X}}$) and is calculated by the formula:

$$\sigma_{\bar{X}} = \frac{\sigma}{\sqrt{N}}. \tag{6.1}$$

(It should be noted that the formula for the standard error of the mean is stated in terms of population parameters. This has been indicated by the use of Greek symbols. Obviously, then, it would not be possible to use this formula to calculate the $\sigma_{\bar{X}}$ unless σ is known.)

How does the preceding formula enable us to estimate where a given sample mean would be expected to fall in a distribution of sample means? The answer is twofold. First, it has been demonstrated previously that means computed from random samples distribute as a normal curve. Second, there is a demonstrable relationship between a population of observations and a distribution of means calculated from random samples drawn from this population of observations. The degree of variability which the sample means will display is a function of the degree of variability of the distribution of observations. Since this is a constant relationship it is possible to estimate the standard deviation of a distribution of sample means *using only one single sample.* This statistic is called a *standard error,* and is an estimate of the standard deviation of the sampling distribution of a statistic; in this case the standard deviation of a distribution of sample means. Whenever the term standard error is used it means, then, that we are referring to the standard deviation of the sampling distribution of a statistic.

The relationship between a population of observations and a sampling distribution of means calculated on samples from this population is as follows: the means will distribute symmetrically and will approach the form of the normal curve. The sampling distribution of means will have the same mean as the population mean (μ) and a standard deviation ($\sigma_{\bar{x}}$) equal to the population standard deviation (σ) divided by the square root of the sample size ($\sqrt{N}$).

Calculation of the Standard Error

By way of illustration we will calculate the standard error of the mean using the formula given earlier, and the population parameters we have been using: $\mu = 75.5$; $\sigma = 4.55$. If we draw samples of $N = 30$ from this population the standard error of the mean is calculated as follows:

$$\sigma_{\bar{x}} = \frac{\sigma}{\sqrt{N}} = \frac{4.55}{\sqrt{30}} = \frac{4.55}{5.48} = .830.$$

This standard error value is interpreted in the same manner as the standard deviation values we have obtained earlier. Thus, between the mean and plus one $\sigma_{\bar{x}}$ we would expect to find .3413 of the total area of curve occurring (and, of course, .3413 of the total number of means); between plus and minus one $\sigma_{\bar{x}}$ we would expect to find .6826 of the total area of the curve, and so forth. Put another way, between the μ of 75.5 (which we know in this example) and $75.5 + .83 = 76.33$ we would expect to find .3413 of the sample $\overline{X}$'s if we drew many samples from the population and calculated the mean for each sample. For the sample means, .6826 would be expected to be between 76.33 and 74.67 (which is 75.5 — .83).

Usually, we do not have a population of sample means at our disposal and must rely on an estimate based on only one sample. In order to evaluate the adequacy of our estimate of the standard error of the mean using only one sample let us draw some actual samples from a population whose parameters we know. We can then compare the estimate based on only one sample mean with the actual distribution of a large number of sample means drawn from the population. Figure 6–2 is the distribution of 100 sample means based on samples of $N = 30$ drawn from the normally distributed population of scores which we have used throughout this book. The mean of these sample means is 75.45 (as compared to the population mean of 75.50). We found earlier that the standard error of the mean based on an N of 30 and the σ of 4.55 is equal to .83. The actual standard error of the mean for 100 means (found by calculating the standard deviation in the usual manner, using each

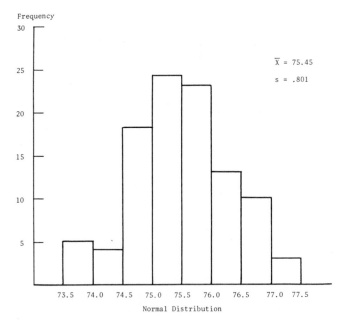

Figure 6–2.   The distribution of 100 sample means each based on random samples of 30 observations from a normal population with $\mu = 75.50$.

mean as a score) is .80. This minor discrepancy from the estimated value of .83 is well within what would be expected on the basis of sampling variation alone.

Let us follow the procedure used to estimate the standard error of the mean as we would do it in actual practice. When we estimate $\sigma_{\bar{X}}$ using only a single sample we do not know the population standard deviation (σ). Therefore, we must use the best estimate of σ that we have available. The best estimate of σ is s, the standard deviation of our sample. The formula for the standard error of the mean thus becomes:

$$s_{\bar{X}} = \frac{s}{\sqrt{N}} . \tag{6.2}$$

The actual calculation of the standard error is done in Table 6–1.

Table 6–1. CALCULATION OF THE STANDARD ERROR FOR A SAMPLE OF 30 OBSERVATIONS.

Observations

78	73	75	69	76
72	76	77	76	78
79	72	78	85	79
72	71	84	80	75
76	70	70	75	71
71	86	71	71	74

$$N = 30$$
$$\sum X = 2260$$
$$\bar{X} = 75.33$$
$$\sum X^2 = 170{,}842$$
$$(\sum X)^2 = 5{,}107{,}600$$
$$(\sum X)^2/N = 170{,}253.33$$
$$\sum x^2 = \sum X^2 - [(\sum X)^2/N] = 588.77$$
$$s^2 = \sum x^2/(N-1) = 20.30$$
$$s = 4.50$$
$$s_{\bar{X}} = \frac{4.50}{\sqrt{30}}$$
$$= 4.50/5.48$$
$$= .82$$

Once the sample standard deviation has been calculated, the calculation of the standard error is quite straightforward. The standard error as estimated for this sample is .82, which compares quite well with the obtained $\sigma_{\bar{x}}$ which was .80. It is also quite close to the $\sigma_{\bar{x}}$ of .83 which we obtained when we computed $\sigma_{\bar{x}}$ using the true σ.

CONFIDENCE INTERVALS

We can now, with a few additional calculations, determine what are called *confidence intervals for the mean*. We know that a population of means calculated from random samples will distribute themselves normally. The one available sample mean may be viewed as a single random case drawn from an infinite population of sample means, each one based on the same number of observations. If the distribution is normal, .95 of the observations lie between plus and minus 1.96 standard deviations from the population mean. The mean of our single sample is the best estimate we have of the true population mean. We will use the standard error of the sample mean $(s_{\bar{x}})$ based on the data of Table 6–1 as an estimate of the standard deviation of the population of means $(\sigma_{\bar{x}})$. Consequently, we can determine the upper and lower limits within which the true population mean would be expected to fall by the following steps:

1. For the upper limit of the confidence interval, the equation is:

$$UL_{.95} = \bar{X} + 1.96s_{\bar{x}}. \tag{6.3}$$

2. For the lower limit:

$$LL_{.95} = \bar{X} - 1.96s_{\bar{x}}. \tag{6.4}$$

If we now apply these equations using the mean and the standard error of the mean taken from the earlier calculations we obtain the following values:

$$UL_{.95} = 75.33 + 1.96(.82) = 75.33 + 1.61 = 76.94$$
$$LL_{.95} = 75.33 - 1.61 = 73.72.$$

What does this mean? We have used the standard error of the mean calculated on the basis of one sample to estimate the standard deviation of a population of means. Then, using the normal curve model we know that .95 of all the observations in a normal curve fall between plus and minus 1.96 standard deviations from the mean.

We multiply the estimate $(s_{\bar{X}})$ of the standard deviation of the populations of means $(\sigma_{\bar{X}})$ by 1.96. This value, when added to the mean to determine the upper limit and subtracted to determine the lower limit, defines *the .95 confidence interval for the mean*. In other words, using the mean and the standard deviation of our sample we expect the value of the population mean to fall between the upper and lower limits specified by $UL_{.95} = 76.94$ and $LL_{.95} = 73.72$. Any hypothesis concerning a value of the population mean which lies outside the limits specified by 76.94 and 73.72 we will reject at the .95 confidence level.

In the first chapter of this book, we remarked that the field of statistics is frequently characterized by a combination of strict rules and arbitrary assumptions. Estimating confidence limits is one example of this situation. We have a set of well-defined procedures for calculating the standard error and a set of requirements (such as minimum sample size) that must be met if the procedures are to be considered valid. However, the setting of confidence limits is a completely arbitrary matter. We could just as easily have determined the .45 confidence limits, or the .64 confidence limits, or any other set of confidence limits for that matter. All that is needed to set any given confidence limit is to determine from the normal curve table the standard scores which define the percentage of observations to be included within the confidence limits. For example, to set the .99 confidence limits, we find the percentage of observations included between the mean and the given standard score value from the table of the normal curve (Table A–2).

Assume we want to set the limits for the .99 confidence interval. We know that half of the .99 will fall between the mean and the lower limit and half will fall between the mean and the upper limit. One-half of .99 is .495. From the body of Table A–2 we find that .495 of the area under the curve falls between the mean and a *z*-score of 2.58 (the real value is 2.576, which becomes 2.58 when rounded up). To determine the .99 confidence limits, we substitute into the UL and the LL equations the value of 2.58 (instead of 1.96 which we used for the .95 level) and multiply our standard error by this value. The results of this calculation are as follows:

$$UL_{.99} = \bar{X} + 2.58s_{\bar{X}} = 75.33 + 2.58(.82)$$
$$= 75.33 + 2.12 = 77.45$$
$$LL_{.99} = 75.33 - 2.12 = 73.21.$$

The interpretation of these values is as before: on the basis of our sample statistics we expect the value of the population mean to be located within the limits defined by the score of 77.45 ($UL_{.99}$) and 73.21 ($LL_{.99}$). Any hypothesis concerning the value of the population mean outside these limits we reject at the .99 confidence level.

Small Samples

The procedure just described is appropriate when the research worker has at least 30 observations in his sample. However, the research worker who has only small samples must employ a slightly different sampling distribution appropriate for small numbers of observations.

By now sampling distributions are nothing new. We have seen how a sampling distribution of means will assume a normal curve shape regardless of the shape of the population on which it is based, and we know that the approximation to the normal curve is usually closer and closer the larger the sample size. By the same logic, we know that a sampling distribution of *differences* constructed by the equation:

$$\frac{\bar{X} - \mu}{\sigma_{\bar{X}}} \tag{6.5}$$

should also distribute normally.

This equation represents the sampling distribution of differences we would obtain if we drew a sample, computed the mean ($\bar{X}$), subtracted from $\bar{X}$ the true population mean (μ), and divided the difference by the standard deviation of the sampling distribution of means ($\sigma_{\bar{X}}$). Such a distribution would have a mean of zero and a standard deviation of one. As you may (or may not) have suspected, this becomes a sampling distribution of mean differences in standard score form. The equation $\dfrac{\bar{X} - \mu}{\sigma_{\bar{X}}}$ is basically a standard score equation.

For sample sizes greater than 30, this sampling distribution will distribute normally. However, for sample sizes smaller than 30, the curve changes shape.

In practice, if we were to develop such a sampling distribution, we would use $s_{\bar{X}}$ instead of $\sigma_{\bar{X}}$, since we would not know either the population mean (μ) or the population standard deviation (σ) and

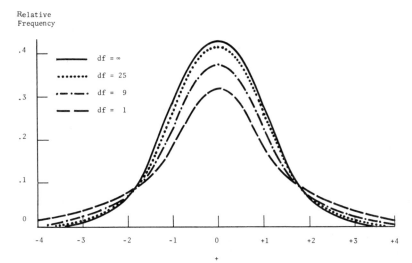

Figure 6–3. (From Ferguson, G. A., *Statistical Analysis in Psychology and Education.* Copyright 1959 by McGraw-Hill Inc. and reproduced with their permission.)

thus could not calculate the $\sigma_{\bar{X}}$. Since the population standard deviation is systematically underestimated using small samples, the normal curve model is inappropriate here. Therefore, an alternative procedure must be found. The sampling distribution for the equation $\dfrac{\bar{X} - \mu}{s_{\bar{X}}}$ can be developed with a correction included for the bias in the estimate of the standard error of the mean due to small sample size. Suppose we draw samples of ten observations each from our population of 1000 observations (for which we know the population mean), calculate the mean of each sample, subtract that mean from the population mean, and then divide by the standard error of the mean estimated on the basis of that sample. After doing this several thousand times we would have the sampling distribution labeled in Figure 6–3 as $df = 9$. (The meaning of the symbol df will be explained in a moment. For our purposes here $df = N - 1$.)

THE t DISTRIBUTION

The relationship of the new sampling distribution to the distribution of the normal curve is shown in Figure 6–3. This new distribution is referred to as the *t* distribution. The mathematical derivation of this distribution was first developed by W. S. Gossett who published his findings under the pseudonym "Student" since the company which employed him had a rule which did not permit the publication of the results of any research performed by its employees. Since the *t* distribution did not reveal any trade secrets dear to the industry concerned (Gossett was employed by the Guinness Brewing Corporation in Dublin) he was allowed to publish under this pseudonym. As a result this statistic is often referred to as Student's *t*.

Inspection of Figure 6–3 indicates (1) that the *t* distribution for ten observations is symmetrical about zero; (2) that the observations are not as densely distributed in the center of the distribution of scores as is the case for the normal distribution; and (3) that there are more observations in the tails of the *t* distribution than in the normal distribution. There are slightly different distributions of *t* for every sample size until $N = 30$, at which point it becomes indistinguishable from the normal curve (which, you will remember, is based on a population of infinite size). Figure 6–3 illustrates the relationship of the *t* distributions for $df = 1, 9, 25$, and infinity (∞). (The distribution for infinity is the normal curve.) Table 6–2 contains a comparison of the values of *t* and the normal curve values (z) for selected numbers of observations.

As is evident from examination of both Figure 6–3 and Table 6–2, the percentage of observations in the tails of the *t* distributions varies as a function of the number of observations. If the sampling distribution is calculated on the basis of samples with five *df*, the percentage of observations in the tails of the distribution is much higher than if the sampling distribution is calculated on the basis of samples with 20 *df*. When the number of *df* reaches 30 the *t* distribution is almost identical to the normal curve.

Table 6–2. COMPARISON OF AREAS BETWEEN LIMITS FOR THE NORMAL CURVE AND THE *t* DISTRIBUTION FOR DIFFERING DEGREES OF FREEDOM.

Area between Confidence Limits	Normal Curve Value	*t* Value for Varying Degrees of Freedom				
	z	5	10	30	120	∞
.90	1.65	2.01	1.81	1.70	1.66	1.65
.95	1.96	2.57	2.23	2.04	1.66	1.96
.99	2.58	4.03	3.17	2.75	2.62	2.58

Degrees of Freedom

The t distribution can be used to set confidence intervals with small samples in the same manner as the normal curve is used with samples of more than thirty observations. To illustrate we will determine the confidence limits of the mean for samples 1 and 2 from Table 2–1. However, before computing an estimate of the standard error of the mean and setting the confidence limits, we should explain the concept of degrees of freedom. The table of the t distribution (Table A–3) is based on the number of degrees of freedom (abbreviated df). The number of degrees of freedom is always one less than the size of the sample on which the value of t is based. For our example in which $N = 10$, the df will be 9. The degrees of freedom for t refer to the freedom of the observations to vary as a function of chance alone. Sample 1 has an N of 10 and a mean of 75.2. When we calculate the mean of that sample we have thereby placed a restriction on the number of observations that are free to vary by chance alone. For example, we could add $+2$ to nine of the observations. However, if the mean is to remain at 75.2, then the tenth value would have to have 18 subtracted from it— there is no other way that the mean of the sample could remain at 75.2. This last value, then, is not free to vary randomly. It is restricted by the value of the mean and the sum of the other observations in the sample. The t distribution is a distribution we use to estimate the extent of variability to be expected on the basis of random sampling errors. Therefore, the equations for the t distribution are based on the number of degrees of freedom rather than the number of observations in the sample. Since we are interested in estimating variability, and since we use the mean as the zero point around which we express variability the mean must remain fixed. For our samples the proper df would be 9, one less than the number of observations. The initial calculations to be carried out for confidence limits are the same as our earlier calculations.

Sample 1	Sample 2
$\sum X_1 = 752$	$\sum X_2 = 724$
$N_1 = 10$	$N_2 = 10$
$\bar{X}_1 = 75.2$	$\bar{X}_2 = 72.4$
$s_1 = 4.89$	$s_2 = 5.95$
$s_{\bar{X}_1} = 1.55$	$s_{\bar{X}_2} = 1.88$

However, when we estimate the confidence limits for the mean we use the table of t values in our UL and LL equations. These values are the small sample equivalent of the normal curve values. Using the normal curve table to determine the .95 confidence limits for our samples of $N = 30$, we multiply the standard error by 1.95, which is the standard score value which encloses .95 of the observations in the normal curve. For the t distribution, we enter Table A–3 and locate the entry 9 in the column labeled "degrees of freedom." Having located 9 in that column, the value of t for the column headed 0.05 is selected. For our samples this value is 2.26. This is the value of t which encloses .95 of the cases in the t distribution for nine degrees of freedom. It encloses exactly the same proportion of observations as does 1.96 for the normal curve, the larger value being due to the fact that the t distribution has more observations in the tails of the distribution than does the normal curve. To calculate our upper and lower confidence limits, we simply substitute the value of t for the normal curve value in the UL and LL equations.

Sample 1	*Sample 2*

$$UL_{.95} = \bar{X} + t_{.05}s_{\bar{X}} \qquad UL_{.95} = 72.4^0 + 2.26(1.88)$$

$$= 75.2^0 + 2.26(1.55) \qquad = 72.40 + 4.25 = 76.65$$

$$= 75.20 + 3.50 = 78.70$$

$$LL_{.95} = 75.20 - 3.50 = 71.70 \qquad LL_{.95} = 72.40 - 4.25 = 68.15$$

Assuming, then, that we had only sample 1 available to us, we could, on the basis of our calculations, estimate that the true population mean is somewhere between 71.70 and 78.70. In addition, we could state these limits with the confidence that, on the basis of random sampling variation, we would be correct .95 of the time.

On the basis of sample 2 we could estimate that the true population mean is somewhere between 68.15 and 76.65, again with the expectation that we would be correct .95 of the time. Both of these estimates, we know, do include the true population mean of 75.5.

The procedure to determine the .99 confidence limits is the same. The value of t in the 0.01 column for 9 df is 3.25 (instead of the 2.58

for the normal distribution).

Sample 1	*Sample 2*

$$UL_{.99} = \bar{X} + t_{.01}s_{\bar{x}}$$

$$= 75.20 + 3.25(1.55)$$

$$= 75.20 + 5.04 = 80.24$$

$$LL_{.99} = 75.20 - 5.04 = 70.16$$

$$UL_{.99} = 72.40 + 3.25(1.88)$$

$$= 72.40 + 6.11 = 78.51$$

$$LL_{.99} = 72.40 - 6.11 = 66.29$$

It can be seen that the range of values we issue when estimating the .99 confidence limits is broader ($80.24 - 70.16 = 10.08$ for sample 1; $78.51 - 66.29 = 12.22$ for sample 2) than those we issued for the .95 confidence limits ($78.70 - 71.70 = 7.00$ for sample 1; $76.65 - 68.15 = 8.50$ for sample 2). The .99 range is broader because we are sacrificing precision of estimate in the interest of greater confidence that the true population mean lies within the stated confidence limits than is the case when the .95 range is used.

Usually, in research applications of statistical methods we are not interested in setting a range of values within which the true population mean would be expected to lie. The most common use of statistical procedures is to determine whether or not two samples could have been drawn from the same population, regardless of what the mean of that population might be. The next chapter develops the logic of statistical inference for this situation.

EXERCISES

1. If you drew a sample of 30 scores from a population and found the mean of these scores to be 75 and the standard deviation to be 2, between what two symmetrically placed raw scores would you expect 97% of the population scores to lie?

2. Given a sample of nine scores with a mean of 25 and a standard deviation of .73, what would be the upper and lower score limits within which 95% of the raw scores would be expected to occur?

3. a. What would you estimate the standard error of the mean to be for the population given a standard deviation of 1.2 based on a sample of 36 cases?

   b. Given that the above population has a mean of 92, between what two symmetrically placed scores would you expect to find .6826 of the total area of the curve for the distribution of raw scores?

   c. Between what two symmetrically placed scores would you expect to find .6826 of the total area of the curve for the distribution of sample means?

4. If the following values are known what is the standard error of the mean? $\bar{X} = 100$; $s_{\bar{x}} = 15$; $N = 40$.

5. Given a sample N of 81 with $\bar{X} = 21.1$ and $s = 3.62$, (a) calculate the standard error of the mean, and determine the confidence limits for the mean at (b) the .95 level of confidence and (c) the .99 level of confidence.

6. Determine the confidence limits for the mean at the .95 and .99 levels of confidence using the same statistics as in problem 5 except that the sample size is now 16 instead of 81.

7. Assume that the value of a population mean is 100 and the standard error of the mean for samples of size 20 is 3.5. What proportion of sample means based on a sample size of 20 would you expect to be between 96 and 103?

8. Find the .95 confidence limits for the mean given the following values: $\bar{X} = 97$; $s_{\bar{x}} = 10$; $N = 40$.

9. Find the .95 confidence limits for the mean given the same values as in problem 8 except that the sample size is now ten instead of 40.

7

DIFFERENCES
BETWEEN
TWO GROUPS

You may have had some difficulty in relating what you have learned about statistics to what you read in your other textbooks. For example, many textbooks in the field of psychology report experiments in which conclusions are drawn on the basis of "significant differences" between groups. These conclusions are based on statistical methods, but to date little that you have learned about statistical inference permits you to understand how these conclusions are reached. We will now examine the area of statistical inference which deals directly with problems of evaluating the results of experiments. Let us consider two types of situations.

(1) A psychologist interested in the physiological bases of learning suspects that a certain class of drugs, because of its mode of action on the central nervous system, may facilitate the rate at which animals learn. To evaluate the likelihood of this suspicion he takes a sample of 20 rats of approximately the same age and randomly assigns them to two groups: Group A, which is injected with an inert substance, and Group B, which is injected with the drug. The animals then learn a multiple choice maze in order to find food. The investigator hypothesizes that the animals who are injected with the drug will learn the maze more quickly than will the

107

animals who are injected with the inert substance. To test this hypothesis he counts the number of trials each animal requires to reach an established criterion of learning; let us assume that the criterion is four errorless runs through the maze. After all the rats have been tested the mean number of trials required to reach the criterion is calculated for Group A and for Group B. On what basis will the experimenter decide whether or not the drug facilitates learning?

(2) A social psychologist is interested in comparing different methods of influencing people's racial prejudices. He wishes to know whether direct contact with a member of a racial group about which prejudicial beliefs are held is more effective in changing attitudes than are methods which do not involve direct contact with a member of the group. To test this, he first administers a questionnaire to determine the degree of racial prejudice within the sample on which he proposes to test his methods. This sample is then divided into two groups which are matched so that the mean prejudice score is the same for both groups. One group is exposed to direct contact with members of the racial group against which prejudicial beliefs are held. The other group is given a series of lectures on the harmful effects of prejudice and is provided with information about the characteristics of the "prejudice group." At the end of the experimental period, a second measure of prejudice is administered. The average scores of the two groups are then compared to see if a positive change in attitudes toward the "prejudice group" has occurred. How big a difference in the amount of change between the two groups would there have to be for the difference to be considered statistically significant?

Although these two experiments, presented in capsule form, differ in many important respects, the fundamental statistical question remains basically the same: Are any differences found between the means of the two groups statistically significant differences? Can we conclude that one drug, or one method, is more effective than another in changing the behaviors in question? The basic paradigm for such experimentation is given in outline form in Figure 7–1. First, two random samples are drawn from the defined population. Each of these samples then receives the appropriate treatment and some relevant characteristic (called a criterion measure) is determined for each subject. Summary statistics are calculated for each group: these will be a measure of central tendency and a measure of variability. The bottom two boxes,

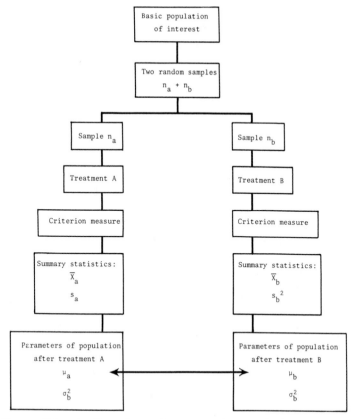

Figure 7-1. Outline of steps in an experiment. (Adapted from Winer, B. J. *Statistical Principles in Experimental Design,* New York: McGraw-Hill, 1962.)

which are connected by a two-headed arrow, represent the inference which is to be drawn from the experiment.

What is needed is an estimate of the probability that the observed difference between location of the means for the two groups could have occurred as a result of random sampling deviations. On what basis do we determine the likelihood that a difference of a certain magnitude between two means is the result of chance factors rather than representing a real difference? Let us consider some data for the first experimental situation in order to clarify the steps of inference involved. In the first situation, you will remember, the effects of a drug on the rate at which rats learn a maze is being tested. The experimenter wishes to test the hypothesis that an injection of a certain amount of a drug will affect the learning of the maze by hungry rats who are rewarded with food at the goal. A group of control rats is injected with the same amount of an inert substance known to have no effect on behavior. The measure of the rate of learning is the number of trials taken by the animals to run the maze without error four consecutive times. Table 7–1 lists the number of trials each animal required to reach the criterion of four errorless runs. Table 7–2 contains the calculation of the mean, the variance, the standard deviation, and the standard error of the mean for both groups of animals.

Examination of these data indicates that the animals of Group B, which were injected with the drug, take fewer mean trials to reach

Table 7–1. NUMBER OF MAZE TRIALS REQUIRED TO REACH CRITERION OF FOUR ERRORLESS TRIALS.

Group A Scores (Inert Substance)	Group B Scores (Drug)
10	5
13	8
13	8
14	9
14	9
14	10
16	10
17	11
17	12
19	12
19	12
19	14
20	14
20	15
22	15
22	17
22	17
24	17
25	23
26	24
$N_A = 20$	$N_B = 20$

Table 7–2. Calculation of Mean, Variance, Standard Deviation and Standard Error of the Mean for Animals in Group A (Control) and Group B (Experimental).

$N_A = 20$	$N_B = 20$
$\sum X_A = 366$	$\sum X_B = 262$
$\sum X_A^2 = 7072$	$\sum X_B^2 = 3882$
$\overline{X}_A = 18.30$	$\overline{X}_B = 13.10$
$(\sum X_A)^2 = 133{,}956$	$(\sum X_B)^2 = 68{,}644$
$(\sum X_A)^2/N_A = 6697.80$	$(\sum X_B)^2/N_B = 3432.20$
$\sum x_A^2 = \sum X_A^2 - (\sum X_A)^2/N_A$	$\sum x_B^2 = \sum X_B^2 - (\sum X_B)^2/N_B$
$= 7072 - 6697.80$	$= 3882 - 3432.20$
$= 374.20$	$= 449.80$
$s_A^2 = 19.69$	$s_B^2 = 23.67$
$s_A = 4.44$	$s_B = 4.87$
$s_{\overline{X}_A} = .98$	$s_{\overline{X}_B} = 1.09$

the learning criterion than do the animals in Group A who were injected with the control substance. Inspection of Figure 7–2 indicates that the distribution of the scores for the two groups is quite different.

How can we decide whether this difference between means could be expected on the basis of chance sampling differences or if

Figure 7–2. Graphic representation of maze learning scores for Group A (inert substance) and Group B (drug).

it is too large to be considered a chance sampling deviation? After all, several of the animals in the two groups have the same scores. How much overlap can the groups have and still be statistically different?

Sampling Distribution of Differences Between Means

To resolve this issue, it is necessary to consider yet another sampling distribution. In Chapter 6, the logic underlying the sampling distribution of means was developed and was discussed in terms of the precision of estimate possible using a single sample mean to estimate the population mean. To evaluate whether a difference in the means of two groups is larger than would be expected on the basis of chance we must refer the obtained difference to a sampling distribution of differences between means.

In previous chapters, we have discussed random sampling and have presented the methods used to estimate population means and standard deviations using statistics calculated from random samples. A sampling distribution of the differences between means can be constructed in much the same manner as is the sampling distribution of differences $\dfrac{(\bar{X} - \mu)}{s_{\bar{X}}}$, which was developed in Chapter 6. If we draw pairs of samples by random methods, calculate the mean for each sample, and then subtract the mean of the second sample of the pair from the mean of the first sample, we could construct a sampling distribution of difference scores.

If we draw sample A and sample B from the same population on a random basis, calculate the mean for A and the mean for B, then subtract the mean for B from the mean for A, and do this several hundred times, we would have a distribution of differences. We can specify several properties of the resulting distribution without carrying out any calculations.

First of all, the mean of such a distribution of differences would be zero, because the population mean will be estimated quite accurately by the majority of the samples drawn. If the mean for sample A is an accurate estimate of the population mean and the mean for sample B is an accurate estimate of the population mean, the two estimates will be very similar, and the difference between them will be very small. A large number of such differences will center around zero. Figure 7–3 is a graphic representation of a

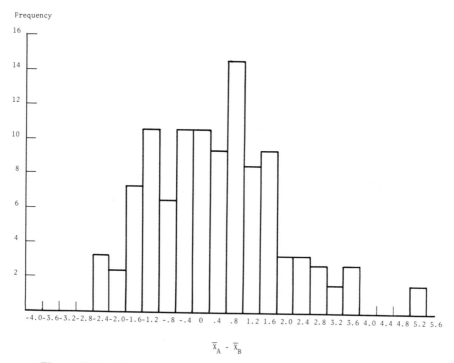

Figure 7-3. One hundred differences between means based on samples of $N = 20$ from a normal population of 6000 cases.

distribution of 100 differences between means, obtained by drawing two random samples of 20 observations each 100 times from a normal population containing 6000 cases, calculating the mean for each sample and then subtracting the mean for the second sample (B) from the first sample (A).

Examination of Figure 7-3 indicates that the mean of the distribution does center on zero. Also, the distribution resembles the normal curve, although many more than 100 differences between means are needed to obtain a closer approximation to the normal curve. Thus, both the means calculated from random samples and the distribution of differences based on these means distribute normally.

The chances of obtaining a difference between means that is not zero diminish as the size of the differences increases, as is true of the other sampling distributions we have considered. In the distribution of differences shown in Figure 7-3, differences between means as large as ± 4.0 occur only one time out of 100.

Could such a distribution be used to assess the probability of

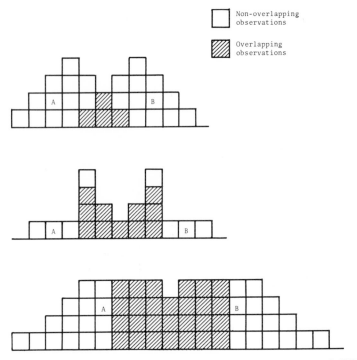

Figure 7–4. Pairs of samples with identical mean differences and differing variances.

obtaining a difference between means of a certain size on the basis of chance alone? The answer is yes, if we take into account the amount of variability to be expected. Several sets of observations could have the same absolute difference between pairs of means but could differ drastically in the extent that the observations vary around their respective means. This point is illustrated in Figure 7–4. The pairs of samples shown all have the same difference between means but quite different variances. As a result there are different percentages of overlapping observations. Obviously some way must be found to take this variability into account.

STANDARD ERROR OF THE DIFFERENCE BETWEEN MEANS

The statistic used to characterize the degree of variability of a distribution of differences between means is called the standard error of the difference between means $(\sigma_{\bar{X}_1 - \bar{X}_2})$.

If pairs of samples are drawn randomly from one single population a distribution of differences between means can be constructed, and this distribution will be normally distributed with $\mu = 0$. This is true only if the pairs of means are drawn from the same population. In the experiment presented earlier, we want to decide whether or not the mean learning scores of the drug and the control groups differ significantly following injection. If they do, then the two groups do not belong to the same population. However, we do not have any expectations on which to base a hypothesis concerning *how much* the population means would be expected to differ as a function of the experimental treatment. Therefore, we have no reasonable *a priori* basis on which we can assign expected values for either of the two population means. We do know, however, that if the treatment has no effect on the learning rate of the two groups they can be considered to still belong to the same population. Therefore, the difference between means expected between the two groups would be zero. For this reason when testing statistical hypotheses we usually test the hypothesis that no difference exists between the two groups (in other words, that the two groups are randomly selected cases from the same population) and evaluate the probability that the difference between means which we have obtained could have occurred on the basis of random sampling deviation from the same population. This hypothesis of no difference between the two underlying population means is called the *null hypothesis*.

In order to decide whether any given difference between means could have occurred as a function of random sampling deviation we must evaluate the probability of this difference occurring in relation to the amount of variability of the sample means. In order to do this we must know the standard error of the distribution of differences between means.

The formula for the standard error of the difference between means is

$$\sigma_{\bar{x}_1 - \bar{x}_2} = \sqrt{\frac{\sigma_1^2}{N_1} + \frac{\sigma_2^2}{N_2}}, \tag{7.1}$$

where σ_1^2 and σ_2^2 are the variances of the respective populations from which the samples are drawn and N_1 and N_2 are the size of each of the samples. Since we do not know the parameters σ_1^2 and σ_2^2 we must use our estimates of those in order to estimate the standard error of the difference as follows:

$$s_{\bar{x}_1 - \bar{x}_2} = \sqrt{\frac{s_1^2}{N_1} + \frac{s_2^2}{N_2}}, \tag{7.2}$$

where s_1^2 and s_2^2 are the variances calculated on the two samples we have taken. The quantity $s_{\bar{x}_1 - \bar{x}_2}$ is an estimate of the standard deviation of a sampling distribution of differences between sample means if the two samples are drawn from a single population of sample means.

t-RATIO FOR INDEPENDENT GROUPS

In order to decide whether or not the obtained difference between means exceeds the difference which would be expected by chance we will compute a t-ratio (see Chapter 6). The t distribution, you will recall, is based on the ratio of sample means to a standard error term. This distribution can be used to determine the probability of obtaining a difference of a given magnitude between two means as a result of sampling error. In order to do this three assumptions are important.

1. The samples are assumed to represent a random selection from the population. For our example, the animals selected are random selections from a population of rats of a given age and species.
2. No differences are assumed to exist between the samples at the time they are selected. We must assume that the two groups of animals do not differ prior to the experimental treatment.
3. A null hypothesis is stated: that there is a zero difference between the means. This makes it possible for us to evaluate the probability of obtaining a difference between means as large as the one observed.

The t-ratio can be calculated using the following formula:

$$t = \frac{\text{Difference between means}}{\text{Standard error of difference between means}}$$

$$= \frac{\bar{X}_A - \bar{X}_B}{\sqrt{s^2 \dfrac{N_A + N_B}{N_A N_B}}} \tag{7.3}$$

Since both s_A^2 and s_B^2 are independent estimates of the same population parameter we will combine them to obtain one pooled estimate of the population variance (the s^2 in formula [7.3] on which to base our standard error estimates). This quantity is calculated by formula (7.4).

$$s^2 = \frac{(N_A - 1)s_A^2 + (N_B - 1)s_B^2}{N_A + N_B - 2} \qquad (7.4)$$

When formulas (7.3) and (7.4) are used it is assumed that σ_A^2 and σ_B^2 are equal (although, of course, they are unknown). This assumption is a reasonable one to make since we are testing the hypothesis that both samples are taken from the same population; hence the statistical model we are applying assumes that they are equal. If the two samples are drawn from the two populations which have unequal variances this will influence the inferential process little, if at all. Departures from the assumption of equal variances have been shown to have practically no effect on the operating characteristics of the t-ratio.*

If we calculate the t-ratio on the data from the drug experiment we obtain the following:

$$s^2 = \frac{(20 - 1)19.69 + (20 - 1)23.67}{20 + 20 - 2}$$

$$= \frac{19(19.69) + 19(23.67)}{38}$$

$$= \frac{374.11 + 449.73}{38}$$

$$= \frac{823.84}{38}$$

$$= 21.68$$

$$t = \frac{18.30 - 13.10}{\sqrt{21.68\,\dfrac{20 + 20}{(20)(20)}}} = \frac{5.20}{\sqrt{21.68\,\dfrac{40}{400}}} = \frac{5.20}{\sqrt{2.168}} = \frac{5.20}{1.47} = 3.53.$$

---

* Boneau, C. A.: *The effects of violations of assumptions underlying the t test;* *Psychological Bulletin*, 1960, 57, pp. 49–64. Baker, B. O., Hardyck, C. D., and Petrinovich, L. F.: *Weak measurements vs. strong statistics: An empirical critique of S. S. Stevens' proscriptions on statistics; Educational and Psychological Measurement*, 1966, 26, pp. 291–309.

How is this t-ratio of 3.53 to be interpreted? We have seen that the distribution of t changes as a function of N. Again, the following rule applies: one degree of freedom is lost for each mean calculated. Since we calculate the means for two samples, two degrees of freedom are lost and when $N = 40$ the total df is equal to 38.

To interpret this obtained value, enter Table A–3. You will recall that the first column lists the number of degrees of freedom and the successive columns list the values of t beyond which a specified proportion of the area under the t-distribution occurs when the null hypothesis is true. Since we have 38 degrees of freedom and there is no exact value given for 38, we will be conservative and use the value entered for 35 degrees of freedom. For 35 df we find the value of 2.72 listed in the column labeled .01. This value — 2.72 — is the value of t that would be exceeded only one time out of one hundred by chance sampling deviation alone. In other words, if we were to draw samples of $N = 20$ from a population and calculate the value of t, only one time out of 100 would we expect to obtain a value of t as large as 2.72. Since our obtained value is 3.53, we conclude that the difference between the means of our two samples represents a real difference and did not occur as a consequence of a random sampling deviation within a single population. Since such a difference would have occurred less than one time in 100 by chance, and since the initial division of the sample into two groups was done randomly, we conclude that the drug administered to Group B does facilitate the rate at which rats learn the maze. In probability terms, the value is less than .01 that this result is due to chance alone. Therefore, we reject the null hypothesis at greater than the .01 level of significance.

This is the basic sequence of steps used to decide whether a mean difference between two groups is due to random sampling differences or is due to the fact that the two groups are members of populations with different means. The t test compares the ratio of the difference between two means to the combined standard error of the difference. On the basis of this ratio the probability of obtaining a difference as large as that observed on a purely chance basis can be determined. While the mathematical basis for determining the critical values of the t distribution is beyond the scope of this book, it can be easily demonstrated, using random sampling methods with a high-speed computer, that this mean-difference/standard error ratio will distribute exactly as do the values of t calculated mathematically.

Other Considerations

Sample size and the t distribution. It can be seen from inspection of the table of the t distribution that as the number of df increases the size of the t-ratio required to reach a given level of significance becomes smaller. Therefore, if everything else remains constant, an increase in sample size permits us to detect differences between means more easily. This point will be discussed further when we discuss the concept of the power of a test.

Significance criteria. In the example presented, the significance level used was .01. This level was chosen arbitrarily and is not related to the type of statistic used or to the number of subjects in the study. It is the arbitrary decision of the experimenter regarding the probability level he will accept. The .05 level could have been chosen and would have been acceptable to most statisticians. There are circumstances where a significance level of .10 might be appropriate, or where we would demand the .001 level of significance before we would reject the null hypothesis. These are considerations that are determined by the nature of the problem and the relative cost of concluding that a chance difference is a real difference. This point will be discussed further when we consider the power of a test.

Unequal samples. In the example used both sets of observations were equal in number. There is no reason why two independent groups have to be equal in the number of observations. However, if the two samples have drastically unequal variances—for example, if one group has twice the variance of the other, then an unfortunate interaction between the number of observations and the inequality of the variance is possible. It has been demonstrated that if two groups are unequal in size, and unequal in variance as well, the t distribution is not that which is tabulated in Table A–3. For example, if one sample has fewer observations and a larger variance than another, then the calculated t-ratio is likely to be larger than the tabled probability levels. Such a condition would result in an experimenter deciding too often that there were real differences between his groups when no real difference existed.

The reverse is true if the sample with the smaller number of observations has the smaller variance. In this case the calculated t-ratio is likely to be smaller than the tabled probability levels. In this case the researcher will fail to detect real differences and will conclude erroneously that his experimental treatment has no effect.

While these considerations may affect the inferences made it has been demonstrated that small fluctuations in sample size and in variance will in general have little effect on the t distribution.

Let us now review the procedures involved in evaluating an experimental hypothesis in order to develop several other considerations:

1. The experimenter must state clearly the experimental hypothesis which he wishes to test. In our example it is that Drug X will facilitate the learning of normal animals.

2. The experimenter must decide on the procedures, apparatus, subjects, etc. that he will use to test the experimental hypothesis. This step does not involve statistical procedures at all but depends on the wisdom of the researcher regarding the experimental procedures and theories of his particular field of specialization.

3. The experimenter, in the course of making the decisions involved in step 2, does become involved in one step requiring a decision on the basis of statistical considerations. If he decides to use the t-test for independent groups, which we have just outlined, then he must take steps to insure that the experimental group and the control group are randomly selected from the same population.

4. At this point the experimenter should formulate his *statistical* hypothesis. In the example we have used the experimenter would have stated a null hypothesis to the effect that with regard to their learning rate, the two groups of animals are two random samples from the same population. It is necessary to state an alternative hypothesis as well. In the example we have presented, the alternative hypothesis is that the two groups are not equal in terms of rate of learning and, hence, are not random samples from the same population. In statistical parlance this is making a *two-tailed test* of the hypothesis since we will consider a deviation in either direction from the hypothesized zero difference between means as a possible basis to reject the null hypothesis. In this case, if we reject the null hypothesis we will accept the alternative hypothesis that the two groups are not equal, and it is possible that the experimental group could be judged to be significantly better or significantly worse than the control group, depending on the direction of the observed difference.

We could state a *one-tailed* alternative hypothesis as well. In this case the alternative to the null hypothesis is that the experimental group will be better than the control group. Here we are deciding (on non-statistical grounds) that the difference between the two groups can either be zero or that the mean differences will all fall in one tail of the distribution. This is tantamount to saying that we do not consider any mean differences in the opposite direction to be possible. The alternative hypothesis can be stated in the opposite direction also. In this case if we reject the null hypothesis, we will conclude that the experimental group is worse than the control group. Again, this type of hypothesis would be justified on the grounds of non-statistical considerations. The use of one-tailed tests of statistical hypotheses merely involves reading a different column of the t table. The ordinary t distribution leaves, for the .05 level of confidence, .025 in each extreme tail of the distribution. If a one-tailed test is used the extreme .05 is entirely within one tail of the distribution. Therefore, to obtain the one-tail entry for the .05 level it is necessary to read the table for the .10 level, since that level leaves .05 in each tail of the distribution. Similarly, if we desire to obtain the one-tail entry for the .01 level the table must be entered for the .02 level of confidence.

Since the advisability of using one-tailed tests at all is still debated by statisticians no more will be said on the matter. The student is advised, at his present level of preparation, to make two-tailed tests at all times since no question concerning the propriety of such tests will be raised.

5. At this point the experimenter is ready to perform the experiment, collect the data, and tabulate it in preparation for statistical analysis.

6. The final step is to calculate the appropriate statistics and either accept or reject the null hypothesis. If the null hypothesis is accepted the experimenter concludes that the experimental manipulations do not affect the behavior under study. If the null hypothesis is rejected the experimenter concludes that the experimental manipulations are effective influences on the behavior.

t-TEST FOR NON-INDEPENDENT GROUPS

Testing the significance of differences between means based on independent groups of subjects has now been presented in some detail. One further situation will be discussed. In this situation we wish to test the significance of a difference between means based on groups which are composed of matched pairs of subjects or to test the significance of a difference between means based on repeated measurements taken on the same subjects.

Suppose that an experimenter is interested in a problem where it is convenient to use the same subjects as both experimental and control subjects. In other words, the pre-experimental level of

Table 7–3. Scores.

S#	Pre-Experimental	Post-Experimental
1	13	17
2	12	15
3	11	15
4	13	16
5	9	10
6	11	16
7	8	7
8	12	15
9	13	18
10	11	15

performance on the variable under study can be obtained as well as the level of performance following the introduction of the experimental manipulation. In this way, it is possible to determine how much subjects change from the initial pre-experimental level as a result of an experimental treatment. Table 7–3 lists pre-experimental and post-experimental scores for ten subjects.

It is possible to treat these two sets of scores as though they were based on independent groups and to carry out the computations shown earlier. However, such a procedure would nullify the precision that the repeated measures design allows. Since each subject provides his own control scores, the amount of variability present is greatly reduced over what would be present in two independent groups. In statistical terms, these scores are called *correlated* scores, meaning that there is a relationship between two sets of scores which are based on the same individual. Under such circumstances many of the factors which produce variability between individuals, such as level of motivation, intelligence level, and physical condition of the subject, would vary less between the pre- and post-experimental tests on the same individual than they would if the two measures were made on different subjects. Similarly, if such variables as intelligence are known to influence the behavior we are measuring, then matching individuals on such related variables will decrease the amount of variability in the scores due to uncontrolled factors.

Correlation methods will not be discussed until Chapters 11 and 12. However, t can be calculated with scores that are not independent by a method which does not require the computation of correlation coefficients. This method allows us to take advantage of the reduction in uncontrolled variability produced when each subject is used as his own control, or when matched subjects are used.

The computation is quite simple and is illustrated with the data from Table 7–3. First, the post-experimental scores are subtracted from the pre-experimental scores, which results in a set of difference scores. The difference scores are then summed, keeping track of signs, and the mean difference $(\bar{D})$ is found. The standard error of these difference scores $(s_{\bar{D}})$ is then calculated, by the same formula used earlier to calculate the standard error of a single mean. The formula for the t-ratio is

$$t = \frac{\bar{D}}{s_{\bar{D}}}, \tag{7.6}$$

where $s_{\bar{D}} = s_d/\sqrt{N}$ and $s_d = \sqrt{\sum d^2/N - 1}$.

We have ten difference scores and have calculated one mean difference. Therefore, we have nine degrees of freedom. Table 7–4 summarizes these calculations.

The t value required for significance at the .01 level with 9 df is 3.25. The calculated t value of 5.30 exceeds this tabled value. Therefore, we reject the null hypothesis at better than the .01 level of significance. We conclude that the two samples are not drawn from the same population, which means that the post-experimental scores are different from the pre-experimental scores in terms of the location of the mean.

Type I and Type II Errors

Obviously, the experimenter does not wish to make a faulty inference on the basis of the experimental data he collects. The

Table 7-4. The Calculation of t for Correlated Scores.

Before	After	Difference (D)	D^2
13	17	-4	16
12	15	-3	9
11	15	-4	16
13	16	-3	9
9	10	-1	1
11	16	-5	25
8	7	$+1$	1
12	15	-3	9
13	18	-5	25
11	15	-4	16

$\sum D = -31 \qquad \sum D^2 = 127$

$\bar{D} = -3.10$

$$\sum d^2 = \sum D^2 - \frac{(\sum D)^2}{N}$$

$$= 127 - \frac{(31)^2}{10}$$

$$= 127 - \frac{961}{10}$$

$$= 127 - 96.10$$

$$= 30.90$$

$$s_D^2 = \sum d^2 / (N-1)$$

$$= 30.90/9$$

$$= 3.43$$

$$s_D = \sqrt{3.43}$$

$$= 1.85$$

$$s_{\bar{D}} = s_D / \sqrt{N}$$

$$= 1.85 / \sqrt{10}$$

$$= 1.85/3.16$$

$$= .585$$

$t = \bar{D}/s_{\bar{D}}$

$= 3.10/.585$

$= 5.30$

$p < .01$ for 9 df

number of faulty inferences the experimenter will make of one type
are dependent on the level of confidence chosen. You will recall
that when we choose a level of confidence we risk making a certain
percentage of mistaken inferences since we will reject the null
hypothesis a certain percentage of the time even though the differences are, in truth, the result of random sampling deviations.
Committing this error of concluding that there is a real difference
between the groups when in fact there is none is known as making a
Type I error. In other words, whenever we reject the null hypothesis
when it is true we are making a Type I error. The probability of
making a Type I error (called α) is determined in advance when we
set our significance levels. Thus, if we set our significance levels at

.05 then we expect to make five Type I errors out of every 100 inferences; if we set our limits at .01 we expect to make one Type I error out of every 100 inferences; if we set our limits at .001 we expect to make only one Type I error out of every 1000 inferences.

Why not always set our significance levels at .001, or even at .0001, in order that we make a minimal number of Type I errors? The reason is that there is another type of faulty inference, called a Type II error. We make this type of error any time we overlook a true difference by concluding that a true difference between means is due to random sampling deviation. A Type II error (called β) is committed whenever we accept the null hypothesis when in actuality it is false. Therefore, if we set our confidence limits so wide that we will practically never make a Type I error, we run the risk of over-looking many real differences and thereby making a large number of Type II errors.

In our example, a Type I error would be made when rats given the drug and rats not given the drug have the same mean learning rate but the mean difference was found to be at or beyond an acceptable significance level. Thus, it would be concluded (wrongly) that the two groups of animals are drawn from populations with different means. A Type II error would be made when the mean learning rates for the two populations of animals are different, but do not reach the predetermined level of significance. Thus, it would be concluded (again, wrongly) that the two groups of animals are drawn from populations with the same mean (this is the same as saying that they are drawn from the same population).

The probability of making a Type I error (α) and the size of the samples (N) are set by the experimenter before collecting the data. When α and N are set the probability of a Type II error (β) is determined. For a fixed N there is an inverse relationship between α and β, such that an increase in α will decrease β. To reduce the possibility of type II errors we must increase N.

POWER OF A TEST

The probability of rejecting the null hypothesis when it is false is called the power of the test. This can also be expressed as $1 - \beta$ since β is the probability of accepting the null hypothesis when it is false (overlooking real differences). The only other possible outcome when null is false is to reject the null hypothesis: therefore, $1 - \beta$

is the probability of rejecting the null when it is, indeed, false. The next section presents a more technical discussion of the power of a test.

POWER OF A TEST

Let us clarify these relationships with a numerical example utilizing the normal curve (Table A–2). Assume that we have a distribution of mean differences $(\overline{X}_1 - \overline{X}_2)$ with $\mu = 0.0$ and $\sigma_{\overline{X}_1 - \overline{X}_2} = 2.0$.

If we let $\alpha = .05$ what is the probability that we will make the correct inference: that $\mu = 0.0$? In this example our "null hypothesis" is that $\mu = 0.0$, and the alternative hypothesis is that μ is not equal to ($\neq$) 0.0.

We know from the table of the normal curve that .025 of the total area in a sampling distribution of differences between means will be located beyond $+1.96\sigma_{\overline{X}_1 - \overline{X}_2}$ and that .025 of the differences between means will be located beyond $-1.96\sigma_{\overline{X}_1 - \overline{X}_2}$. Our confidence limits for the mean will be 1.96 (2.0) = 3.92; $UL_{.95} = 0.00 + 3.92$; $LL_{.95} = 0.00 - 3.92 = -3.92$. Any time we obtain a difference between means which is greater than 3.92 or less than -3.92 we will reject the hypothesis that $\mu = 0.0$, and will do so at the .05 level of confidence.

Consider the operation of this test if we assume that $\mu = 0$ when actually $\mu = 0.5$. What is the power of our test to detect this true difference? In other words, we are interested in the power of our test to detect a difference between means of 0.5 when we assume a μ of 0.0 to be the true difference. We assume that reality is as illustrated in Figure 7–5 A and we will reject the hypothesis of $\mu = 0$ whenever a difference between means falls in the shaded region. If, however, the reality is as indicated in Figure 7–5 B, what is the probability that we will detect the difference? In other words, what is the probability that we will reject the hypothesis that $\mu = 0.0$ and will accept the alternative hypothesis that $\mu \neq 0.0$ when really $\mu = 0.5$. Again, we will reject the hypothesis that $\mu \neq 0.0$ whenever the sample mean falls in the shaded region of Figure 7–5 B.

Since the population distribution is centered around $\mu = 0.5$, rather than 0.0 we will have to recalculate our z-score values. We are going to reject any difference between means below

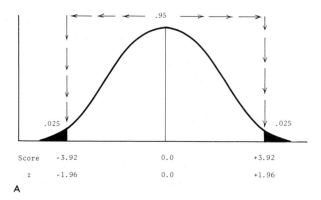

Score   -3.92   0.0   +3.92

z   -1.96   0.0   +1.96

A

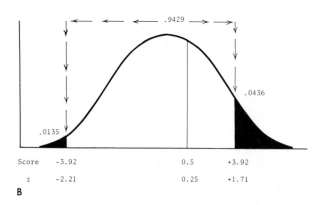

Score   -3.92   0.5   +3.92

z   -2.21   0.25   +1.71

B

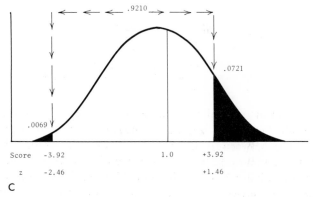

Score   -3.92   1.0   +3.92

z   -2.46   +1.46

C

Figure 7–5.

−3.92 and above +3.92 and, therefore, must find the z-score values corresponding to those differences between means.

$$UL_z = \frac{3.92 - 0.50}{2.0} = \frac{3.42}{2.00} = 1.71$$

$$LL_z = \frac{-3.92 - 0.05}{2.0} = -\frac{-4.42}{2.00} = -2.21.$$

Referring to the normal curve table we find that .4564 of the total area falls between μ and a z of 1.71 and that .4864 of the total area falls between μ and a z of −2.21. It follows then that .0436 of the total area falls beyond a z of 1.71 and .0135 falls beyond a z of −2.21. Therefore, $1.0000 - .0436 - .0135 = .9429$ which is the area contained in the unshaded portion of the curve shown in Figure 7–5 B.

The probability of *failing* to detect the difference between the "true" mean difference of 0.5 and the "assumed" mean difference of 0.0 equals $\beta = .9429$. The power of the test to detect a difference of this magnitude equals $1 - \beta = 1 - .9429 = .0571$.

Now, let us assume that the true mean difference is 1.0. The statistical model we are using assumes that the reality is the same as illustrated in Figure 7–5 A (shown again as 7–5 C). However, the reality is illustrated in Figure 7–5 D.

We wish to determine the power of our test to detect a difference between means of 1.0 when we assumed a μ of 0.0 to be the true difference. We will reject the hypothesis of $\mu = 0$ whenever a difference between means falls in the shaded region of Figure 7–5 D.

$$UL_z = \frac{3.92 - 1.00}{2.00} = \frac{2.92}{2.00} = 1.46$$

$$LL_z = \frac{-3.92 - 1.0}{2.00} = \frac{-4.92}{2.00} = -2.46.$$

From the normal curve table we find that .4279 of the total area falls between μ and a z of 1.46, and that .4931 of the total area falls between μ and a z of −2.46. Therefore, $1.0000 - .0721 - .0069 = .9210$ which is the unshaded area of the curve shown in Figure 7–5 D. The probability of *failing* to detect the difference between the "true" mean difference of 1.0 and "assumed" mean difference of 0.0 equals $1 - \beta = 1 - .9210 = .0790$.

We could, by this procedure, determine the power function (with a fixed α) to detect any presumed mean differences. Leaving α fixed we could calculate a family of curves with N varying, such as is illustrated in Figure 7–6 for the t-test. A family of curves of this type could be generated for any given confidence level we wished and for any statistical test.

Power curves

To illustrate the concept of the power of a test in relation to differences between groups, assume that 10 subjects are selected from a population and assigned to two equal groups of five subjects each. One group is exposed to an experimental manipulation hypothesized to produce a change in the measured variable while the other group serves as the control and receives no special treatment. Upon completion of the experiment, the significance of the difference between the means for the groups is evaluated using the t-test. The null hypothesis is that the two groups are still from the same population following the differential treatment. Thus, any differences which occur are due to chance fluctuations around a population mean difference of zero.

t is computed using formula (7.3) and a value of t is obtained. Suppose there is a real difference between the groups following the experimental treatment. What is the probability that the t-test will detect this difference? We can determine the power of the t-test to detect a difference from Figure 7–6. Along the horizontal axis the population difference is scaled in standard score units ranging from zero to ± 3. Along the vertical axis the power of the test to detect a difference is scaled. The curves in the figure indicate the power of detecting a difference significant at the .05 level for different values of N. For our example, $N = 10$, and the power curve for $N = 10$ would be used. Suppose that there is a real difference between our two groups and, as a result of the experimental treatment, the two groups now belong to different populations. Suppose that our population difference is $\mu_0 = +.5\sigma$ in standard score values. We can determine from inspection of Figure 7–6 that there is about a 70 per cent chance of *failing* to detect this population difference. The power of the test to detect a difference of this size is .30. However, suppose that the population difference was $\mu_0 = -2.0\sigma$. Examination of the other side of the curve for $N = 10$ indicates that we would fail to detect this difference less than 1 per cent of the time. The power of the test to detect differences of this size is greater than .99.

$1 - \beta$

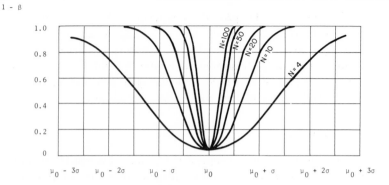

Population difference (in standard scores)

Figure 7-6. Power curves for the t-test; $\alpha = .05$; two-tailed test. (Reprinted from Dixon, W. J. and Massey, F. J. *Introduction to Statistics*. New York: McGraw-Hill, 1957.)

Suppose that our population difference was $\mu_0 = +.5\sigma$ and our N is 50. Examination of the curve for $N = 50$ indicates that we would fail to detect such a difference at the .05 level of significance only about 5 per cent of the time. The power of the test to detect a difference this large is, therefore, .95.

Inspection of these curves indicates the importance of sample size as a determinant of the power of a test to detect population differences. A comparison of the probability of detecting a real difference with $N = 10$ as compared to $N = 50$ should provide at least second thoughts for any experimenter who decides that an N of 10 observations is enough to detect possible differences. If you suspect that a population difference is small, there is simply no substitute for large samples. On the other hand, the experimenter must decide whether a population difference that is so small that 100 observations are necessary to detect it is really of practical importance. The importance of a psychological, political, or any other kind of phenomenon is not a question to be decided statistically.

The choice of a significance level rests on a consideration of how costly, in practical terms, it is to the investigator to make a Type I as compared to a Type II error. If the decision to reject the null hypothesis carries with it sweeping implications (say in terms of financial expense or social consequences) the experimenter might well decide to demand a significance level of .0001, for example. We know that if he does demand such an extreme significance level he will probably overlook real differences. If he does reject the null hypothesis at this level of significance, however, he can be relatively certain that the observed difference is a real one. On the other hand, if he is performing a series of experiments to understand the effect of several environmental manipulations on behavior, it is extremely wasteful in terms of research energy as well as an accurate construction of reality to overlook real differences that do exist. The relative cost to the investigator of making a Type I and a Type II error, then, can only be decided on non-statistical grounds by the researcher. Once he has made his decision he can choose the proper significance level to minimize the expected number of Type I or Type II errors.

EXERCISES

1. An experimenter wants to test the effect of a new drug on perception. He injects the experimental group with the drug and injects the control group with saline. He records the number of seconds between presentation of a light and the time when the presence of the light was reported. Did his drug have any effect on perceptual threshold? (Use .05 level of confidence.)

Control	Experimental
13	9
12	8
11	9
9	12
12	10

2. In order to use a t-test, what three assumptions must be made?

3. Compute a t for the difference between means using the following data: $N_1 = 11$; $N_2 = 26$; $\bar{X}_1 = 17.5$; $\bar{X}_2 = 14.8$; $\sum x_1^2 = 44$; $\sum x_2^2 = 68$.

4. A test of musical aptitude was given to a group of eighth grade and a group of tenth grade students. Is the difference between the means significant?

	8	10
$\bar{X}$	90.76	99.32
s	19.32	18.36
N	200	200

5. The strength of the patellar reflex under two conditions, tensed and relaxed, was measured for 10 minutes. Does tensing the patella make any significant difference?

133

Tensed	Relaxed
31	35
19	14
22	19
26	29
36	34
30	26
29	19
36	37
33	27
34	24

6. Subjects were given an attitude test before and after viewing a motion picture designed to influence their attitudes favorably. A high score indicates a favorable attitude, and a low score an unfavorable attitude. Can we conclude that the motion picture resulted in a significant mean change?

Subject	Pretest	Post test
1	2.6	2.5
2	4.6	5.7
3	8.9	9.3
4	5.5	6.7
5	1.9	1.5
6	8.2	7.8
7	4.6	4.7
8	5.6	5.9
9	6.9	7.3
10	6.9	7.0

7. An experimenter found that the mean running speed of several groups of subjects with a specific magnitude of reinforcement was 50, $\sigma = 10$. He wishes to test the hypothesis that a change in magnitude of reinforcement will change the mean running speed. Accordingly, he employs a group of 100 subjects in a study and obtains a mean of 51.75. If $\alpha = .05$:

a. Is he justified in concluding that running speed is a function of magnitude of reinforcement within the limit of the studies?

b. What is the statistical hypothesis being tested?

c. What is the probability of a Type I error in this experiment?

d. What is the probability of a Type II error if the true mean (r) is 50.65 $(\alpha = .05)$?

e. What is the power of the test?

8

ANALYSIS OF VARIANCE

The principles of statistical inference as presented to this point have been developed to evaluate the significance of mean differences between the means of two groups. Other techniques exist which offer the research worker tremendous advantages in terms of flexibility in experimental design, and which enable the experimenter to extract the maximum amount of information from an experiment. These are called "analysis of variance" techniques and are most often used when there are more than two groups in an experiment. They provide the research worker with some of the most powerful statistical tools available.

By now, the logic underlying the comparison of two groups should be clear. However, what do we do if we wish to make a comparison among more than two groups? Perhaps the first answer to come to mind would be to do all of the possible t-tests among the groups. Practical considerations alone suggest the limitations of this approach. For example, if we have three groups we wish to compare we must make only three t-tests. If we have ten groups to compare, however, we must make 45 t-tests! Apart from the incredible amount of computation required, the prospect of trying to make sense out of this number of comparisons would be sufficient to discourage even the most determined and obsessive investigator.

Entirely apart from both of these considerations is the simple fact that such comparisons violate the randomness requirement of the t-test. In comparing two groups by means of the t-test, we draw two samples randomly from the same population. Following experimental treatment the two samples are compared to determine whether the experimental treatment has had any significant effect upon the variable being measured. If the groups differ more than we would expect on the basis of the size of the variability estimates, we conclude that our experimental treatment has had some effect; if the groups differ less than we would expect, we conclude that our experimental treatment has had little or no effect.

The critical assumption in the above formulation is that the two groups are random samples from the same population. If we have three groups and we compare groups one and two by means of the t-test, we are carrying out a perfectly legitimate comparison. However, if we now compare group two with group three, the requirement of randomness has been violated, since after having performed a t-test to compare groups one and two, the comparison of groups two and three is not independent of this first comparison. As the number of groups (and comparisons) increases, the seriousness of this problem becomes more extreme. The analysis of variance technique offers a way around this difficulty.

The concept of variance is scarcely new by now. It was first introduced in Chapter 4 and is defined as the average of the sum of the squared difference scores when each score is subtracted from the mean:

$$s^2 = \frac{\Sigma (X - \bar{X})^2}{N - 1}.$$

The computational formula we use to calculate the variance of a set of observations is the following:

$$s^2 = \frac{\Sigma X^2 - \dfrac{(\Sigma X)^2}{N}}{N - 1}.$$

The effectiveness of analysis of variance is due to the fact that the variability of several sets of observations can be divided into several parts with each part being associated with a given source of variability. To illustrate this we will draw three random samples of ten observations each from our population of 1000 observations.

We will first calculate the variance for each of the samples by the rather cumbersome definitional formula:

$$s_1^2 = \frac{\Sigma (X - \bar{X})^2}{N - 1} = \frac{116.40}{9} = 12.93$$

$$s_2^2 = 112.00/9 = 12.44$$

$$s_3^2 = 144.00/9 = 16.00.$$

Table 8-1. CALCULATION OF THE SUMS OF SQUARES FOR THREE RANDOM SAMPLES OF TEN OBSERVATIONS EACH.

	Sample 1			Sample 2			Sample 3		
	Score	x	x^2	Score	x	x^2	Score	x	x^2
	68	−5.6	31.36	75	−1.0	1.00	76	−2.0	4.00
	71	−2.6	6.76	78	2.0	4.00	79	1.0	1.00
	73	−.6	.36	70	−6.0	36.00	81	3.0	9.00
	69	−4.6	21.16	73	−3.0	9.00	78	.0	.00
	75	1.4	1.96	76	.0	.00	72	−6.0	36.00
	75	1.4	1.96	74	−2.0	4.00	74	−4.0	16.00
	78	4.4	19.36	76	.0	.00	86	8.0	64.00
	72	−1.6	2.56	76	.0	.00	75	−3.0	9.00
	78	4.4	19.36	83	7.0	49.00	80	2.0	4.00
	77	3.4	11.56	79	3.0	9.00	79	1.0	1.00
$\sum X$	736	.0	116.40	760	.0	112.00	780	.0	144.00
$\bar{X}$	73.6			76.0			78.0		
$\sum x^2$			116.40			112.00			144.00

THE TOTAL VARIANCE

Since these are three random samples from the same population, we are justified in combining them to determine the total variance (s_T^2) for all the observations. We will use the standard computational formula $s_T^2 = \dfrac{\sum x_T^2}{N-1}$, where $\sum x_T^2 = \sum X_T^2 - (\sum X_T)^2/N$ rather than the definitional formula. To use this formula we must first calculate the sum of the squared scores. For our total sample of 30 observations the sum of all the scores $(\sum X_T)$ is 2276, the sum of all the squared scores $(\sum X_T^2)$ is 173,142, and the sum of all the scores, quantity squared $(\sum X_T)^2$ is 5,180,176. These quantities can be substituted into the formula for the sum of squares:

$$\sum (X - \bar{X}_T)^2 = \sum x_T^2 = \sum X_T^2 - (\sum X_T)^2/N \qquad (8.1)$$
$$= 173,142.0 - 5,180,176/30$$
$$= 173,142.0 - 172,672.5$$
$$= 469.5$$

$$s_T^2 = \sum (X - \bar{X}_T)^2/(N-1) = 469.5/29 = 16.19. \qquad (8.2)$$

At this point in the calculations an interesting discrepancy can be noted. The sum of squares obtained when we add the $\sum x^2$ for the three separate samples in Table 8–1 together are 116.4, 112.0, and 144.0; the sum of which is 372.4. The sum of squares for the total group (which we have just calculated) adds up to 469.5. Since both of these sums are based on the same scores it would seem logical that the total sum of squares calculated directly would be the same as the sum obtained by adding the sums of squares from the three sets of samples together. After all, the sums of the *scores* for the three samples can be added together to provide a total sum of *scores*. Why then does the total *sum of squares* calculated directly not equal the total *sums of squares* arrived at by adding the individual sums of squares together?

Components of the Total Sum of Squares. The answer is that when the three samples are added together (as was done in the last calculation), and the sum of squares is calculated using the overall mean $(\overline{X}_T)$ as a base for the $\sum (X - \overline{X})^2$ term a source of variation is introduced which is not present when the variance is calculated for each sample separately. When we calculate the sum of squares for each of the separate samples, we express the variance of the sample scores around the mean of each sample. The sum of squares on which the total variance is based will always be at least as large as the sum of the individual sums of squares since the sum of squares for the total variance is made up of two separate components: the first component is a function of the variability of the scores in each sample around their respective sample means; the second component is a function of the variability of the sample means around the overall mean. In fact, the total sum of squares will almost always be larger than the sum of the individual sums of squares.

A figure will help to clarify this point. Assume that the sum of squares is 100.00 for each of the three equal size samples depicted in Figure 8–1. Assume, also, that each of the samples is drawn from the same population, but that the means are slightly different as a function of small sampling deviations. The mean of sample A $(\overline{X}_A)$ is 48; $\overline{X}_B = 50$; $\overline{X}_C = 52$; and $\overline{X}_T$ (overall mean) is 50. If we calculate the total sum of squares using $\overline{X}_T$ as a base we will have a total sum of squares which is larger than the value 300 which is the sum of the sums of squares. This can be understood by examining the contribution of an individual score to the total variance. The score $X_A = 43$ is a score taken from the first sample, which has a

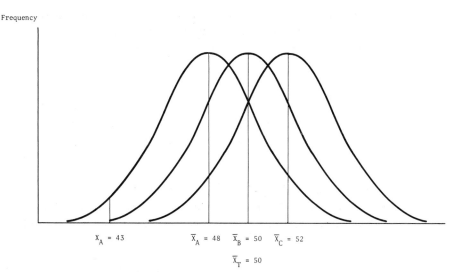

Frequency

$X_A = 43$ $\overline{X}_A = 48$ $\overline{X}_B = 50$ $\overline{X}_C = 52$

$\overline{X}_T = 50$

Score

Figure 8–1.

mean of 48. One portion of the contribution of this score to the sum of squares is based on the deviation of X_A from $\overline{X}_A$ which is $(43 - 48)^2 = 25$. Another portion of this score's contribution to the total variance is not expressed here, however. Remember that we are expressing our total variance using $\overline{X}_T = 50$. Therefore, the score X_A is contributing the squared deviation of X_A from $\overline{X}_T$, which is $(43 - 50)^2 = 49$ to the total variability. In order to include this second component of the variability (that portion which is reflected by the difference between a squared deviation of 25 as compared to 49) we have to take into account the variability which is due to the differences *between* the sample means. In the example outlined in Figure 8–1 the total variation contributed by score X_A is $X_A - \overline{X}_T$ which itself is composed of two parts—$X_A - \overline{X}_A$ and $\overline{X}_A - \overline{X}_T$— both the amount the score differs from its sample mean and the amount the sample mean differs from the total mean.

Between Groups Sum of Squares. The sum of squares between means $(\sum x_b^2)$ is determined by finding the squared deviations of each sample mean from the overall mean and weighting these squared deviations by the number of cases in each sample as follows:

$$\sum x_b^2 = n_1(\overline{X}_1 - \overline{X}_T)^2 + n_2(\overline{X}_2 - \overline{X}_T)^2 + n_3(\overline{X}_3 - \overline{X}_T)^2. \quad \textbf{(8.3)}$$

Table 8–2. Tabulation of $\bar{X}$, $\sum x^2$, and s^2 for Each Sample and for the Combined Observations.

Sample	$\bar{X}$	$\sum x^2$	s^2
1	73.6	116.40	12.93
2	76.0	112.00	12.44
3	78.0	144.00	16.00
Total	75.87	469.50	16.19

The values of $\bar{X}$, $\sum x^2$, and s^2 for each of the three samples on which we have based our calculations are listed in Table 8–2.

If we apply formula (8.3) to the data of Table 8–2 we obtain the following:

$$\sum x_b^2 = 10(73.60 - 75.87)^2 + 10(76.00 - 75.87)^2$$
$$+ 10(78.00 - 75.87)^2$$
$$= 10(5.15) + 10(0.17) + 10(4.54)$$
$$= 51.5 + 1.7 + 45.4$$
$$= 98.6.$$

When the sum of squares calculated in this manner is added to the total of the sums of squares calculated for the separate samples, this combined total is identical (within rounding errors) to the sum of squares calculated on p. 138 for the total sample.

$$\sum x_T^2 = \sum x_{w_1}^2 + \sum x_{w_2}^2 + \sum x_{w_3}^2 + \sum x_b^2 \tag{8.4}$$
$$= 116.4 + 112.0 + 144.0 + 98.6$$
$$= 471.0 \text{ (as compared to 469.5 when calculated directly)}.$$

What would be the state of affairs if all three samples were drawn from the same population, that is, if the null hypothesis is true? If all three samples are drawn from the same population and if each sample mean was an accurate representative of μ, then each of the sample means would be identical. This can be formulated as follows:

$$\bar{X}_1 = \bar{X}_2 = \bar{X}_3 = \bar{X}_T = \mu.$$

If this null case were true then $\sum x_{w_1}^2 + \sum x_{w_2}^2 + \sum x_{w_3}^2 = \sum x_T^2$, since the total amount of variability present in this example is due to the variability of the individual scores around their respective sample means—all of which are the same. The $\sum x_b^2$ would equal zero, since none of the variability is due to differences between sample means. Even though the null hypothesis is true there will probably be some differences between the sample means due to sampling error. In this case the three sample means will not be the same and $\sum x_T^2$ is not equal to ($\neq$) $\sum x_w^2$. In order to account for the total variability in this instance we must take into account the variability between the sample means. Therefore, $\sum x_T^2 = \sum x_w^2 + \sum x_b^2$. It can be demonstrated that $\sum x_w^2$ and $\sum x_b^2$ are actually two independent estimates of the variability within a set of scores.

Source of Between and Within Sums of Squares. If we conduct an experiment by selecting subjects and randomly assigning them to groups which then are subjected to different treatment conditions, any variability within the groups is considered to be variability due to chance variation of the individual scores around their sample means. The sources of this error variability are many in number: it could be due to individual differences among subjects in initial ability; it could be due to errors of measurement on the part of the experimenter; it could be due to fluctuations of interest, attention, or motivation in the subjects participating in the experiment; it could be due to small unnoticed changes in the experimental procedures as the experiment progresses. In short, these factors are all considered to be sources of unwanted error variance which exists in every actual experiment. All of these factors contribute to $\sum x_w^2$.

The $\sum x_b^2$ is also an estimate of chance variability among individuals plus any variability that may be due to systematic differences between groups. Some of this difference may be due to random sampling errors resulting in differences in ability between groups. However, it may also be due to the different experimental treatments given the groups.

If the variability attributed to the differences between groups is large relative to the variability attributed to the differences within groups, then the differential experimental treatment can be considered to be effective.

Variance Estimates

We have, up to this point, been concerned with the sums of squares and not with the variances. The variance, you will recall, is a value indicating the arithmetic average of the variability which has been expressed in terms of squared deviations from the mean. The variance estimates, then, will be a function of the sums of squares. It is preferable to work with variance estimates since this enables us to have unequal numbers of cases in each sample. Therefore, we divide our sums of squares by the appropriate number of degrees of freedom (df) to obtain what is called the Mean Square. This Mean Square is called the *variance estimate*.

We obtain the total Mean Square (s_T^2) as follows:

$$s_T^2 = \sum x_T^2/df_T, \tag{8.5}$$

where

$$df_T = N - 1. \tag{8.6}$$

The mean square between groups (s_b^2) is:

$$s_b^2 = \sum x_b^2/df_b, \tag{8.7}$$

where

$$df_b = k - 1 \qquad (k = \text{number of groups}). \tag{8.8}$$

The mean square within groups (s_w^2) is:

$$s_w^2 = \sum x_w^2/df_w, \tag{8.9}$$

where

$$df_w = N - k. \tag{8.10}$$

If the degrees of freedom are correctly assigned, $df_T = df_b + df_w = N - 1$.

F-RATIO

When we have divided our sums of squares by the appropriate number of degrees of freedom we have an estimate of the total variance, the variance within the groups, and the variance between the groups. As mentioned earlier, if there is a large variance *between* the groups as compared to the variance *within* the groups this indicates that the experimental effect is quite large relative to the experimental error.

The ratio s_b^2/s_w^2 is called the F-ratio. $\tag{8.11}$

Just as the t-ratio is used to determine the statistical significance of differences between two groups, the F-ratio may be used to determine the probability of obtaining differences greater than would be expected on the basis of chance for more than two groups. In fact, the F-ratio is the more general statistic and it can be demonstrated that the t-ratio is a special case of the more general F-ratio.

CALCULATION OF ANALYSIS OF VARIANCE

The use of the F-ratio in statistical inference will be illustrated using another three group problem. The data for this example represent the number of correct choices out of a total of 25 choices in a discrimination learning problem. The experiment was performed to determine the effects of a central nervous system stimulant on discrimination learning. Laboratory rats of the same age were randomly assigned to one of three groups. Group 1 is a control group which was injected with an inert substance known to have no effect on behavior. Group 2 was injected each day with .10 milligrams of the drug per kilogram of body weight. Group 3 was injected each day with .05 milligrams of the drug per kilogram of body weight. The scores indicate the number of times out of the 25 choices each rat chose the correct stimulus card to find food. The data are shown in Table 8–3.

Table 8–3. ACCURACY SCORES FOR DISCRIMINATION OF LEARNING IN THREE GROUPS OF LABORATORY RATS WITH DIFFERENT DRUG DOSAGES.

Group 1 (Control)	Group 2 (.10 mg/kg)	Group 3 (.05 mg/kg)
7	21	18
10	17	19
10	12	23
14	18	13
13	13	15
13	12	12
10	16	16
16	20	16
12	10	20
	16	

Table 8–4. Summary Statistics for the Analysis of Variance.

	1	2	3	*Total*
n	9	10	9	$N = 28$
$\bar{X}$	11.67	15.50	16.89	$\bar{X}_T = 14.71$
$\sum x$	105	155	152	$\sum X_T = 412$
$\sum x^2$	1283	2523	2664	$\sum X_T^2 = 6470$
$(\sum X)^2$	11,025	24,025	23,104	$(\sum X_T)^2 = 169{,}744$
$(\sum X)^2/n$	1225.00	2402.50	2567.11	$\sum \dfrac{(\sum X)^2}{n} = 6194.61$
				$\dfrac{(\sum X_T)^2}{N} = 6062.29$

Note that groups 1 and 3 contain nine animals each while group 2 contains ten animals. At the start of the experiment all of the groups were equal, but shortly after the start, an animal in group 1 was found to have a severe infection and was removed from the study. An animal was lost from group 3 when a careless assistant injected the animal with the wrong solution. Problems such as these arise in experiments and it is well to be aware of the likelihood of such problems arising when an experiment is planned. As we will see, the small difference in the size of the groups will not affect the analysis.

Calculation of the sums of squares will be done by the usual computational formulas in this example. The summary statistics required to calculate the analysis of variance are contained in Table 8–4.

COMMON CALCULATION ERRORS IN THE ANALYSIS OF VARIANCE

The symbols used to indicate the quantities needed to calculate the analysis of variance are complex, and, in a few instances, quite similar in appearance. It is important that you keep in mind the distinctions among these symbols. The following two comments may help:

1. Quantities such as $\sum X_T$ and $\sum X_T^2$ are obtained by summing the values for the separate groups. In the computational example, $\sum X_T$ is obtained by adding $\sum X_1 + \sum X_2 + \sum X_3$ to obtain $\sum X_T$. $\sum X_T^2$ is obtained by adding $\sum X_1^2 + \sum X_2^2 + \sum X_3^2$.

Quantities such as $(\sum X_T)^2$ and $(\sum X_T)^2/N$ *cannot* be obtained by adding the quantities for the separate groups together. $(\sum X_T)^2$ is obtained by squaring $\sum X_T$. $(\sum X_1)^2$ is obtained by squaring $\sum X_1$. Similarly, $(\sum X_T)^2/N$ is obtained by dividing $(\sum X_T)^2$ by the total number of observations in all of the groups combined and should not be confused with $\sum \dfrac{(\sum X)^2}{n}$, which is obtained by adding the values of $(\sum X)^2/n$ which have been calculated for each group.

2. Keep in mind the difference between $(\sum X)^2$ and $(\sum X^2)$. $(\sum X)^2$ instructs you to sum the scores in the column labeled X and *then* to square that sum. $(\sum X)^2$ is read "the sum of X, quantity squared." $(\sum X^2)$ instructs you to square each of the scores and then to sum those squares. $(\sum X^2)$ is read "the sum of X-squared."

The number of quantities needed for even a simple analysis of variance may seem forbiddingly large, and the arithmetic may appear to be overwhelming. However, if a certain order of operations is followed, the computations are reasonably easy to follow. The number of observations in each of the samples is represented by the lower case letter n. The total number of cases in the analysis is represented by the upper case letter N. If necessary, subscripts can be used to identify particular samples, i.e., n_1, n_2, n_3, and N_T (for total sample). The mean for each of the samples is symbolized as $\bar{X}_1$, $\bar{X}_2$, and $\bar{X}_3$, and the total (or overall) mean is identified by the symbol $\bar{X}_T$. The next quantities in the table should be quite familiar: $\sum X$ and $\sum X^2$ are the sum of the scores and the sum of the squared scores. The subscripts indicate which quantities are summed: $\sum X_T$ and $\sum X_T^2$ indicate that the sums are based on the total cases; $\sum X_1$ indicates that the sum is taken over sample 1, and so forth. $\sum X_1 = 105$; $\sum X_2 = 155$; and $\sum X_3 = 152$. The total of these is 412, which is the value of $\sum X_T$. $\sum X_T^2$ is obtained by adding the values $\sum X_1^2$, $\sum X_2^2$, and $\sum X_3^2$. $\sum X_1^2 = 1283$; $\sum X_2^2 = 2523$; and $\sum X_3^2 = 2664$. The sum of these quantities is 6470, which is the value of $\sum X_T^2$. The value $(\sum X_T)^2$ in the column headed "total" has a box around it. This is purely an attention getting device, since this quantity is *not* the sum of the quantities for groups 1, 2, and 3. $(\sum X_T)^2$ is calculated by squaring $\sum X_T$, exactly as $(\sum X_1)^2$ is calculated by squaring $\sum X_1$.

The next item in the table, $(\sum X)^2/n$, is obtained by dividing each $(\sum X)^2$ by its corresponding number of observations. The quantity $\sum \dfrac{(\sum X)^2}{n}$ is obtained by summing each of the separate quantities obtained in this way for samples 1, 2, and 3.

The quantity $(\sum X_T)^2/N$ is calculated by dividing $(\sum X_T)^2$ (the first boxed item in the table) by N. For our example, 169,744 is divided by 28, which gives the value 6062.29 for $\dfrac{(\sum X_T)^2}{N}$.

The sums of squares needed for the analysis of variance can be obtained by the process of simple subtraction once the above sums have been calculated. The calculations are as follows:

For the total sum of squares:

$$\sum x_T^2 = \sum X_T^2 - (\sum X_T)^2/N. \tag{8.12}$$

For the sum of squares between groups:

$$\sum x_b^2 = \sum \frac{(\sum X)^2}{n} - \frac{(\sum X_T)^2}{N}. \tag{8.13}$$

For the sum of squares within groups:

$$\sum x_w^2 = \sum X_T^2 - \sum \frac{(\sum X)^2}{n}. \tag{8.14}$$

For our example, the total sum of squares $(\sum x_T^2) = 6470 - 6062.29 = 407.71$. The sum of squares between groups $(\sum x_b^2) = 6194.61 - 6062.29 = 132.32$. The sum of squares within groups $(\sum x_w^2) = 6470 - 6194.61 = 275.39$. If the calculations are correct, the sums of squares for $\sum x_b^2$ and $\sum x_w^2$ should equal $\sum x_T^2$.

To obtain our variance estimates the sums of squares are now divided by the appropriate number of degrees of freedom. For the within groups sum of squares, the *df* is equal to the number of observations minus the number of groups. For our example, $N = 28$ and $k = 3$; therefore $df_w = 25$. For the between groups sum of

Table 8–5. SUMMARY TABLE FOR ANALYSIS OF VARIANCE.

Source of Variation	Sum of Squares	df	Mean Square	F
Between groups	132.32	2	66.16	6.003
Within groups	275.39	25	11.02	
Total	407.71	27		

squares, the df_b is equal to the number of groups minus one. For our example, $k = 3$; $df_b = 3 - 1 = 2$. The value of the between groups and within groups variance estimates are usually arranged in an analysis of variance table such as Table 8–5.

In Table 8–5 the sums of squares are listed for the two independent estimates of variation. The degrees of freedom are listed and the mean square is calculated by dividing each of the sums of squares by the df for that sum. For the between groups variance, the calculation of the mean square is 132.32/2, which equals 66.16. For the within groups variance the mean square is 275.39/25, which equals 11.02.

The only remaining step is the calculation of the F-ratio which is done by dividing the mean square between groups by the mean square within groups. For our example, F is equal to 66.16/11.02, which equals 6.003.

Interpretation of the F-Ratio

How is the value of F to be interpreted? The logic is basically the same as that used with the normal curve. If we were to randomly draw three samples from a normally distributed population, compute both the variance estimate between groups and the variance estimate within groups, and then compute the F-ratio, we would have one F value. This value of F is, you will recall, the ratio of the between variance estimate to the within variance estimate. The null hypothesis to be tested is that $\mu_1 = \mu_2 = \mu_3$. If this hypothesis is true, then $\bar{X}_1 = \bar{X}_2 = \bar{X}_3$ should be the case. As was indicated earlier, if the null hypothesis is true all the variance will be due to the variance within groups, and any variance due to differences between groups is assumed to be the result of chance sampling deviation. Since we know that there will always be a certain amount of

A

B

Figure 8–2. *A*, comparison of theoretical F distribution (smooth line) for two and 12 degrees of freedom with the distribution (bar graph) of 19,486 F-ratios for two and 12 degrees of freedom. *B*, comparison of theoretical F distribution (smooth line) for nine and 98 degrees of freedom with the distribution (bar graph) of 1000 F-ratios for 9 and 98 degrees of freedom.

sampling variability of means the values of F will, in the true null case, have a sampling distribution. Most of the values of F will be centered around one, and the frequency of an F value becomes smaller and smaller as the F value becomes larger.

The F distribution for two and 12 degrees of freedom is illustrated in Figure 8–2 A. The smooth line represents the theoretical distribution of F and the bar graph represents the obtained distribution of 19,486 actual F values obtained by drawing random samples and calculating the values of F with the aid of a high-speed computer.

In Figure 8–2 B the theoretical distribution of F for nine and 98 degrees of freedom is shown as a smooth line and the actual distribution of 1000 F values is plotted as a bar graph. There will be a different sampling distribution for F depending on the number of degrees of freedom and on the manner in which they are apportioned to the within and the between variances. Each of these distributions of F, then, are what would be expected if the null hypothesis is true. Therefore, it is possible to state the probability of obtaining an F-ratio of any given size by determining the proportion of the total area under the F distribution which falls beyond the given F value.

Table of F. The F distribution has been derived mathematically and complete tables of F can be constructed. However, such tables would fill several large volumes. Since investigators are usually interested in evaluating the null hypothesis only at certain stated probability levels, tables have been constructed which list the critical values for the 5 per cent and the 1 per cent points on the distribution of F. Table A–4 contains the 5 per cent and the 1 per cent points of the distribution of F for degrees of freedom ranging from 1 and 1 to ∞ and ∞.

The sampling distribution of F with which we are concerned in our computing example is for · 2 and 25 degrees of freedom: 2 df are associated with the between group effect (which is the greater mean square) and 25 df are associated with the within group effect (which is the smaller mean square). We enter Table A–4 by locating the entry at the intersection of the column headed 2 and the row headed 25. The F value for the 5 per cent level is 3.38 and that for the 1 per cent level is 5.57. The F-ratio in our example is 6.003. Since this F-ratio is larger than the tabled 1 per cent value we can reject the null hypothesis at the .01 level of significance since an F-ratio as large as the one obtained would occur less than 1 per cent of the time when the null hypothesis is true.

Table 8–6. CALCULATION OF F WHEN THE NUMBER OF GROUPS $= 2$.

	A			B	
	17	21		10	14
	19	21		12	17
	11	16		18	12
	11	16		8	10
	11	16		10	12

$$\sum X_A = 159 \qquad \sum X_B = 123 \qquad \sum X_T = 282$$

$$n_A = 10 \qquad\qquad n_B = 10 \qquad\qquad N = 20$$

$$\sum X_A^2 = 2663 \qquad \sum X_B^2 = 1605 \qquad \sum X_T^2 = 4268$$

$$(\sum X_A)^2 = 25{,}281 \qquad (\sum X_B)^2 = 15{,}129 \qquad (\sum X_T)^2 = 79{,}524$$

$$(\sum X_A)^2/n_A = 2528.1 \qquad (\sum X_B)^2/n_B = 1512.9 \qquad \sum \frac{\sum X^2}{n} = 4041.0$$

$$\bar{X}_A = 15.9 \qquad\qquad \bar{X}_B = 12.3 \qquad\qquad (\sum X_T)^2/N = 3976.2$$

Calculation of t

$$s^2 = \frac{\sum x_A^2 + \sum x_B^2}{n_A + n_B - 2} \qquad \sum x_A^2 = 2663 - 2528.1 \qquad t = \frac{\bar{X}_A - \bar{X}_B}{\sqrt{\dfrac{s^2}{n_A} + \dfrac{s^2}{n_B}}} = \frac{15.9 - 12.3}{\sqrt{\dfrac{12.61}{10} + \dfrac{12.61}{10}}}$$

$$= \frac{134.9 + 92.1}{18} \qquad\qquad = 134.9 \qquad\qquad\qquad = \frac{3.6}{\sqrt{2.52}} = \frac{3.6}{1.59} = 2.26$$

$$\sum x_B^2 = 1605 - 1512.9$$

$$= 12.61 \qquad\qquad\qquad = 92.1 \qquad\qquad\qquad t_{.95} = 2.10$$

Calculation of F

$$\sum x_T^2 = \sum X_T^2 - (\sum X_T)^2/N = 4286 - 3976.2 = 291.8$$

$$\sum x_b^2 = \sum \frac{(\sum X)^2}{n} - \frac{(\sum X_T)^2}{N} = 4041.0 - 3976.2 = 64.8$$

$$\sum x_w^2 = \sum X_T^2 - \sum \frac{(\sum X)^2}{n} = 4268 - 4041 = 227$$

Source of Variation	Sum of Squares	df	Mean Square	F
Total	291.8	19	15.36	
Between	64.8	1	64.80	5.14
Within	227.0	18	12.61	

$$F_{.95} = 4.41$$

Upon rejecting the null hypothesis we will accept the alternative hypothesis that the three sample means are not drawn from the same population. The means of the three groups are $\overline{X}_1 = 10.89$; $\overline{X}_2 = 15.50$; and $\overline{X}_3 = 16.89$. The greatest difference among the groups is between the control group (1) and the smallest drug dosage group (3) while the difference between the largest drug dosage group (2) and group 3 is much smaller. We might suspect from this that the facilitating effect of the drug does not increase linearly with the dosage level. However, there is nothing in the present data to confirm this directly. To test this additional hypothesis, we would need several groups of animals given systematically increased amounts of the drug. We could then test for differences between the groups by more elaborate methods than are presented in this text. At present we can conclude that our first hypothesis—that the drug facilitates discrimination learning—is indeed supported by the data.

Relationship of F and t. The normal curve, the t distribution, and the F distribution are all related to one another. This can be illustrated by calculating F-ratios for two groups. The data and the calculation of both t and F are listed in Table 8–6.

The value of t is 2.26 and the value of F is 5.14. The square root of F (5.14) equals 2.26. This value is the value of t. For all situations with two groups $F = t^2$. The t-test is actually a special case of the more general F distribution applicable only to two-group problems.

On the basis of both sets of calculations in Table 8–6, we reject the null hypothesis at the .05 level of significance. The F-test, it should be mentioned, is always a two-tailed test since the probability of obtaining a deviation as large as the one obtained, irrespective of the direction of the deviation, is being evaluated.

Complex Analysis of Variance

Analysis of variance techniques can be adapted to a wide variety of complex, multiple variable problems. However, the development and exposition of these complex designs is not appropriate for this text. There are an almost unlimited variety of analysis of variance models available. There are models available for designs in which there are several independent groups of subjects, each one being tested under one combination of two treatment variables. For example, we might wish to study the effect of three different methods of instruction on the level of scholastic achievement. In addition, we might want to know if there is any interaction between method of instruction and intelligence of the pupils. To study this we form three independent groups on the basis of IQ scores: high IQ, average IQ, and low IQ. One-third of each IQ group receives instruction under one of the instructional methods. The complete design is shown in Table 8–7.

Table 8–7. INSTRUCTIONAL METHODS.

		r	s	t	
	High	$n_a = 10$	$n_b = 10$	$n_c = 10$	$n_h = 30$
IQ	Medium	$n_d = 10$	$n_e = 10$	$n_f = 10$	$n_m = 30$
	Low	$n_g = 10$	$n_h = 10$	$n_i = 10$	$n_l = 30$
		$n_r = 30$	$n_s = 30$	$n_t = 30$	$N = 90$

It is possible by combining and recombining the variance due to the different treatments to determine whether or not there is a significant difference in achievement level between the methods of instruction independent of IQ effect (i.e., does $n_r = n_s = n_t$); whether there is a significant difference in achievement between IQ independent of instructional method (i.e., does $n_h = n_m = n_l$); and whether there is an interaction between method of instruction and IQ level such that students of a certain IQ level score higher (or lower) using one particular method. Designs of this type are called *factorial* designs, and there are a large variety of models available: the same individual can be tested on only one combination of the factors; he can be tested on only one level of the first factor and every level of the second factor; or he can be tested on all levels of both factors.

The student interested in these topics should consult an advanced text.*

---

* McNemar, Q.: *Psychological Statistics;* New York: Wiley, 1962. Winer, B. J.: *Statistical Principles in Experimental Design;* New York: McGraw-Hill, 1962. Lindquist, E. F.: *Design and Analysis of Experiments in Psychology and Education;* Boston: Houghton Mifflin, 1953. Walker, H. M., and J. Lev: *Statistical Inference;* New York: Holt, 1953.

EXERCISES

Indicate, for each of the computational problems, the value of F, the values of each of the sums of squares, mean squares, and df's. State whether the F is significant and at what probability level.

1. An experimenter was interested in studying the effects of distribution of practice on the rate of learning. He performed an experiment in which three groups of subjects learned a list of ten nonsense syllables to a criterion of learning. The first groups had syllables presented to them every two seconds, the second group had a syllable presented every four seconds, and the third group had a syllable presented every six seconds. The number of trials required to reach criterion are listed for each subject below. Can you conclude that the rate at which the syllables are presented influences the rate of learning?

2 sec.	4 sec.	6 sec.
10	8	4
12	10	8
15	12	6
10	12	5
		4

2. Three methods of instruction were used to train army recruits to shoot a rifle. Method 1 involved lectures only on the principles of marksmanship. Method 2 involved a combination of lectures and demonstrations. Method 3 involved practice only. The final

marksmanship scores in terms of the number of "hits" in 15 shots are recorded below.

Method 1	Method 2	Method 3
3	4	6
5	4	7
2	3	8
4	8	6
8	7	7
4	4	9
3	2	10
9	5	9

What would you conclude regarding the relative merit of the three methods of instruction?

3. An experiment was performed to determine whether or not changes in the ratio of reinforced responses to total responses influenced the strength of a learned response. Five groups of rats were run 50 trials in a maze: the animals in Group I were reinforced on every trial; Group II animals were reinforced on 40 of the trials; Group III animals were reinforced on 30 of the trials; Group IV animals were reinforced on 20 of the trials; Group V animals were reinforced on ten of the trials. The measure of the strength of response was the number of trials required to reach an extinction criterion. What would you conclude concerning the effect of the partial reinforcement on the resistance to extinction based on the data presented below?

I	II	III	IV	V
4	10	15	12	30
5	12	14	10	12
8	10	10	15	20
6	14	8	13	15
4	15	12	14	20
7	12			18
	10			20
				20

9

CHI-SQUARE AND
PROPORTIONS

The statistical techniques considered so far have all been based on observations scaled on some continuous scale of measurement. There are situations in which data are not based on measurements, but on categorization. Instead of continuous measurements the data are based on frequencies of occurrence of various discrete events. If we want to decide whether or not there are any systematic deviations from some *a priori* pattern, we need a method by which we can compare frequencies of occurrence. The method which is most often used in this situation is called chi-square (χ^2): if we can categorize individuals in some way we can use the χ^2 test.

For example, assume that we are interested in learning whether or not the voters of a state are for or against capital punishment. We conduct a survey and determine the number opposed to capital punishment and the number in favor of capital punishment. Assume that of a sample of 40 people questioned, 13 favor capital punishment, and 27 oppose it. Does this represent a large enough deviation from a 20-20 split to conclude that more people oppose capital punishment than favor it in this state (assuming, of course, that our poll results are based on a representative sample of the voters)?

The χ^2 technique is applicable in more complex situations, also. For example, suppose we want to know whether or not there is a relationship between preference for television programs and type of job. We might, in this instance, conduct a poll in which we categorize television preference into three types (e.g., current events, drama, and musicals) and categorize jobs into four types (e.g., laborers, blue collar workers, white collar workers, and professionals). Each individual is assigned to one of the job types and is asked to choose his preferred television fare. We could then determine whether or not the observed frequencies in each cell deviate from the frequencies that would be expected on the basis of chance distribution.

Usually, we want to know whether the frequencies observed in a sample deviate significantly from some theoretical, or expected frequency. In both of the examples above we have assumed a chance distribution as our expected distribution. We could, however, assume any *a priori* distribution and use the χ^2 technique. The χ^2 test can be used to test any hypothesis regarding the expected frequency of events.

ONE-WAY CLASSIFICATION PROBLEM

Let us use the example of opinions regarding capital punishment. Assume that we wish to test the hypothesis that there is an even split among the voters of the state. Since we have asked the opinion of 40 voters we expect that 20 will oppose capital punishment and 20 will be in favor of capital punishment. These expected frequencies are contained in the small rectangle at the upper right-hand corner of the cells in Table 9–1.

We stated earlier that 13 people favored capital punishment and 27 opposed it. Now, we wish to determine whether the observed 13-27 split can be considered to be a significant deviation from our expected 20-20 split.

Table 9–1.

For	*Against*	
20		20
13	27	40

The formula for χ^2 is:

$$\chi^2 = \sum \frac{(O - E)^2}{E}, \tag{9.1}$$

where O = observed frequency and E = expected frequency. For our problem the calculation would be as follows:

$$\chi^2 = \frac{(27 - 20)^2}{20} + \frac{(13 - 20)^2}{20} = \frac{49}{20} + \frac{49}{20}$$

$$= 2.45 + 2.45 = 4.90.$$

To interpret this value we refer to Table A–5. The table is organized with n standing for the number of degrees of freedom, and the probability of obtaining a χ^2 equal to or larger than the tabled value listed in the body of the table.

Degrees of Freedom in a One–Way Classification. The number of degrees of freedom in this instance does not depend on the number of observations (N), as was the case with the t and F distributions. Rather, the number of df depends on the number of deviations which are free to vary between the observed and the expected frequencies. In a one-way classification, such as the one we have here, only one deviation value is free to vary because the sum of the expected values must equal the sum of the observed values. The latter sum is fixed in our example at 40 (the number of individuals polled). Therefore, we have one df in our χ^2 problem.

In general, in a one-way classification the number of df equals the number of cells minus one. Therefore, if we had categorized our data into four degrees of opinion (strongly opposed; opposed; favor; strongly favor) we would have four cells on which the χ^2 is based, and, hence, four deviation scores. This would give us 3 df. The method used to determine the number of df in a two-way classification will be referred to in a later section.

χ^2 **Table**

The χ^2 table (Table A–5) is interpreted in the same manner as is a t table. If the value of the calculated χ^2 exceeds the tabled value it is significant at or better than the probability level indicated at the head of the column. With 1 *df* the value of χ^2 required to reject the *a priori* hypothesis of a 20–20 split at the .05 level of significance is 3.84. Since our $\chi^2 = 4.90$ we will conclude that there is *not* an even balance of opinion among the voters. On the basis of our results we will conclude that a majority of the voters in the state do not favor capital punishment.

We could, if we had some logical reason for doing so, assume any distribution of expected frequencies. For example, assume that on the basis of prior surveys we had reason to believe that twice as many people prefer candidate *A* over either candidate *B* or *C*, who are equally preferred. We ask 300 voters to choose their favorite candidate. Table 9–2 contains the data.

Table 9–2.

Candidate			
A	B	C	
150	75	75	
237	24	39	300

On the basis of our *a priori* hypothesis we would expect 150 voters to choose candidate *A*, 75 to choose candidate *B*, and 75 to choose candidate *C*. We observed that 237 choose *A*, 24 choose *B*, and 39 choose *C*. Can we consider the deviation from our expected frequencies to be within that expected by chance alone?

$$\chi^2 = \frac{(237-150)^2}{150} + \frac{(24-75)^2}{75} + \frac{(39-75)^2}{75}$$

$$= \frac{(87)^2}{150} + \frac{(-51)^2}{75} + \frac{(-44)^2}{75}$$

$$= \frac{7569}{150} + \frac{2601}{75} + \frac{1936}{75}$$

$$= 50.46 + 34.68 + 25.81$$

$$= 110.95.$$

Entering Table A–5 with 2 df (the number of cells minus one) we find a χ^2 value of 5.99 listed for the .05 level of significance. Since our χ^2 value exceeds the tabled value more than 18 times, we are safe in concluding that our hypothesis concerning the respective popularities of the candidate is certainly supported by our results.

TWO-WAY CLASSIFICATION PROBLEM

Now consider some data which have been categorized in two ways. Assume that we are interested in the problem-solving ability of college students as related to their academic major. We choose a difficult reasoning problem and decide to categorize individuals according to whether or not they are able to solve the problem. We categorize each individual according to academic major as well: Physical Science majors, Humanities majors, and Social Science majors. Sixty individuals are selected randomly from the college roster. They are then categorized according to academic major and are given the problem to solve. The data are in Table 9–3.

Table 9–3.

Problem Solving Ability	Academic Major			
	Physical Science	Humanities	Social Science	
Solve problem	10 10	13 11	15 17	38
Do not solve problem	6 6	8 10	8 6	22
	16	21	23	60

It was observed that 38 of the 60 students could solve the problem and 22 of them could not. Sixteen of the students were Physical Science majors (of whom ten solved the problem and six did not); 21 were Humanities majors (of whom 11 solved the problem and ten did not); and 23 of the students were Social Science majors (of whom 17 solved the problem and six did not). We have no reason to expect any differences in ability to solve the problem among the students in the three academic majors. Therefore, we expect an even distribution of cases in each cell. Determining the random distribution of frequencies is more complicated for this problem since we do not have the same number of individuals in each category. To determine the expected frequency for each cell when the expected distribution is random, we multiply the number of frequencies contained in the entire row by the number of frequencies contained in the entire column in which the cell is located and divide that product by N. In order to determine the expected frequency for those Physical Science majors who could solve the problem we multiply 38 (the total number who could solve the problem) by 16 (the total number of Physical Science majors), and divide that product by 60 (the total number of cases):

$$f_e = \frac{(38)(16)}{60} = \frac{608}{60} = 10.$$

The expected frequency of ten has been indicated in the small rectangle in the upper right-hand corner of the appropriate cell. If ten of the Physical Science majors are expected to solve the problem, and there are 16 Physical Science majors, then $16 - 10 = 6$ would be expected to be unable to solve the problem. That number is added to the table.

To determine the number of Humanities majors who would be expected to solve the problem, we perform the following calculation:

$$f_e = \frac{(38)(21)}{60} = \frac{798}{60} = 13.$$

The expected frequency is 13, and that number is added in the appropriate place in the table. Since there are 21 Humanities majors and 13 of them would be expected to solve the problem, $21 - 13 = 8$ of them would be expected to be unable to solve the problem. Since our marginal totals must be 38 and 22, the last two expected frequencies are fixed: $38 - 10 - 13 = 15$; $22 - 6 - 8 = 8$. The sum of the observed frequencies ($\sum O$) and the sum of the expected frequencies ($\sum E$), therefore, are the same, as they must be.

It was necessary to perform only two computations to determine the expected frequencies. The sum of the expected cell frequencies must equal the expected marginal frequencies and the expected marginal frequencies must equal the observed marginal frequencies. Once two cell frequencies are assigned the others are all determined by the marginal frequencies. Thus, only two values are free to vary in this instance; there are 2 df.

The general formula used to determine the number of df is:

$$df = (r - 1)(c - 1), \tag{9.2}$$

where $r = $ number of rows and $c = $ number of columns.

We can now calculate our χ^2 value:

$$\chi^2 = \sum \frac{(O - E)^2}{E}$$

$$= \frac{(10.0 - 10.0)^2}{10.0} + \frac{(11.0 - 13.0)^2}{13.0} + \frac{(17.0 - 15.0)^2}{15.0}$$

$$+ \frac{(6.0 - 6.0)^2}{6.0} + \frac{(10.0 - 8.0)^2}{8.0} + \frac{(6.0 - 8.0)^2}{8.0}$$

$$= \frac{(0.0)^2}{10.0} + \frac{(-2.0)^2}{13.0} + \frac{(2.0)^2}{15.0} + \frac{(0.0)^2}{6.0} + \frac{(2.0)^2}{8.0} + \frac{(-2.0)^2}{8.0}$$

$$= \frac{0.0}{10.0} + \frac{4.0}{13.0} + \frac{4.0}{15.0} + \frac{0.0}{6.0} + \frac{4.0}{8.0} + \frac{4.0}{8.0}$$

$$= .00 + .30 + .27 + .00 + .50 + .50$$

$$= 1.57.$$

The number of $df = (r - 1)(c - 1) = (2 - 1)(3 - 1) = 2$. From Table A–5 we find that, with 2 df, χ^2 must be 5.99 to reach the .05 level of significance. Since out χ^2 value falls far short of the critical value we will conclude that the observed distribution of frequencies is within the deviation expected on the basis of chance. We conclude that there is no reason to believe that the ability to solve the problem is different for the different academic majors.

χ^2 **DISTRIBUTION**

With one degree of freedom χ^2 distributes the same as does F (and, of course, t^2). However, with more than one degree of freedom the sampling distribution of χ^2 is not the same as F. There are a large number of χ^2 distributions depending on the number of degrees of freedom. The χ^2 distributions for 1, 2, 4, 6, and 10 degrees of freedom are illustrated in Figure 9–1. With 30 df the χ^2 distribution is essentially normal. The χ^2 test is a two-tailed test (see Chapter 7, pp. 120 and 121), as is F, since it does not take into account the direction of the deviation, but is based on the size of the deviation.

The χ^2 Table is used to determine the proportion of the total area which would be expected to be beyond the listed χ^2 value if the *a priori* hypothesis is true, and the deviations from that hypothesis are due to chance deviations.

With over 30 df the calculated χ^2 value can be converted to a z and the z can be interpreted with a normal curve table. The formula

Figure 9–1. Approximate forms of χ^2 distribution for certain degrees of freedom. (From Lindquist, E. F., *Design and Analysis of Experiments in Psychology and Education.* Copyright 1953 by Houghton Mifflin Co. and reprinted with their permission.)

to convert χ^2 to z, with over 30 df, is as follows:

$$z = \sqrt{2\chi^2} - \sqrt{2n - 1}, \qquad (9.3)$$

where $n = df$.

FOUR-FOLD CONTINGENCY TABLE

One of the most common uses of χ^2 is in cases in which the data are arranged in a 2×2 table. In these instances individuals are categorized two ways. For example, we could categorize individuals according to sex and according to blue vs. brown eye color. If the two ways of classifying the individuals are independent of one another the χ^2 will not be significant.

Since χ^2 is used so often with the 2×2 table a formula has been derived for this special case which eliminates the necessity to calculate the expected frequencies. When using this method we assume that there is a random distribution of one trait on the other; that is, that they are independent traits. Assume for our sex-eye color example that when 40 individuals are categorized according to sex and eye color the data are as shown in Table 9–4.

Table 9–4.

Sex	Eye Color		
	Blue	Brown	
♂	6 [A]	9 [B]	15
♀	4 [C]	21 [D]	25
	10	30	40

The formula to determine the value of χ^2 in this example is:

$$\chi^2 = \frac{N(AD - BC)^2}{(A + B)(C + D)(A + C)(B + C)} , \qquad (9.4)$$

where $N = $ number of observations.

$$\chi^2 = \frac{40[(6)(21) - (9)(4)]^2}{(6 + 9)(4 + 21)(6 + 4)(9 + 21)}$$

$$= \frac{40[126 - 36]^2}{(15)(25)(10)(30)}$$

$$= \frac{40[90]^2}{112,500}$$

$$= \frac{324,000}{112,500}$$

$$= 2.88.$$

To determine the number of degrees of freedom for this example we use formula (9.2); $df = (r - 1)(c - 1) = (2 - 1)(2 - 1) = 1$. Since our χ^2 of 2.88 falls short of the value of 3.84 tabled at the .05 level we accept the hypothesis that the two traits—eye color and sex—are independent of one another.

Yates' Correction for Continuity

If our χ^2 had been significant, or if we want to estimate the true probability level more accurately we should apply Yates' correction for continuity. This correction will lower the χ^2 value slightly and should be used if the χ^2 is based on 1 df, or if any expected cell frequency is less than ten.

When we correct for continuity we allow for the fact that our computed χ^2 is based on observed frequencies which are whole numbers. Therefore, our observed frequencies vary in discrete steps. The χ^2 table, however, lists values which are based on a continuous scale. To correct for this we reduce each observed difference by 0.5. This reduces the χ^2 value. It is important to make this correction whenever N is small and when the χ^2 is on the borderline of significance.

Table 9–5.

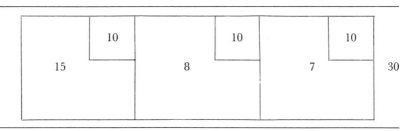

Let us calculate a χ^2 with and without the correction for the data of Table 9–5.

First, we will calculate χ^2 without the correction:

$$\chi^2 = \Sigma \frac{(O - E)^2}{E} = \frac{(15 - 10)^2}{10} + \frac{(8 - 10)^2}{10} + \frac{(7 - 10)^2}{10}$$

$$= \frac{(5)^2}{10} + \frac{(-2)^2}{10} + \frac{(-3)^2}{10}$$

$$= \frac{25}{10} + \frac{4}{10} + \frac{9}{10}$$

$$= 2.5 + .4 + .9$$

$$= 3.80.$$

With Yates' correction the formula becomes:

$$\chi^2 = \Sigma \frac{(|O - E| - .5)^2}{E}, \tag{9.5}$$

where $|O - E| - .5$ indicates that we should reduce the absolute size of the deviation by .5.

$$\chi^2 = \frac{(|15 - 10| - .5)^2}{10} + \frac{(|8 - 10| - .5)^2}{10} + \frac{(|7 - 10| - .5)^2}{10}$$

$$= \frac{(4.5)^2}{10} + \frac{(1.5)^2}{10} + \frac{(2.5)^2}{10}$$

$$= \frac{20.25}{10} + \frac{2.25}{10} + \frac{6.25}{10}$$

$$= 2.025 + .225 + .625$$

$$= 2.875.$$

In neither instance is the χ^2 value significant at the .05 level of significance. However, it can be seen that the size of the χ^2 has been reduced considerably.

To apply Yates' correction with the four-fold contingency table the formula becomes:

$$\chi^2 = \frac{N(|AD - BC| - N/2)^2}{(A + B)(C + D)(A + C)(B + D)} \qquad (9.6)$$

Again, $|AD - BC| - N/2$ indicates that the size of the $AD - BC$ term is to be reduced toward zero by $N/2$, regardless of the sign of the deviation.

Restrictions on the Use of χ^2

χ^2 is a useful and simple statistic to calculate as well as to interpret. However, it is also a frequently misused statistic. The requirement that all the individual events be independent is the most often violated in the use of χ^2. To meet this requirement no one individual can contribute more than one frequency to the χ^2, since the frequencies would no longer be independent. Several measures based on the same individual are all dependent on that individual's abilities and background and cannot be used in a χ^2 test.

χ^2 can only be used with frequency data. It cannot be used to test differences, for example, between an expected mean and an observed mean since the χ^2 values would then vary with the size of the units of measurement and the χ^2 table would not be appropriate.

There must be some rational basis for the manner in which the data are categorized. If the categorization is not meaningful then there will be no way to draw a meaningful inference on the basis of the calculated χ^2 value.

In order to obtain accurate estimates of probability there should not be too many small theoretical (E) frequencies. Some statisticians believe that the use of χ^2 is inadvisable if there are any expected frequencies less than ten. This is perhaps an extreme position.

Walker and Lev (1953) have outlined some "rules of thumb" which we believe are the most sensible positions on this issue:

1. If there is only one degree of freedom, follow the suggestion previously given for the use of Yates' correction.

2. If there are two or more degrees of freedom and the expectation in each cell is more than five, the chi-square table assures a good approximation to the exact probabilities.

3. If there are two or more degrees of freedom and roughly approximate probabilities are acceptable for the test of significance, an expectation of only two in a cell is sufficient.

4. If there are more than two degrees of freedom and the expectation in all the cells but one is five or more, then an expectation of only one in the remaining cell is sufficient to provide a fair approximation of the exact probabilities.

5. If the logic of the problem permits, combine some of the classes to increase the expectations in the cells when several cells have very small expectations.

PROPORTIONS

There is another circumstance in which the data are not in the form of measurements, and in which we might want to evaluate the significance of a deviation from an *a priori* hypothesis. This circumstance is one in which the data are in the form of proportions. Assume that a cigarette company claims that 70 per cent of doctors smoke their brand (Brand A). We are suspicious of their advertising claims and conduct a survey on the smoking habits of doctors. The results of polling a random sample of 50 doctors indicate that 60 per cent of the 50 (30 of them) smoke Brand A.

The question now arises whether or not the proportion of doctors we found to smoke Brand A (.60) could have occurred as a result of sampling error when the true proportion is as the cigarette company claimed (.70). In other words, what is the probability that we would obtain a proportion of .60 when $N = 50$ if the true proportion is .70?

The solution to this problem is based on the fact that if a large number of random samples are drawn from a population of proportions, the resulting distribution of proportions will distribute in a form similar enough to the normal curve to allow the use of the normal curve table. We have a statement concerning the true proportion in the population, which we assume is the μ of the distribution. We also know that the proportions around μ will be distributed almost normally. Therefore, if we can determine the standard error of this distribution of proportions we can make the usual inferences based on the normal curve table. The formula for the standard error of a proportion is as follows:

$$\sigma_p = \sqrt{\frac{pq}{N}},\qquad\qquad (9.7)$$

where p = hypothetical true proportions,

$\qquad q = 1 - p$,

$\qquad N$ = sample size.

The standard error of the proportion in our example, then, is

$$\sigma_p = \sqrt{\frac{(.7)(.3)}{50}} = \sqrt{\frac{.21}{50}} = \sqrt{.0042} = .065.$$

We can now determine the probability that we would obtain a proportion of .60 when the true proportion is .70. The problem is illustrated in Figure 9–2. We wish to find the proportion of the total area under the curve indicated by the shaded section. This proportion is the proportion of cases which would be expected to deviate as greatly as .10 from the true proportion on the basis of random sampling error, given the size of our sample.

To use the normal curve table we must calculate a z-score:

$$z = \frac{x}{\sigma_p} = \frac{.70 - .60}{.065} = 1.54.\qquad\qquad (9.8)$$

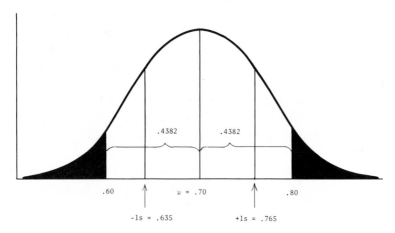

Figure 9–2.

From Table A–2 we find that .4382 of the area under the curve falls between the mean and a z of 1.54: .4382 + .4382 = .8764 of the area under the curve would be expected to fall between a z of −1.54 and a z of +1.54. Therefore, .1236 of the area would remain in the tails of the distribution. Thus, the probability of observing a difference of .10 from the true proportion of .70 based on a sample of 50 cases is .1236. Since this probability is larger than the probability we usually require to reject a hypothesis (usually, we demand a significance level of .05) we conclude that the proportion we observed could reasonably have occurred due to chance sampling error from a population whose true proportion was .70. Hence, we accept the cigarette company's claim regarding the proportion of doctors who smoke Brand A.

Corrections for Continuity. A problem arises when the value of p becomes extreme. If, for example, $p = .10$ we will undoubtedly have a skewed distribution since the smallest p possible is .00, while the highest p possible is 1.00. However, the degree of skewness is also dependent on the size of N. In order to compensate for the bias introduced in such instances we should correct for continuity when *either* N_p or N_q is between five and ten. If *both* N_p and N_q exceed ten we need not be concerned with correcting for continuity.

To correct for continuity we should reduce the value of the deviation of the observed proportion from the hypothetical proportion by $.5/N$. In our example the correction would be applied as follows:

$$z = \frac{|.7 - .6| - .5/50}{.065} = \frac{.1 - .01}{.065} = \frac{.09}{.065} = 1.38. \qquad (9.9)$$

Applying the correction reduces the size of z from 1.54 to 1.38. The correction should always be applied when the size of N_p or N_q warrants it, and when the probability level is of a borderline value.

EXERCISES

1. A die was tossed 60 times. The number of times each side was up is as follows: one, 8; two, 9; three, 8; four, 8; five, 10; six, 16. Would you conclude that the die is not evenly balanced?
2. It is claimed that 75 per cent of college students favor co-educational residential facilities. A sample of 100 students is polled and it is found that 65 of the students favor such housing arrangements. On the basis of these data, can you accept the claim?
3. It is further claimed that while 75 per cent of the total are in favor, 90 per cent of male students are in favor while only 60 per cent of female students are in favor of the proposed housing arrangements. The sample of 100 students is composed of 50 males and 50 females. Forty of the males and 32 of the females were found to be in favor. Can you accept this further claim that 90 per cent of males and 60 per cent of females are in favor on the basis of these data?
4. An experiment is performed in which subjects are categorized according to political affiliation and then are asked to state their preference for four political candidates. The data are tabled below:

		A	B	C	D	
	Liberal	5	5	20	0	30
Political Preference	Democrat	10	20	30	20	80
	Republican	21	19	20	20	80
	Conservative	8	2	0	20	30
		44	46	70	60	220

On the basis of these findings can you conclude that the obtained is other than that expected on the basis of a random distribution?

5. It is claimed that 85 per cent of college students favor fraternities on campus. A poll is conducted and it is found that of 60 students polled, 75 per cent favor fraternities. On the basis of these data, can you accept the claim? (Answer this using both the χ^2 method and the standard error of a proportion.)

10

DISTRIBUTION-FREE METHODS

The chi-square method discussed in Chapter 9 is called a distribution-free, or non-parametric, method. This means that it is not necessary to make any assumptions about the shape of the underlying population distribution from which the samples are drawn. In contrast, to use statistical methods such as t and F you must assume that the statistics on which inferences are to be based distribute themselves normally.

In practice, these assumptions can be largely ignored. Several recent studies* indicate that statistics such as t and F, which are based on normal curve models, are not sensitive to violations of the normal distribution requirement. Therefore, the nature of the underlying distribution of scores can, in general, be disregarded since statistics computed from non-normal populations of scores distribute in a form sufficiently close to the normal curve to permit the use of methods based on the normal distribution.

While it is comforting to know that these assumptions are not essential some misleading inferences can be made under certain

---

* Boneau, C. A.: *The effects of violations of assumptions underlying the t test; Psychological Bulletin*, 1960, 57, pp. 49–64. Baker, B. O., Hardyck, C. D., and Petrinovich, L. F.: *Weak measurements vs. strong statistics: An empirical critique of S. S. Stevens' proscriptions on statistics; Educational and Psychological Measurement*, 1966, 26, pp. 291–309.

A

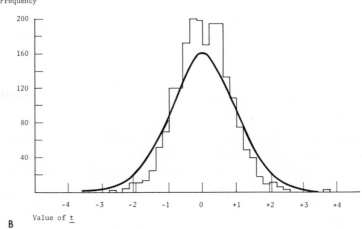

B

Figure 10–1. *A* and *B*. (From Boneau, C. A., *The effects of violations of assumptions underlying the t test*; *Psychological Bulletin*, Vol. 57, No. 1, 1960, and reprinted with permission.)

circumstances. Perhaps the clearest demonstration of such circumstances was provided by Boneau, who used a computer to draw random samples and to calculate values of t under conditions in which certain of the underlying assumptions for the use of t were systematically violated. He found very few conditions which produced any systematic bias in the t-test. However, if samples are of unequal sizes and have unequal variances, some serious discrepancies do appear. The shape of the t distribution is shown in Figure 10–1 A for the circumstances in which the smaller sample of the two has the larger variance. In Figure 10–1 B we see the t distribution for the circumstances in which the larger sample has the larger variance. Examination of these two figures indicates that when the smaller sample has the larger variance the t-ratio will fall beyond the .95 confidence limits many more times than the .05 expected on the basis of chance. When the larger sample has the larger variance, the reverse occurs—the t-ratio will fall beyond the .95 limits many *fewer* times than the .05 expected on the basis of chance.

For such occasions inferential methods have been developed which do not require any assumptions regarding the nature of the parent population. In this chapter a few additional techniques will be discussed which do not require normal curve assumptions.

SIGN TEST

The sign test takes its name from the fact that only the difference, + or −, around some reference point enters into the calculations; the actual score values themselves are not used in the computation. Suppose an investigator is interested in the accuracy of visual recognition of objects under conditions of sunrise vs. sunset illumination. He obtains accuracy scores on a group of subjects, half of which are first tested at sunrise and half of which are first tested at sunset. The variances for the two conditions are so different that he decides not to use the t-test for correlated means. Rather, he decides to use a sign test to decide whether or not there is any significant difference in accuracy scores under the two conditions of illumination. Since his measures differ greatly in variability he decides to subtract the sunset measurement from the sunrise measurement for each of the subjects. He then tallies the number of times the difference between the sunrise and the sunset score is + or −. Table 10–1 contains the data.

Table 10–1. CALCULATION OF THE SIGN TEST.

A—Sunrise Accuracy Scores	B—Sunset Accuracy Scores	A-B Sign Difference
12	18	−
19	20	−
11	17	−
8	24	−
12	18	−
17	17	0
22	19	+
14	14	0
18	15	+
13	21	−

Number of − signs = 6

Number of + signs = 2

The number of times the sign with the smaller number of occurrences appears is counted (ignoring zero differences) and this number is called r. Then Table A–6 is entered. If the observed r is equal to or less than the value in the table, it can be concluded that r occurs less frequently than would be expected by chance. For the data of Table 10–1, the total N is equal to ten. This is reduced by two, because of zero differences and the value of r is 2. Entering Table A–6 with an N of 8 we find that r can be no larger than 0 to reach the 5 per cent level of confidence. Since the r in our example is 2 we will accept the hypothesis that there is no difference in the two sets of accuracy scores.

MEDIAN TEST

Given the situation where we have two independent groups and do not wish to use the t-test, it is possible to test the hypothesis that the two groups come from populations having the same median. This test is a χ^2 test; the only unique feature is that the groups are split at the median for all scores. To test this hypothesis, the two groups are combined and the overall median is determined (see Chapter 3, pp. 33 , for computing methods). Once the median has been located, a four-fold contingency table (cf. Chapter 9) is constructed. A tally is entered for each score of each group in the appropriate cell according to whether it is above or below the median for the combined groups. Once the tally has been completed the hypothesis that the two groups are drawn from a population with the same median is tested using the chi-square statistic. Table 10–2 contains the calculation.

Since the critical χ^2 value with one degree of freedom at the .05 level is 3.84, we accept the hypothesis that these two groups are drawn from populations with the same median. We conclude, therefore, that our experimental treatment has had no effect.

Ranking Methods

Situations frequently arise in which data are collected in the form of ranks or in which scores are changed to ranks when they are unsuitable for analysis with parametric techniques. Two techniques for testing hypotheses using ranked data will be presented here.

Mann-Whitney U Test. The Mann-Whitney U test is the equivalent of the t-test for ranked measurements. If we wish to test the hypothesis that two sets of scores come from the same population, we first combine the sets of scores and rank them, giving the value of 1 to the lowest score, 2 to the next lowest, and so forth, until all scores have been ranked. Ties in rank are dealt with by assigning the average of the ranks that would have been assigned if they were not identical. Let us rank the following scores: 5, 7, 8, 10, 10, 10, 11, and 12. The first three scores which are identical in value are assigned the average of ranks 4, 5, and 6, which is 5. The rank order would read, then, 1, 2, 3, 5, 5, 5. Since rank positions 4, 5, and 6 have all been used by the scores of 10, we continue the ranking by assigning the rank of 7 to the score of 11. The completed ranking is 1, 2, 3, 5, 5, 5, 7, 8. The value of U is found by the following formula:

$$U = \left[n_1 n_2 + \frac{n_1(n_1 + 1)}{2} \right] - \Sigma R_1, \qquad \textbf{(10.1)}$$

where n_1 and n_2 = the number of cases in sample 1 and 2, respectively, and ΣR_1 = the sum of ranks for group 1, where group 1 is the smaller sample.

Table 10–2. CALCULATION OF THE MEDIAN TEST.

	Sample A	Sample B
Step 1: Determine the median by finding the score above which 50 per cent of the cases lie.	16	15
	22	14
	20	12
	10	9
	23	8
	21	13
	10	19
	$N = 7$	$N = 7$

10   13

8   9   10   12   13   14   16   19   20   21   22   23

↑

Median $= 13.5$

(Scores in order of increasing magnitude)

Step 2: Prepare a contingency table

A	B
C	D

	Sample A	Sample B	
Above median	5	2	7
Below median	2	5	7
	7	7	

Step 3: Calculate χ^2 for a four-fold table with correction for continuity (formula [9.6]) and $df = 1$.

$$\chi^2 = \frac{N(|BC - AD| - N/2)^2}{(A + B)(C + D)(A + C)(B + D)}$$

$$= \frac{14(|4 - 25| - 14/2)^2}{(7)(7)(7)(7)}$$

$$= \frac{14(|-21| - 7)^2}{2401} = \frac{14(14)^2}{2401}$$

$$= \frac{14(196)}{2401} = \frac{2744}{2401}$$

$$= 1.14$$

The critical values of U for the .01 and .05 levels of confidence are listed in Table A–7 as a function of the size of the smaller sample (n_1) and the size of the larger sample (n_2). In order to be significant at the given level of confidence the calculated value of U must be as small as or smaller than the value listed in the table. Table 10–3 contains the computations.

To evaluate the U, we turn to Table A–7 and find that our U is considerably larger than the tabled value of 23. Consequently, we conclude that our obtained difference is not significant and accept the hypothesis that the two samples have been drawn from the same population.

Large Samples.   If either of the samples contains more than 20 cases the normal curve table (Table A–2) can be used since the following formula gives a good approximation of z:

$$z = [\,U - (n_1 n_2/2)\,] \,/\, \sqrt{(n_1)(n_2)(n_1 + n_2 + 1)/12}, \quad \textbf{(10.2)}$$

where z is 1.96 for the .05 level and 2.58 for the .01 level.

Kruskal-Wallis H Test.   The U test just described is a ranked data analogue to the t-test for two independent groups. Similarly, the Kruskal-Wallis H test is a ranked data analogue to the one-way analysis of variance. It is used to test the hypothesis that a number of groups have been drawn from the same population. The computational procedure is quite similar to the Mann-Whitney U. All groups are combined and ranked as in the Mann-Whitney. The statistic, H, is then calculated by the formula:

$$H = \frac{12}{N(N + 1)} \Sigma \frac{R^2}{N} - 3(N + 1), \quad \textbf{(10.3)}$$

where $N =$ the total number of observations over all samples,

$n =$ the number of observations in any one sample,

$R =$ the sum of ranks for any one sample.

The calculation of H is illustrated with data based on three groups of subjects. The scores, their rank, and the sum of the ranks for each group are listed in Table 10–4.

Table 10–3. Calculation of the Mann-Whitney U Test.

Step 1: Rank the scores. Ties are settled by determining the average rank of the positions taken by the tied scores.

Rank	1	2	3.5	3.5	5.5	5.5	7	8	10
Score	8	11	12	12	13	13	14	15	17
Rank	10	10	13	13	13	15.5	15.5	17	18
Score	17	17	18	18	18	19	19	20	21
Rank	19	20
Score	22	24

Step 2: Arrange the ranks by groups.

	Group 1		Group 2	
	Score	Rank	Score	Rank
	18	1	13	5.5
	11	2	15	8
	12	3.5	17	10
	12	3.5	17	10
	13	5.5	18	13
	14	7	18	13
	17	10	19	15.5
	18	13	20	17
	19	15.5	21	18
	22	19	24	20

Step 3: Sum the ranks for each of the groups. Σ | 80.0 | 130.0

Step 4: Since Group 1 has the smaller sum, we will solve for U using Group 1

$$U = n_1 n_2 + \frac{n_1(n_1 + 1)}{2} - \sum R_1$$

$$= (10)(10) + \frac{(10)(11)}{2} - 80.0$$

$$= 100 + 55 - 80$$

$$= 75.0$$

Step 5: The obtained value of U is larger than the tabled value for .05, which is 23 (Table A–7).

Step 6: Accept the hypothesis that the two samples are drawn from the same population.

180

Table 10-4.

Group 1		Group 2		Group 3	
Score	*Rank*	*Score*	*Rank*	*Score*	*Rank*
.50	1	.73	3	2.00	9.5
.93	2	1.27	6	2.60	11
.84	4	1.55	7	3.00	12
.87	5	2.00	9.5	3.40	13
1.66	8				
$\sum R_1 = 20$		$\sum R_2 = 25.5$		$\sum R_3 = 45.5$	

The value of H calculated using formula (10.3) is

$$H = \frac{12}{13(14)}\left[\frac{20^2}{5} + \frac{25.5^2}{4} + \frac{45.5^2}{4}\right] - 3(14)$$

$$= \frac{12}{182}\left[\frac{400.0}{5} + \frac{650.25}{4} + \frac{2070.25}{4}\right] - 42$$

$$= .066[80 + 162.6 + 517.6] - 42$$

$$= 50.17 - 42$$

$$= 8.17.$$

To evaluate the obtained H of 8.2, we use Table A–8 which lists the values of H for all combinations of three groups, where no n is larger than five, at the .05 and .01 levels of confidence. For n's of 5, 4, and 4 we find that the listed H value is 7.74 at the .01 confidence level. Our value of 8.2 is larger than the tabled value and we reject the null hypothesis at the .01 level. We can conclude that the three samples are not drawn from the same population.

The size of H is affected by the number of ties in rank. Therefore, a correction for ties should be made using the formula:

$$1 - \frac{\sum T}{N^3 - N}, \tag{10.4}$$

where $T = t^3 - t$, where t is the number of tied observations in a set which is summed over all sets of ties,

N = the total number of observations in the sample.

The correction is made by dividing the obtained value of H by the result of the preceding formula. In our example one tie occurred. Since two observations are involved in this tie, the number of tied observations is two. Applying the formula, we find

$$T = t^3 - t = 8 - 2 = 6$$

$$N^3 - N = 2197 - 13 = 2184$$

$$1 - \frac{6}{2184} = 1 - .0027 = .9973.$$

The corrected value of H is equal to:

$$H_c = 8.17/.9973$$

$$= 8.19$$

Since there was only one tie in this example the difference between the corrected H (8.19) and the uncorrected H (8.17) is quite small. If the H value is at the borderline of significance or if we want a precise estimate of significance level the H value should be corrected for ties.

Larger Samples. When the number of observations exceeds the values listed in Table A–8, H can be evaluated by computing a chi-square with the degrees of freedom equal to the number of groups minus one. If we have more than three groups of subjects or have more subjects than five in any one of three groups, our calculated H can be treated as a χ^2 value. If we do evaluate the H statistic using the χ^2 distribution Table A–5 should be entered with

$$df = k - 1,$$

where $k =$ the number of groups.

If we have six groups of subjects the $df = 6 - 1 = 5$; the tabled value for χ^2 at the .05 level of confidence with 5 df (Table A–5) is 11.07. In order to reject the null hypothesis at the .05 level of confidence the value of H must be at least as large as 11.07.

Advantages and Disadvantages of Non-parametric Methods

As a general rule, parametric methods are preferred because they have superior power and allow greater precision of estimation than do the corresponding non-parametric methods. Occasionally a non-parametric method is used because it is easier to compute. However, the efficiency of non-parametric methods is not as great as that of parametric methods. For example, a sign test done on 20 subjects is equivalent in power to a t-test done with 14 subjects at $\alpha = .04$. Use of the sign test in this case could be equivalent to throwing away six subjects! The U and H tests have somewhat better power, but still do not equal the power of the corresponding parametric measure. If a difference is significant with a non-parametric test it will usually be at least as significant with the corresponding parametric test, so it is usually not necessary to carry out the additional computation.

In general, the use of non-parametric measures disregards information when compared to the corresponding parametric test. A sign test, for example, merely takes into account the sign of a difference; the magnitude of the differences is not taken into account.

Very few circumstances are encountered in which a parametric method is inappropriate. The only case in which one must use a non-parametric method are those instances in which the data are incomplete because some of the extreme measurements are not scaled. The empirical investigations cited earlier have established the fact that the parametric methods remain relatively unaffected by wide departures from the conventional normal curve models. In many situations it has been shown that parametric methods are *less* affected by unusual distributions than are the non-parametric methods.

EXERCISES

1. Two experimenters are concerned about sampling biases in their selection of rats for their studies. In particular, they have been told that when rats are housed two to a cage the rat picked up first will be the larger and more aggressive rat of the two. Since they are conducting studies in emotionality in which any such biases would influence the outcome of their studies they decide to test this claim. They cage ten pairs of rats together for one month; then an experimenter who is unaware of the purpose of the study picks one of the rats from each cage. They note which rat is chosen and they weigh all of the rats. The weights are listed below in grams:

Cage #	1	2	3	4	5	6	7	8	9	10
Chosen rat	250	241	232	215	283	200	234	189	250	226
Cage mate	225	236	234	180	198	200	220	210	231	207

   One experimenter decides to run a sign test on these data. Can he conclude that there is a significant effect?

2. The second experimenter decided to do a median test on the data. Can he conclude that there is a significant effect?

3. The original informants explain to the two experimenters that the observed effect holds only for male rats. Since the experimenters used females in the first experiments they performed the study again with males. The weights are listed below in grams:

Cage #	1	2	3	4	5	6	7	8	9	10
Chosen rat	282	270	313	305	267	315	308	291	316	302
Cage mate	250	273	319	302	240	312	314	266	300	271

   The second experimenter again decides to analyze the data using a median test. Can he conclude that there is a significant effect?

185

4. The first experimenter decides to do a sign test on the data. Can he conclude that there is a significant effect?

5. An experimenter is interested in studying the effect of motivation on the ability to make fine motor movements. He uses a task in which tweezers are used to insert tiny pegs into holes in a board. The score is expressed in terms of the number of pegs inserted in a five minute work period. One group of randomly selected subjects is paid 1¢ for each peg inserted (Group M). The other group of randomly selected subjects is not paid to do the task but is merely urged to do as well as they can (Group U). The data are listed below.

Rank	4	9	8	3
Group M	$X_1 = 254$	$X_2 = 201$	$X_3 = 210$	$X_4 = 264$
	2	1	5	
	$X_5 = 276$	$X_6 = 281$	$X_7 = 233$	
Rank	10	7	12	13
Group U	$X_1 = 195$	$X_2 = 212$	$X_3 = 173$	$X_4 = 140$
	11	6		
	$X_5 = 183$	$X_6 = 215$		

The experimenter evaluates the significance of the difference between the two groups with the Mann-Whitney U test. Can he conclude that there is a difference between the two groups?

6. (a) Another experimenter decides to test the difference between the two groups using the t-ratio. Can he conclude that there is a difference between the two groups?

(b) Which procedure to test the difference between the two groups is preferable? Why?

7. The following learning scores are based on three groups of subjects of different ages. The scores are expressed in terms of the number

of items correctly recalled from a list of 20 nonsense syllables which the subjects had been instructed to learn.

15 year olds		30 year olds		45 year olds	
Score	Rank	Score	Rank	Score	Rank
10	5	13	2	9	7
9	7	8	9	7	10
12	3	6	11.5	4	13
11	4	7	7	2	14
15	1		29.5	6	11.5
	20				55.5

What is the value of the Kruskal-Wallis H test calculated from these data? Can it be concluded that there is a significant difference among these groups?

11

REGRESSION

The first ten chapters of this book have been used to develop the logic underlying the methods used to make inferences concerning the central location of a population of scores. We have presented the methods used (1) to estimate the location and variability of a sampling distribution of means, and (2) to evaluate whether or not two samples can be considered to have come from the same population. The logic underlying these inferences has been developed for data which take the form of measurements, frequency counts, proportions, and ranks.

This chapter and the next one will have as their central focus another concern. We will now discuss the methods used to evaluate the degree to which variables are associated with one another. In this chapter we will consider the problem of predicting values of one variable from values of another variable. In the next chapter we will consider the problem of expressing the degree of relationship by means of an "average" value.

PREDICTION

Regression is defined as the prediction of unknown values of one variable from known values of another variable. The variable we are using as the predictor is labeled X, and the to-be-predicted variable is labeled Y. For example, we might wish to use scores in a test of arithmetical reasoning ability (X) given at the beginning of the semester to predict grades in a statistics course (Y) at the end of the semester.

If knowing the values of X provides information about the value of Y, then X and Y are said to be related, or to be associated. Our central concern in regression problems is to make the best estimate possible of an individual's Y score from knowledge of his X score.

LINEAR REGRESSION

The problem is quite simple when we have a perfect linear regression of variable Y on X. To illustrate the nature of such a relationship assume that we want to predict the yearly income of a small business. Assume that the monthly income throughout the year is the same since all income comes from fixed amount contracts for a 12-month period. In addition to this income the company receives $1000 interest on investments over the year. Knowing this information we can calculate the yearly income. The equation we use is the equation for a straight line:

$$Y = a + bX, \qquad\qquad \textbf{(11.1)}$$

where $Y =$ the to-be-predicted yearly income,
  $X =$ the monthly income from contracts,
  $a =$ the interest income,
  $b =$ the number of months over the year the income is
      collected.
In this equation a and b are constants, the function of which we will discuss later. We will assume the following values: $X = \$1000$, $a = \$1000$, $b = 12$ months. Therefore: $Y = 1000 + 12(1000) = 13{,}000$.

Keeping everything else constant let us assume that X takes the value $1500. Therefore: $Y = 1000 + 12(1500) = 19{,}000$. Again, keeping everything else constant let us assume that X takes the value $2000. Therefore: $Y = 1000 + 12(2000) = 25{,}000$. Let X take the value $2500. Therefore: $Y = 1000 + 12(2500) = 31{,}000$.

Figure 11–1 is a graph of these four points which are plotted as crosses and connected by a solid straight line. If both constant a and constant b stay the same we can predict the yearly income from knowing the monthly income with complete accuracy. In fact, we could do so after calculating only two points, connecting them, and

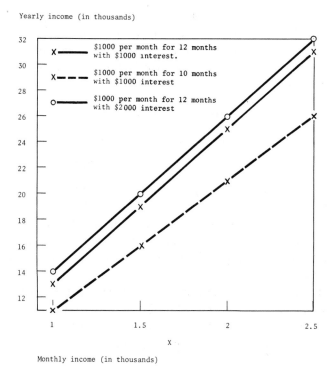

Figure 11–1.

using the regression line to predict Y contingent on a given value of X.

Suppose that everything stays the same except the number of months over which the income is collected. The decision of the company president is to close the business for two months during the summer for a vacation. Thus, b will take the value of 10, rather than 12. Our four equations will now give the following values:

$$Y = 1000 + 10(1000) = 11,000$$

$$Y = 1000 + 10(1500) = 16,000$$

$$Y = 1000 + 10(2000) = 21,000$$

$$Y = 1000 + 10(2500) = 26,000$$

These four points are plotted as crosses in Figure 11–1 and connected by a dashed line. The effect of changing the constant b is to change the slope of the straight line.

If we change the value of the constant a we will not affect the slope but will change the position of the line on Y. For example, assume that the investment income (a) becomes $2000 per year and everything else is as depicted in the solid line. Now, our four equations become:

$$Y = 2000 + 12(1000) = 14,000$$

$$Y = 2000 + 12(1500) = 20,000$$

$$Y = 2000 + 12(2000) = 26,000$$

$$Y = 2000 + 12(2500) = 32,000$$

These four points are represented in Figure 11–1 as open circles connected with a solid line. It can be seen that changing the constant a does not affect the slope of the line at all but merely the position of the line on Y.

On the basis of this example it is evident that if a perfect linear relationship exists all of the points in the distribution fall on the regression line: if we know the parameters a, b, and are given a value of X we can predict Y with complete accuracy.

Scatter Diagram

In most prediction problems we do not have an exact relationship between the variables we are considering. However, we still want to make the best estimate of an individual's Y score from knowledge of his X score. If some degree of relationship does exist between X and Y we will increase the accuracy of our predictions using the X score to predict Y over what would be possible if we did not use the information provided by the X score. This lack of an exact relationship is due to uncontrolled influences which also influence the value of X and Y and which are not measured. For example, assume that we wish to predict school grades (Y) from IQ scores (X). If a zero relationship exists between the two variables, the best possible prediction we could make given any X score would be the mean of the Y scores. There will be some degree of relationship between school grades and IQ, but certainly not a perfect relationship. Other variables which would influence school grades would be such things as level of motivation, amount of outside work, the number of extracurricular activities, emotional stresses, and so forth. Even though our data points do not all fall on the regression line we can still determine the best fit regression line through the data points.

When we suspect that there is a relationship between two variables the first step is to construct a scatter diagram (also called a correlation chart). The scatter diagram is a special type of graph based on two values: the values of X and the values of Y for each member of a group of individuals. Such data on a two-scaled trait are called *bivariate data*. When constructing scatter diagrams the variable which is the predictor (in our example, IQ scores) is called the X variable and is scaled along the horizontal axis of the graph. The variable which is to be predicted is called the Y variable (in our example, school grades) and is plotted along the vertical axis of the graph. Figure 11–2 is a scatter diagram based on the data in Table 11–1.

Table 11–1 contains a pair of scores for each of ten subjects. The score on one variable is labeled X and the score on the other is labeled Y. The table also contains X^2 (which we will need in a later calculation) and the cross products of X and Y. This term, XY, is obtained by multiplying each subject's X score by his Y score. The $\sum XY$ is obtained by summing these cross products.

Figure 11–2 is constructed by placing a tally mark in the box at the intersection of the appropriate X and Y scores for each subject. Subject A has an X of 1 and a Y of 1. Therefore, a tally mark has been placed in the lower left-hand box which is the intersection of the appropriate X and Y values and which would be identified as X_1Y_1. Note that the box at the intersection of an X value of 4 and a Y value of 5 (X_4Y_5) contains two tally marks since both subjects D and J have this combination of X and Y scores (this would be written $_fX_4Y_5 = 2$). As a check on the accuracy of the tallying, the frequency of each X score ($_fX$) is noted at the top of each column and the frequency of each Y score ($_fY$) is noted along the right margin of each column. The sum of the X scores ($\sum_f X$) should equal 10, as should the sum of the Y scores ($\sum_f Y$).

We can now calculate what is called the "best fit line" through these tallies. It must be emphasized that if the relationship between the two variables is not a linear relationship the best fit line will not be a straight line. We cannot use the method to be described here when a curved line would be the best fit line. This method works *only* when the best fit line is a straight line. We could, of course, draw in the best fit line by visual inspection. The drawbacks of this

Table 11-1.

Subject	X	X^2	Y	Y^2	XY	Y'	$Y - Y'$	$(Y - Y')^2$
A	1	1	1	1	1	1.97	−.97	.94
B	2	4	3	9	6	2.87	.13	.00
C	3	9	3	9	9	3.77	−.77	.59
D	4	16	5	25	20	4.67	.33	.11
E	4	16	4	16	16	4.67	−.67	.45
F	6	36	5	25	30	6.47	−1.47	2.16
G	7	49	8	64	56	7.37	.63	.40
H	3	9	6	36	18	3.77	2.23	4.97
I	3	9	4	16	12	3.77	.23	.05
J	4	16	5	25	20	4.67	.33	.11
	$\sum X = 37$	$\sum X^2 = 165$	$\sum Y = 44$	$\sum Y^2 = 266$	$\sum XY = 188$		.00	9.78
	$\bar{X} = 3.70$		$\bar{Y} = 4.40$					

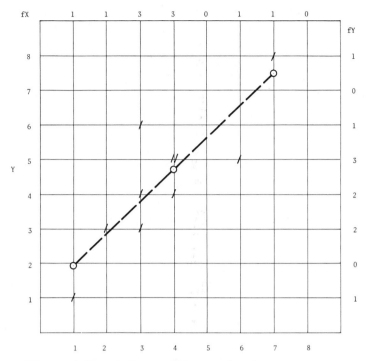

Figure 11–2. Tabulation of bivariate data from Table 11-1.

procedure are that different people might draw slightly different best fit lines through the tallies and the result would be different predictions of Y based on the value of X. Therefore, we want a method which will not depend on the subjective judgment of the investigator. By computing a regression equation (which you will remember is the equation for a straight line) we obtain a line which allows us to make the best estimates of an individual's Y score from knowing his X score.

At this point, the question might arise as to why we use the regression line rather than the average values of Y contingent on a given value of X. Suppose we had four individuals each with an X score of 7 and whose Y scores were 6, 7, 7, and 8. Why not take the arithmetic mean of these values and use that average as the best prediction of Y from X? This question might seem even more meaningful in situations in which, for some values of X, the regression line might not be at any of the obtained values of Y. The answer is that from the standpoint of sampling stability the regression line is more stable than any other value indicating the relationship between X and Y since it is based on *all* the scores. Predictions based on the regression line will not be influenced by minor sampling fluctuations as much as would be the case if we used the values in the individual columns to make the predictions.

To fit the regression line by more objective means than would be possible by visual inspection we will solve an equation which fits a straight line to the observations such that the sum of the squares of the deviations from the line are as small as possible.

The equation is the earlier equation for the best fitting straight line: $Y' = a + bX$, where Y' (Y-prime) = the predicted value of Y given a certain value of X. The constant a will be used to adjust the line so that it passes through both $\bar{X}$ and $\bar{Y}$, and is called the Y *intercept*; b will determine the slope of the line, and is called the *slope constant*.

$$b = \frac{N \sum XY - (\sum X)(\sum Y)}{N \sum X^2 - (\sum X)^2} \tag{11.2}$$

$$a = \bar{Y} - b\bar{X}. \tag{11.3}$$

Solving for the example of Table 11–1 we obtain the following:

$$b = \frac{(10)(188) - (37)(44)}{10(165) - (37)^2} = \frac{1880 - 1628}{1650 - 1369} = \frac{252}{281} = .90$$

$$a = 4.40 - (.90)3.70 = 4.40 - 3.33 = 1.07.$$

Having obtained the necessary constants our regression equation becomes:

$$Y' = 1.07 + .90(X).$$

We can now determine Y' conditional on any given value of X.

Let us solve the equation for three different values of X: 1, 4, and 7.

$$Y' = 1.07 + .90(1) = 1.97,$$

$$Y' = 1.07 + .90(4) = 4.67,$$

$$Y' = 1.07 + .90(7) = 7.37.$$

These three points have been plotted as open circles in Figure 11–2, and the regression line has been fitted through them.

Error of Estimate

It can be seen that our predictions compare quite favorably with the obtained Y's. The discrepancy of an actually obtained Y from the predicted Y is symbolized $Y - Y'$. This discrepancy is called the error of estimate, the error of prediction, or the residual error.

For each X column we have what is called a conditional distribution of Y. This is the distribution of Y on condition that X has a certain value. For each value of X the value of Y' is the mean of the conditional distribution of Y based on all of the cases in the scatter diagram. From inspection of Figure 11–2 we can see that the actual mean of each conditional distribution of Y is not the same as the mean estimated by our calculations. However, as pointed out earlier, it is more stable from a sampling standpoint than would be the case if we used the actual conditional Y means because it is based on all of the cases.

Standard Error of Estimate

As when estimating a population mean from a sample mean (cf. Chapter 6), we would like to estimate the probability that our predictions will be within a certain range of values. Again, we have techniques which make it possible to estimate the standard deviation of a set of conditional Y's. If N is large we would find that the variability of the various Y distributions are very similar. We assume that all the Y distributions have the same standard deviation and compute this standard deviation based on all the scores in the entire distribution. This standard deviation, called the standard error of estimate or standard error of prediction, is for all the conditional Y distributions. The standard error of estimate is symbolized as $s_{y \cdot x}$.

$$s_{y \cdot x} = \sqrt{\frac{\sum (Y - Y')^2}{N - 2}} \qquad (11.4)$$

where N = the number of subjects, each of whom contributes an
X and a Y value.

This formula is quite similar to the basic formula for the standard deviation of a distribution of scores: $s = \sqrt{\dfrac{\sum (X - \bar{X})^2}{N - 1}}$. The difference is that the standard error of estimate is based on the deviation scores from the estimated conditional distribution of Y. We divide by $N - 2$ since we have computed two constants, a and b, and this places two restrictions on the variability.

$\sum (Y - Y')$ can be computed directly as is illustrated in Table 11–1. The $\sum (Y - Y')$ must equal zero if our calculations are correct, just as the $\sum (X - \bar{X})$ must equal zero.

We can now calculate $s_{y \cdot x}$ by substituting into formula (11.4):

$$s_{y \cdot x} = \sqrt{\frac{9.80}{10 - 2}} = \sqrt{\frac{9.80}{8}} = \sqrt{1.225} = 1.11.$$

Since we do not wish to perform all of the subtractions required to calculate the deviation scores directly we can use the following formula which uses the same terms involved in solving the regression equation.

$$\sum (Y - Y')^2$$

$$= \frac{1}{N} \left\{ N \sum Y^2 - (\sum Y)^2 - \frac{[N \sum XY - (\sum X)(\sum Y)]^2}{N \sum X^2 - (\sum X)^2} \right\}. \quad \textbf{(11.5)}$$

It should be noted that much of the second portion of this formula,

$$\left\{ \frac{[N \sum XY - (\sum X)(\sum Y)]}{N \sum X^2 - (\sum X)^2} \right\},$$

has already been obtained in the course of computing the b constant by formula (11.2).

$$\sum (Y - Y')^2 = \tfrac{1}{10} \left\{ 10(226) - (44)^2 - \frac{[10(188) - (37)(44)]^2}{10(165) - (37)^2} \right\}$$

$$= .1 \left\{ 2260 - 1936 - \frac{252^2}{281} \right\}$$

$$= .1\{98.0\}$$

$$= 9.80.$$

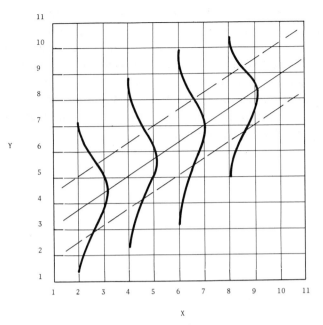

Y

X

Figure 11–3.

The standard error of estimate is interpreted in the same way any standard deviation is in relation to the normal curve. We could construct confidence limits on either side of the regression line depicted in Figure 11–3 (which is based on the data depicted in Figure 11–2) and estimate Y' in terms of a level of confidence. The dotted lines have been placed at $1.96s_{y \cdot x}$ on either side of the solid regression line.

$$1.96s_{y \cdot x} = 1.96(1.11) = 2.18.$$

Given any X value we would predict the value of Y on the basis of the regression line. We assume that around each Y' value the actual values will assume a normal distribution. $s_{y \cdot x}$ is an estimate of the standard deviation of that estimate. Our estimates of Y' can then be made within the limits of plus and minus 2.18 score units, and we can make this estimate at the .05 level of confidence. Only .05 of the cases would be expected to fall beyond these score limits in a normal distribution.

If there is a relationship between X and Y we will make better predictions of the values of Y using information regarding this relationship than we will by merely predicting some most frequent value of Y, such as the mean, median, or mode of Y.

Although prediction problems are not encountered very often in experimental settings, the logic of using regression equations to predict values of one variable from information on another has been developed at some length since an understanding of linear regression permits a clearer understanding of correlational methods, which are the subject of the next chapter.

EXERCISES

1. Given the following data for test X and test Y

$$\sum X = 183 \qquad\qquad \sum Y = 144$$
$$\sum X^2 = 1119 \qquad\qquad \sum Y^2 = 962$$
$$(\sum X)^2 = 33489 \qquad\qquad (\sum Y)^2 = 20736$$
$$N = 35 \qquad\qquad \sum XY = 846.97$$

compute the regression equation for Y.
2. Predict Y given $X = 25$.
3. Predict Y given $X = -1.877$.
4. Given the following data on two forms of the same test

$$\sum X = 87 \qquad\qquad \sum Y = 97$$
$$\sum X^2 = 592 \qquad\qquad \sum Y^2 = 1203$$
$$(\sum X)^2 = 7569 \qquad\qquad (\sum Y)^2 = 9409$$
$$N = 25 \qquad\qquad \sum XY = 1356.87$$

calculate the regression equation for Y.
5. Predict Y with $X = 3.48$.
6. Predict Y with $X = 4.85$.
7. Compute the standard error of estimate ($s_{y \cdot x}$) for the data of problem 1.
8. Compute the .05 confidence limits for problem 2.
9. Compute the .01 confidence limits for problem 3.
10. Compute $s_{y \cdot x}$ for problem 4.
11. Compute the .05 confidence limits for problem 5.
12. Compute the .01 confidence limits for problem 6.

12

CORRELATION

In the last chapter we discussed the methods used to predict values of Y from knowledge of X. We discussed the fact that we gain information concerning Y from knowledge of X only if there is some relationship between X and Y. Frequently, however, we have a situation in which we are not interested in making predictions of Y, but want instead to estimate the *degree* of relationship between X and Y. In these instances we would like a single number to express this degree of relationship: to express the degree to which a change in one variable is associated with change in another variable.

Problems dealing with the relationship between variables are referred to as correlation problems. In such problems we want to know if there is a tendency for an individual who stands high (or low) on one characteristic to be high (or low) on a second variable as well. We speak of a *positive correlation* when individuals who score high on one variable tend to score high on another and individuals who score low on one variable tend to score low on the other. An example of a positive correlation would be if families with many children tend to have higher incomes than do families with few children. If this were the case there would be a positive correlation between size of family and amount of income.

We speak of a *negative correlation* when individuals scoring high on one variable tend to score low on another. In our example of family size and income a negative correlation would exist between family size and income if families with many children tend to have lower incomes than do families with few children.

There would be *zero correlation* (no correlation), if the amount of income does not vary as a function of family size.

Correlation and Causation

It is important to emphasize that the existence of a correlation between two variables does not tell us anything about causation. If a correlation is found we cannot tell which variable is influencing which. In the preceding example a positive correlation could exist because people with many children must earn more income to support the children. Or, it could be the other way around and families with large incomes might have many children because they can afford them.

Another factor which makes it difficult to imply causation from the existence of a correlation is the fact that both of the variables might really be caused by changes in a third variable. Using the same example, perhaps there is a relationship between religion and both family size and income for the sample under consideration. In this case the religious background of the individual would be the causative factor influencing both the variables we are considering. Therefore, the existence of a correlation between two variables does not imply causality.

Several other examples can be offered in which it is obvious that the mere existence of a correlation does not mean there is any causation involved. An educator has discovered that there is a correlation between the size of school children's feet and the quality of their handwriting. Are we to assume that the size of feet is a factor determining the quality of handwriting? Perhaps the increase in quality of handwriting causes the feet to grow longer. If this is true, to obtain children with larger feet we should give them practice aimed at improving the quality of their handwriting. Obviously, neither of these alternatives is the correct one. Both size of feet and quality of handwriting are related to a third variable, age of the child; older boys have larger feet and a higher quality of handwriting than do younger boys.

Similarly, it has been pointed out that there is a relationship between teachers' salaries and the amount of beer consumed in the United States. Can we conclude from this that teachers are, therefore, consuming more beer as their incomes increase? Or perhaps we should conclude that as beer consumption increases those controlling teachers' salaries relax their control and raise salaries in their beery condition? It seems that the most likely possibility is that the change in both variables is related to the economic condition of the country. As the economic conditions improve both teachers' salaries and beer consumption increase.

COEFFICIENT OF CORRELATION
(PEARSON r)

The correlation coefficient is a number which indicates the degree of linear relationship between two variables. It is an expression of the degree to which a straight line relating X and Y summarizes the trend shown by a scatter diagram. It is, therefore, inappropriate to calculate a correlation coefficient which estimates the degree of linear relationship if the relationship is not linear. Figure 12–1 contains four scatter diagrams illustrating a positive relationship (A), a negative relationship (B), no relationship (C), and a curvilinear relationship (D). Only in the first three instances can we

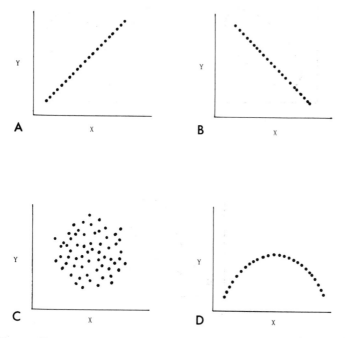

Figure 12–1. A, positive relationship. B, negative relationship. C, no relationship. D, curvilinear relationship.

justify the use of the coefficient of correlation for a linear regression, called either the *Pearson r* (after Karl Pearson, who developed it), or the product-moment correlation coefficient. If inspection of the scatter diagram shows a curvilinear relationship we cannot use the linear regression method but must use special correlation techniques designed for use with curvilinear relationships. It is clear that a curved line will fit the points shown in Figure 12–1 *D* quite well, but that no straight line can be a "best-fit" line.

Even though the relationship of *X* and *Y* in Figure 12–1 *C* is near zero, there is a line that will provide better prediction than any other line. In circumstances in which there is no relationship between *X* and *Y*, a line drawn through the mean of *Y* will be a better predictor than any other line. With zero relationship, the best prediction of *Y* for any *X* is the mean of *Y*.

If the distribution of cases in the scatter diagram is elliptical, as in Figure 12–2 *A* we can justifiably compute a Pearson *r*. The underlying distribution of the *X* and *Y* variables should be fairly symmetrical and unimodal if we are to use a Pearson *r* to describe

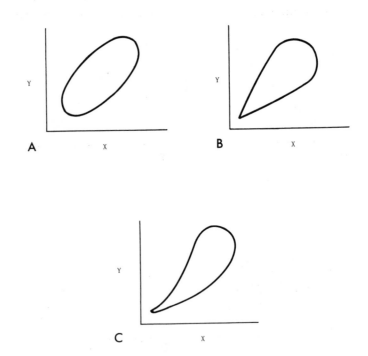

Figure 12–2. *A*, linear and homoscedasticity. *B*, linear and lack of homoscedasticity. *C*, curvilinear and lack of homoscedasticity.

the degree to which X and Y are related. It is not necessary, however, that the two distributions be normal. The important consideration is that the dispersion in all the columns is about the same. This equal dispersion is called *homoscedasticity*. In Figure 12–2 A the regression is linear and we have homoscedasticity.

Figure 12–2 B is a case where there is a linear regression but a lack of homoscedasticity. The reason for this is that both the X and Y distributions are negatively skewed. In Figure 12–2 C we have a curvilinear regression and a lack of homoscedasticity since variable Y is negatively skewed. Here, the Y variable is negatively skewed and the X variable is positively skewed. Only in the case of 12–2 A should we calculate a Pearson r.

Definitional Formula for Pearson r.   A beginning definitional formula for Pearson r is

$$r = \frac{\sum (X - \bar{X})(Y - \bar{Y})}{\sqrt{\sum (X - \bar{X})^2 \sum (Y - \bar{Y})^2}} . \qquad \textbf{(12.1)}$$

This formula can be rewritten as

$$r = \frac{\sum xy}{\sqrt{\sum x^2 \sum y^2}} . \qquad \textbf{(12.2)}$$

The Pearson correlation coefficient is best considered to be a ratio which indicates the degree to which variation in one variable is associated with variation in another variable. The denominator in formula (12.3) you will recognize as the square root of the sum of squares for variable X times the sum of squares for variable Y. This term is actually a type of arithmetic mean. We did not discuss this among the measures of central tendency referred to in Chapter 3 simply because this type of average has only limited use. The value $\sqrt{\sum x^2 \sum y^2}$ is called the *geometric mean* of the sums of squares for X and Y. A geometric mean is defined as the nth root of the product of n values. For example, the geometric mean of 3, 5, and 6 is equal to $\sqrt[3]{90}$ since three values enter into the total. If four values were involved, the fourth root would be taken. For correlation where only two values are involved in determining the geometric mean, the square root is taken.

The numerator represents the sum of squares for the cross products of X and Y. Just as

$$\sum x^2 = \sum X^2 - \frac{(\sum X)^2}{N}, \sum xy = \sum XY - \frac{(\sum X)(\sum Y)}{N}.$$

Put in this fashion, the formula for r can be written as follows:

$$r = \frac{\sum XY - \frac{(\sum X)(\sum Y)}{N}}{\sqrt{\left[\sum X^2 - \frac{(\sum X)^2}{N}\right]\left[\sum Y^2 - \frac{(\sum Y)^2}{N}\right]}}, \qquad \textbf{(12.3)}$$

where $\left[\sum X^2 - \frac{(\sum X)^2}{N}\right]$ and $\left[\sum Y^2 - \frac{(\sum Y)^2}{N}\right]$ are the familiar formulas for determining a sum of squares as shown in Chapter 4.

COVARIANCE

The only new quantity involved in the calculation of the correlation coefficient is the *covariance*. The covariance of two variables such as X and Y is the degree to which a proportional change in one variable is related to a proportional change in the other variable.

The concept of covariance is more easily understood if it is put in terms other than those of simple cross-multiplication. To illustrate this, r will be defined in terms of standard scores. If our variables X and Y are in conventional standard score form, $\frac{(X - \bar{X})}{s_X}$ and $\frac{(Y - \bar{Y})}{s_Y}$, the formula for r can be written as:

$$r = \frac{\sum z_x z_y}{N} \qquad \textbf{(12.4)}$$

from which we see that, if the variances of X and Y are equalized by standard score transformations, r is simply the covariance of two variables. Note that the larger the value of the covariance (whether positive or negative) the larger the value of r. To illustrate this, examine Table 12–1 which contains three sets of standard score

Table 12–1. ILLUSTRATION OF CORRELATION AS THE MEAN OF CROSS-PRODUCTS WHEN VARIANCES ARE IDENTICAL

	a			b			c		
	Std. Score	Std. Score		Std. Score	Std. Score		Std. Score	Std. Score	
Subject	z_x	z_y	$z_x z_y$	z_x	z_y	$z_x z_y$	z_x	z_y	$z_x z_y$
1	−1.58	−1.58	+2.50	−1.58	+1.58	−2.50	+1.58	+1.58	+2.50
2	−1.26	−1.26	+1.59	−1.26	+1.26	−1.59	−1.26	+1.26	−1.59
3	−.95	−.95	+.90	−.95	+.95	−.90	+.95	+.95	+.90
4	−.63	−.63	+.40	−.63	+.63	−.40	−.63	+.63	−.40
5	−.32	−.32	+.11	−.32	+.32	−.11	+.32	+.32	+.11
6	.00	.00	.00	.00	.00	.00	.00	.00	.00
7	+.32	+.32	+.11	+.32	−.32	−.11	−.32	+.32	−.11
8	+.63	+.63	+.40	+.63	−.63	−.40	+.63	+.63	+.40
9	+.95	+.95	+.90	+.95	−.95	−.90	+.95	−.95	−.90
10	+1.26	+1.26	+1.59	+1.26	−1.26	−1.59	+1.26	+1.26	+1.59
11	+1.58	+1.58	+2.50	+1.58	−1.58	−2.50	−1.58	+1.58	−2.50

$$\sum z_x z_y = 11.00 \qquad \sum z_x z_y = -11.00 \qquad \sum z_x z_y = .00$$

$$r = \frac{\sum z_x z_y}{N} \qquad r = \frac{-11.00}{11.00} \qquad r = \frac{.00}{11.00}$$

$$= \frac{11.00}{11.00} \qquad\qquad = -1.00 \qquad\qquad = .00$$

$$= +1.00$$

values: one for a high positive correlation; one for a high negative correlation; and one for a zero correlation.

In part (a) of the table the standard scores for the individuals on X and Y match perfectly and the algebraic sum of the covariance is equal to N, resulting in an r of $+1.00$ (remember that a negative number times a negative number results in a positive number). In part (b) the algebraic sum of the $z_x z_y$ multiplications is -11.00 (again equal to N), and the r is -1.00. In part (c) the algebraic sum of the covariances is zero and the r is also zero. The use of formulas (12.1), (12.2), (12.3), and (12.4) all result in the same answers.

Relation of Pearson r to the Regression Line

Remember that the Pearson r can vary between $+1.0$ and -1.0. A coefficient of $+1.0$ indicates that there is a perfect positive relationship between X and Y. In this case every XY point would fall exactly on the regression line, such as the line drawn in Figure 12–1 A. As the points cluster more and more widely around the regression line the value of r will decrease from $+1.0$ to zero. At zero the points are so evenly distributed that no one regression line will fit them any longer (as in Figure 12–1 C). A coefficient of -1.0 indicates that there is a perfect negative relationship between X and Y such that every XY point falls exactly on the regression line drawn in Figure 12–1 B.

One way to understand the relationship of r to the regression line is to consider the ratio of the sum of the squared deviations from the regression line, $[\sum (Y - Y')^2]$ to the sum of the squared deviations from the mean of Y, $[\sum (Y - \bar{Y})^2]$. If prediction of Y from X were exact then every Y' would fall on the regression line and every $(Y - Y')^2$ value would be zero. Therefore the ratio $\sum (Y - Y')^2 / \sum (Y - \bar{Y})^2$ would be zero if prediction were exact. If X led to no information about Y the numerator would equal the denominator, since the "best-fit" regression line would fit the data no better than would any other arbitrarily chosen straight line. The arbitrary line we have chosen to compare against the regression line is a line drawn through the mean of Y. If X led to no information about Y the numerator would equal the denominator, since the points deviate from the two lines the same amount, and the ratio is equal to one. (It is impossible, by the way, for the numerator to be larger than the denominator since $\sum (Y - \bar{Y})^2 = \sum (Y - Y')^2 + \sum (Y' - \bar{Y}^2)$. The reasons for this will not be developed any further.)

At this point, the question may well arise: is r of any help in computing regression constants? We have seen that as accuracy of prediction increases, r will also increase. Remember that the formula (11.2) for determining the slope of the regression line for predicting Y from X

$$b = \frac{N \sum XY - (\sum X)(\sum Y)}{N \sum X^2 - (\sum X)^2}$$

is basically the ratio of the covariance to the variance of X. Since r is also a measure of covariation, its use in calculating the b coefficient greatly simplifies matters. All that is needed to calculate b if we have r are the standard deviations of X and Y and the following relationship will hold:

$$b = r \left(\frac{s_Y}{s_X} \right).$$

If we apply this formula to the data of Table 11–1, we have

$$b = .83\left(\frac{5.70}{5.29}\right) = .83(1.077) = .90$$

which is identical to the value obtained by formula (11.2).

Computing Formula for Pearson r. The most efficient calculating machine formula for r does not require the subtractions required by the definitional formula (12.1).

$$r = \frac{N \sum XY - (\sum X)(\sum Y)}{\sqrt{\{N \sum X^2 - (\sum X)^2\}\{N \sum Y^2 - (\sum Y)^2\}}} \qquad \textbf{(12.5)}$$

The following formula can be used if the means and the standard deviations have been computed:

$$r = \frac{\sum XY/N - \bar{X}\bar{Y}}{s_X s_Y}. \qquad \textbf{(12.6)}$$

In both of these formulas N = the number of individuals, each of whom contribute an X and Y value. $\sum XY$ is found by multiplying each X by its corresponding Y and *then* summing the resulting products.

Calculation of r. The value of r will be calculated using the data from Table 11–1. (You will note that several steps of this calculation have been done when the slope constant, b, is calculated.)

$$
\begin{aligned}
r &= \frac{10(188) - 37(44)}{\sqrt{\{10(165) - (37)^2\}\{10(266) - (44)\}^2}} \\
&= \frac{1880 - 1628}{\sqrt{\{1650 - 1369\}\{2260 - 1936\}}} \\
&= \frac{252}{\sqrt{\{281\}\{324\}}} \\
&= \frac{252}{\sqrt{91,044}} \\
&= \frac{252}{302} \\
&= .83.
\end{aligned}
$$

The obtained value of r indicates quite a high degree of relationship between these two variables. However, interpretation of the correlation coefficient, as the next few sections will show, is dependent upon a number of considerations.

Factors Affecting the Size of Correlation Coefficients

There are several factors which affect the size of correlation coefficients. One is linearity of regression. If the regression is not linear then the Pearson r will underestimate the degree of relationship.

Another factor which will lead to an underestimation of the degree of relationship is variable errors of measurement. This reduction in r as a result of variable errors of measurement is called attenuation. We can correct for attenuation to estimate the true degree of the relationship between two variables. However, r's corrected for attenuation cannot be used in prediction equations because prediction is based on fallible, rather than on true scores.

The magnitude of a correlation coefficient also varies as a function of the degree of heterogeneity of the sample with respect to the variables being correlated. Assume that we are correlating IQ and grades. If all of the students have an IQ of 100, then the range of IQ scores is zero. Since r is an estimate of the proportional change in one variable in relation to the proportional change in another variable, r under these conditions will be an indeterminate value near zero. As the range of scores becomes greater, other things being equal, the obtained correlation will become higher. There are methods used to correct for spread of talent and for attenuation. The student is referred to the advanced texts cited in Chapter 8 for a presentation of these methods.

A highly spurious correlation coefficient might be obtained as a function of the manner in which cases are selected. If, for some reason, we eliminate cases near the mean, r will increase since we have eliminated cases from the middle of the distribution where the dispersion is likely to be the greatest. If any relationship exists between the two variables it should be most apparent at the extremes.

Figure 12–3 illustrates why the correlation of a composite group made up of subgroups with unequal means is misleading. In Figure 12–3 A groups with unequal means on both X and Y are combined. Within each group there is no relationship between X and Y

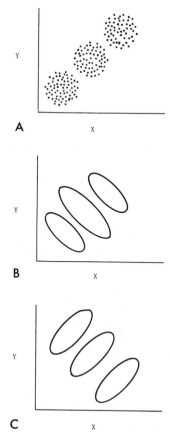

Figure 12–3. *A*, *B*, and *C*. See text for explanation.

$(r = 0)$. However, the composite correlation is positive and fairly high. In Figure 12–3 *B* we see the effect of combining three groups whose means differ on *X* and *Y*. Within each group the *r* is highly negative while in the composite it is zero. In Figure 12–3 *C* the *r* within each group is positive while in the composite it is negative. Therefore, extreme caution must be exercised when combining groups for the purpose of determining the degree of relationship if the means of the individual samples tend to be quite different.

Inferences Regarding *r*

Usually we test the hypothesis that the population correlation (ρ, following the convention of using Greek letters to represent population parameters) is zero, and test our obtained r against this hypothesis. In a sense, we are testing a null hypothesis: that there is no relationship between the two variables in the population. If we reject this hypothesis we will accept the alternative hypothesis: that there is a statistically significant relationship between the two variables. We could test two obtained correlation coefficients against one another to determine whether or not they are drawn from the same population. However, the occasions on which this is done are so rare that the procedures for doing so will not be presented here. We could also test for population values other than zero. To do this we must transform r to normalize the distribution since the sampling distribution of r depends on the size of ρ. As ρ approaches $+1.00$ or -1.00 a skewed sampling distribution of r's results because r cannot exceed these values. For example, if $\rho = .80$ the distribution of ρ will be negatively skewed since the highest value r can be is $+1.00$ (.20 points away from ρ) while the lowest value r can take is -1.00 (1.80 points from ρ). Figure 12–4 contains the sampling distributions for $\rho = .80$ and $\rho = .00$. It can be seen that the distribution around $\rho = .00$ is symmetrical, while that around $\rho = .80$ is highly negatively skewed.

The transformation used to test for population values other than zero is called the r to z transformation and the methods used to make this transformation can be found in Walker and Lev: *Statistical Inference* and McNemar, Q.: *Psychological Statistics.**

The only case we will consider here is testing the hypothesis that no relationship exists between the two variables: that is, that the population correlation is zero. Again, if we reject this hypothesis we will conclude that *some* relationship exists.

The coefficient of correlation, as with every statistic we have considered, is subject to errors of sampling. If $\rho = 0$ and we take successive samples of ten pairs of observations each, the sample r's will fluctuate around the population value. Some of the sample r's will be above the mean, some will be below, and the distribution will be normal around ρ. (Remember, this is true only if $\rho = 0$.) Therefore, if we could determine the standard error of r we could apply normal curve methods to evaluate our statistical hypothesis concerning the value of ρ.

The formula for the standard error of r (σ_r) when $N > 30$ is as

---

* Walker, H., and Lev, J.: *Statistical Inference;* New York: Holt, 1953 and McNemar, Q.: *Psychological Statistics;* New York: Wiley, 1962.

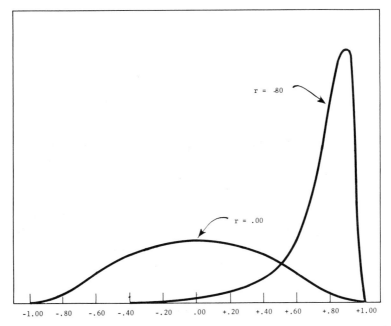

Figure 12–4. Sampling distribution of correlation coefficients for samples of eight pairs drawn from two populations having the indicated values of r. (From Edwards, A. L., *Statistical analysis for students in psychology and education*. New York: Rinehart and Company, Inc., 1948, and reprinted with their permission.)

follows:

$$\sigma_r = \frac{1 - \rho^2}{\sqrt{N - 1}}.$$

If $\rho = 0$ as it does in the case we are considering this formula reduces to:

$$\sigma_r = \frac{1}{\sqrt{N - 1}}. \tag{12.7}$$

Assume that we have gathered data on 37 subjects and found an r of .30. We now want to determine the likelihood that an r this large could have arisen in the course of sampling from a population in which $\rho = 0$. We decide that we will use the .05 level of significance. We know that a z of ± 1.96 defines this significance level.

$$\sigma_r = \frac{1}{\sqrt{37 - 1}} = \frac{1}{\sqrt{36}} = \frac{1}{6} = .167.$$

To determine the z-ratio we use the formula:

$$z = \frac{r - \rho}{\sigma_r} = \frac{.30 - 0}{.167} = 1.80. \tag{12.8}$$

From the table of the normal curve, Table A–2, we find that .4641 of the total area falls between the mean (ρ) and a z of 1.80. Thus, .9282 of the total area will fall between z's of ± 1.80, and $1 - .9282 = .0718$. Since this proportion of the total area is greater than .05 we conclude that an r of .30 could have occurred by chance when $\rho = 0$. Therefore, we conclude that there is no relationship between the two variables.

Let us now test the hypothesis that the r calculated from the data in Table 11–1 could have arisen by chance when $\rho = 0$. Since N is only ten we must use small sample statistics. Therefore, we will calculate a t value by the following formula:

$$t = \frac{r\sqrt{N - 2}}{\sqrt{1 - r^2}} \tag{12.9}$$

$$= \frac{.83\sqrt{10 - 2}}{\sqrt{1 - .83^2}}$$

$$= \frac{.83\sqrt{8}}{.5578}$$

$$= \frac{2.31}{.5578}$$

$$= 4.14.$$

With 8 df we find, from Table A–3, that a t value of this size would occur fewer than .01 times by chance, and reject the hypothesis that $\rho = 0$. We accept the alternative hypothesis that $\rho \neq 0$ and we conclude that there is a relationship between the two variables.

TABLE OF SIGNIFICANT VALUES OF r. We do not have to calculate σ_r and then find a z or a t value, however, since the size of σ_r varies as a function of N alone when $\rho = 0$. Consequently, it is a simple task to table the values of r which would occur at the 5 per cent and 1 per cent levels of significance as a function of the number of degrees of freedom. Table A–9 lists these values. The number of degrees of freedom are listed in the left column and the values of r

for the .10, .05, .02, and .01 per cent levels are listed in the columns headed level of significance for two-tailed tests. Once r is calculated no further calculation is necessary since its significance can be evaluated using the table.

In the example for which we computed the t-ratio we have 8 df. The values of r which reach the 5 per cent and the 1 per cent levels of confidence for 8 df are .632 and .765. Since our r of .83 exceeds these values, we, again, reject the hypothesis that $\rho = 0$.

Interpretation of r

As we have seen, r can range between $+1.0$ and -1.0. A correlation coefficient is not expressed in the units of measurement from which it is obtained, as are the mean and standard deviation. Therefore, we must exercise some caution in deciding on the meaning of a correlation coefficient. A coefficient of .60 does not indicate twice as great a relationship as does an r of .30. One useful interpretation of r is to consider the amount of the total variance in Y which is accounted for by knowledge of X. This can be determined by squaring r: $r^2 =$ coefficient of determination. Therefore,

$$r^2 \times 100 = \text{the percentage of the variation in } X \text{ associated}$$
$$\text{with variation in } Y. \qquad \textbf{(12.10)}$$

$\left(\text{Remember that } r^2 = 1 - \dfrac{\Sigma (Y - Y')^2}{\Sigma (Y - \bar{Y})^2}.\right)$ Thus, if $r = .60$, $r^2 = .36$; this indicates that 36 per cent of the variance in X and Y are associated. If $r = .30$, $r^2 = .09$; only nine per cent of the variance in X and Y are associated. If we wished to predict values of Y from knowledge of X, an r of .60 is four times as useful as is a value of .30.

Statistical vs. Practical Significance. We can, of course, interpret the meaning of r solely in terms of statistical significance. But we must remember not to confuse statistical significance with practical significance. For example, we see from examination of Table A–9 that with 1000 degrees of freedom an r of .062 is significant at the 5 per cent level of confidence. However, $r^2 = .0036$, which means that we are accounting for only 0.36 per cent of the variance in Y from knowledge of X. Predictions of Y from X will be very poor. These predictions of Y will, of course, be better than would be expected without using X, but the gain will be very small.

The same point is true when we test the significance of differences between means. A difference between means might be highly significant statistically if the N is large enough, but might not mean anything *practically*. Only the researcher's judgment can be used to decide if statistically significant results have any practical meaning.

One other way to interpret an r is in terms of the use for which it is intended. Often, correlation coefficients are calculated to determine either the reliability or the validity of a measuring instrument, such as a test. The next two sections will discuss the use of r to estimate reliability and validity.

Reliability of Measurement. The problem of the reliability of measurements is one of the most important that a scientist must face. A measurement is said to be reliable if it is dependable, in the sense that you obtain the same reading each time you measure the same thing on different occasions. A reliable ruler, for example, would be one which does not change from reading to reading, while an unreliable ruler would be one, say, made of rubber which must be stretched to make the reading. If you do not stretch it the same amount on repeated measurements of the same thing you will not obtain the same reading.

What sorts of factors lower the reliability of a measuring instrument? One factor would be errors in the instrument, or test, itself, such as intermittent mechanical defects in a piece of apparatus or mistakes in printing on some copies of a printed test. Another factor would be any physiological variations in the individual which occur from testing to testing: perhaps on one testing the individual is rested and not hungry while on the second testing he is tired and very hungry. Another factor lowering reliability would be errors due to extraneous physical disturbances present during the testing: perhaps on one testing the room is quiet and of normal temperature while on the second testing there is a great deal of noise and it is quite warm. Yet another factor lowering reliability would be errors in reading the instrument or in scoring the test. Each of these factors would make it difficult to obtain the same reading on successive measurements of the same thing, and would be said to lower the reliability of the measurement. If we want to use a measuring instrument for some purpose it, at least, must be reliable.

The correlation coefficient between any two measurements of the same thing is called a reliability coefficient. It is simple to determine the reliability of such things as measurements of length and time: measure the same objects twice and calculate the correlation coefficient between the two sets of readings. Many times, however, repetition of the measurement is not feasible since the measurement cannot be made without changing the object of the measurement. An example of this is a learning task in which the second reading would not be the same as the first because the individual remembers some of the items from the first reading. In such cases we could construct comparable alternate forms of the test, and correlate the performance on these two forms. This involves a considerable amount of effort and would probably underestimate the true reliability since the two separate testings would still be influenced by the factors which produce day to day variation, such as physiological variations in the subjects and extraneous physical distractions.

Split-Half Reliability. The other solution to this problem is to estimate what is called the split-half reliability. This method requires us to compare the results of one half of the test with the results of the second half of the test. If the test does not vary systematically in difficulty we can compare the first half of the test directly with the second half. If the test is one which gets progressively more difficult we can compare alternate items, thereby obtaining a score for even numbered items and another score for the odd-numbered items. The estimate of reliability based on two halves of the same test is found using what is known as the Spearman-Brown prophecy formula:

$$R = \frac{2r}{1 + r}, \qquad (12.11)$$

where R = the correlation between two comparable test forms,
       r = the correlation between two half-tests.

This formula compensates for the fact that the correlation between two half-tests will be lower than the correlations between two complete tests. The use of this formula will probably lead to an overestimation of the reliability because chance day-to-day errors will be correlated. However, this method will provide a closer estimation of the true reliability than will the use of the uncorrected r based on two half-tests.

A detailed discussion of reliability theory will be found in Ghiselli's book.*

Validity.   A valid measurement is one which measures what it is supposed to measure. If we are using a ruler to measure length in centimeters it is important that the centimeter scale be accurate. If the basic scale units are inaccurate we can obtain highly reliable measurements, but they will not be valid since the centimeters as indicated on the scale do not correspond to the agreed upon length for a centimeter.

When we report a correlation coefficient between some predictor and the measure which is to be predicted we call that correlation a validity coefficient. Assume that we wish to know whether or not the IQ of mothers is a valid predictor of the IQ of their first born children. To decide this we might measure the IQ of the mother using a standard test and also measure the IQ of the first born children using another standard test. We could then correlate the IQ score of each mother with the IQ score of the first born child. This validity coefficient would then be used to decide whether or not a mother's IQ is a valid predictor of a first born child's IQ.

If we are in a situation in which we wish to use, for example, a measure of a person's aptitude (say, clerical aptitude) to predict his success on a job, two problems arise. The first problem involves the selection of a measure of performance which relates to the ultimate job performance. The second problem involves the selection of a criterion which is an indicator of on-the-job performance. Since the solution to these problems depends on the specific situation and on the ingenuity of the investigator, there is little more that can be said here.

Validity depends directly on reliability. If a test is not reliable it *cannot* be valid. We must have stable indicators of the values under consideration in order to make measurements which have meaning as predictors. However, a test can be highly reliable, and still not be valid. An example of this would be a clock which runs at the wrong speed. It might be highly reliable since the same results would be obtained on successive readings, but the readings would not be valid since they would not conform to the standards agreed upon for seconds, minutes, and hours.

---

* Ghiselli, E.: *Theory of Psychological Measurement;* New York: McGraw-Hill, 1964.

Spearman's Rank Order Correlation

One special correlational method will be presented because of its usefulness in a wide variety of situations. This method, Spearman's rank order (or rank difference) correlation (rho), is used with data which are in the form of ranks. If all we have is the rank order of data and do not know the value of the actual measurements we can use this technique. With a small number of cases rho can be determined quickly and provides a fast and accurate estimate of r.

To use this method the data must be in the form of ranks. The formula is as follows:

$$\text{rho} = 1 - \frac{6 \sum d^2}{N(N^2 - 1)}, \qquad (12.12)$$

where N = number of paired ranks,
$\qquad d$ = difference between pairs of ranks.

Let us compute rho for a sample of ten pairs of observations. Table 12–2 lists the scores and their corresponding ranks as well as the difference scores and their squares. The lowest score has been assigned the rank of one. Again, it is important to square each difference score and then sum the squared difference scores. The rho, which is calculated in Table 12–2, is +.77. (You will recall that the r for these same data is +.82.)

The rank difference correlation has a larger standard error than does r. Therefore, it is not as powerful a test as is r. To determine whether or not a rho of .77 based on an N of ten could have arisen from chance when the true population correlation is zero we will use Table A–10. This table is entered using N and *not* the degrees of freedom. We see that, with an N of ten a rho of .65 is significant at the .05 level of significance. Since a rho of .77 exceeds the tabled value we assume that a correlation this large did not occur by chance from a population whose true correlation is zero. Therefore, we will conclude that there is a relationship between the two variables. Since the table is a two-tailed table we accept the hypothesis that the population correlation is not zero.

It is important to remember that the rank difference correlation can *only* be calculated after the scores have been transformed to ranks. It cannot be used with the raw scores themselves.

In the last two chapters the basic methods used to express the

Table 12–2.

Subject	X	Y	X Rank	Y Rank	d	d²
A	12	11	1	1	.0	.00
B	13	13	2	2.5	−.5	.25
C	14	13	4	2.5	1.5	2.25
D	14	16	4	9	−5.0	25.00
E	14	14	4	4.5	−.5	.25
F	15	15	7	7	.0	.00
G	15	14	7	4.5	2.5	6.25
H	15	15	7	7	.0	.00
I	16	15	9	7	2.0	4.00
J	17	18	10	10	.0	.00
					Σ	38.00

$$\text{rho} = 1 - \frac{6 \sum d^2}{N(N^2 - 1)}$$

$$= 1 - \frac{6(38)}{10(99)}$$

$$= 1 - \frac{228}{990}$$

$$= 1 - .23$$

$$\text{rho} = .77$$

degree of relationship have been presented. Many other coefficients of correlation have been developed for use with special kinds of measurement scales. For example, it is possible to estimate the correlation between two variables when one is a continuous variate and the other can take only two values. It is possible to estimate the correlation between two variables when both variables can take only two values. Earlier it was indicated that the degree of correlation can be determined between two variables which are related curvilinearly. In addition, methods exist which allow us to hold a third variable constant which might affect the size of the correlation between two variables. It is possible to determine the correlation of several variables with one variable. The basic logic underlying this variety of techniques all stems from that of the Pearson *r*. These techniques, which are among the most elegant and sophisticated in statistics, are the topics of advanced courses in statistics and will not be presented here.

At this point in the text we have, in addition to discussing measures of relationship, covered the logic of statistical inference. Particularly, we have discussed the methods which are used to draw inferences concerning the central location of population values. The last chapter of this text will consider the practical application of the statistical methods you have learned to the types of experimental data you are likely to encounter in your further course work in the behavioral sciences.

EXERCISES

1. Calculate a Pearson product-moment correlation from the following data:

$$N = 54,$$

$$\sum z_X z_Y = 19.71.$$

2. Is the obtained correlation significant at the .05 level of significance?

3. Calculate the Pearson r for the following two measures of social adjustment:

$$\sum X = 183 \qquad\qquad \sum Y = 144$$
$$\sum X^2 = 1119 \qquad\qquad \sum Y^2 = 962$$
$$(\sum X)^2 = 33489 \qquad\qquad (\sum Y)^2 = 2037$$
$$\sum XY = 864.97 \qquad\qquad N = 35$$

4. Is the obtained r significant at the .01 level? What would you conclude about the relationship between these two measures?

5. Transform the following set of data to ranks and calculate a Spearman rank-difference correlation:

Case	X Score	Y Score
1	16	14
2	14	17
3	13	11
4	10	5
5	8	8
6	7	15
7	5	6
8	4	9
9	2	2
10	1	3

6. Determine the significance of the obtained Spearman rank-difference correlation.

7. Calculate the Pearson r on the following data:

$$\sum X = 60 \qquad\qquad \sum Y = 40$$
$$\sum X^2 = 494 \qquad\qquad \sum Y^2 = 212$$
$$(\sum X)^2 = 3600 \qquad\qquad (\sum Y)^2 = 1600$$
$$\sum XY = 288 \qquad\qquad N = 10$$

8. Determine the significance of the correlation for the data of problem 7.
9. A psychologist, dissatisfied with all existing measures of work aptitude, decided to develop another test which would measure work aptitude for precision tasks more effectively than any existing measures. In order for him to evaluate his new test it was necessary (1) to give the test twice over a two month interval to determine reliability, (2) to compare his test scores with actual ratings of job performance on precision tasks. On a small sample, he obtained the following data:

Individual	Score on First Administration	Score on Second Administration	Score on Work Sample
A	104	104	104
B	98	100	98
C	130	127	133
D	76	85	85
E	109	119	111
F	110	111	111
G	68	63	64
H	149	145	143
I	100	105	100
J	103	100	102
K	96	96	93
L	85	86	87
M	121	118	118
N	118	115	118
O	86	85	80

Calculate the reliability coefficient for these data and determine the significance.

10. Determine the validity coefficient and determine its significance.
11. On the basis of these data he concluded that his test was both reliable and valid and decided to publish his test. Do you think that his decision was justified? Why?

13

SOME APPLICATIONS TO EXPERIMENTAL PSYCHOLOGY

This chapter contains a series of experiments similar to those which most students will encounter in an experimental psychology laboratory course. Usually, the beginning experimental psychology course is the first stage at which the psychology student must apply statistical methods to experimental data. Frequently, the transition from the study of statistics to the application of statistical methods to an experimental problem is a difficult one for the student to accomplish. The material in this chapter is intended to provide the student with "real data" on which he may practice and to illustrate the types of problems to which the various statistical procedures can be applied.

We will illustrate six statistical techniques used to test for the significance of differences between two or more groups and two methods to determine correlation. These techniques are presented in the following order:

1. The t-test for independent groups (Chapter 7).
2. The t-test for correlated groups (repeated measures) (Chapter 7).
3. The one-way Analysis of Variance (Chapter 8).
4. The Chi-square (χ^2) test (Chapter 9).

5. The Mann-Whitney U test (Chapter 10).

6. The Kruskal-Wallis analysis of variance of ranks (Chapter 10).

7. The Pearson coefficient of correlation (Chapter 12).

8. The Spearman rank difference correlation (Chapter 12).

Each method is complete within its section; thus, the order in which the methods are considered is completely arbitrary.

1. A Reaction–Time Experiment: The t-Test for Independent Groups (Chapter 7). An experimenter wished to test what is called a "response compatibility hypothesis" using reaction time as his outcome measure.

He used a two choice reaction time apparatus with two stimulus lights 12 inches apart. A response key was located beneath each stimulus light. Figure 13–1 is an illustration of the type of apparatus used.

The experimenter's hypothesis is that reaction time will be longer if the response is not compatible with the stimulus. A compatible response is defined as one in which the response key to be pressed is located beneath the stimulus light that is illuminated. An incompatible response is defined as one in which the key to be pressed is located beneath the stimulus light that is not illuminated. Each subject was seated at the apparatus and neither light was illuminated. Each subject was instructed to keep his left forefinger on the left key and his right forefinger on the right key. Those subjects assigned to the compatible condition were instructed to

Figure 13–1. Two choice reaction-time apparatus.

press the left key as quickly as possible when the left stimulus was illuminated and to press the right key as quickly as possible when the right stimulus was illuminated. Those subjects assigned to the incompatible condition were instructed to press the right key as quickly as possible when the left stimulus was illuminated and to press the left key as quickly as possible when the right stimulus was illuminated.

A total of 25 subjects were available for this experiment and were randomly assigned to either the compatible or incompatible response groups. Thirteen subjects were assigned to the compatible group and 12 were assigned to the incompatible group. Each subject was given 20 trials. The stimulus light was presented on the left for one-half of the trials and on the right for the other half in a random order. When the stimulus light was illuminated, a timer registering thousandths of a second was started. When the subject pressed the key this stopped the timer. Each subject's score for each trial was recorded in thousandths of a second and the average for each subject over his 20 trials was taken as that subject's "score."

The statistical hypothesis to be tested is that the compatible and incompatible response groups are drawn from a population with common mean reaction time. In terms of the experimental treatment, the statistical hypothesis would be that "compatibility" or "incompatibility" of a response as defined in the experiment has no effect on the subjects' reaction time. The alternative statistical hypothesis is that they are drawn from different populations in terms of mean reaction time. The statistic used to test these hypotheses is the t-test for independent groups.

The subject's scores and the computations for the t-test are given in Table 13–1.

The value of the t statistic, as shown in Table 13–1, is 9.30. Examination of Table A–3 reveals that for 23 degrees of freedom, a t value of 2.069 is required to reach the .05 level of significance and a t value of 2.807 is required to reach the .01 level of significance. The obtained t of 9.30 exceeds both of the tabled values. Therefore, the experimenter rejects at the .01 level of significance the hypothesis of "no difference." He accepts the alternative hypothesis that the two means are drawn from different populations. Also, since the mean response time of the "incompatible" group is much higher he considers his "response compatibility hypothesis" to be supported by the data.

Table 13–1. Reaction Times in Thousandths of a Second for Subjects Making Compatible and Incompatible Responses. (Each Score is the Average of 20 Responses.)

	A				B		
		Compatible				Incompatible	
Subject #		Response Group		Subject #		Response Group	
2	4	230	207	1	3	320	315
6	9	196	217	5	7	289	335
11	12	235	265	8	10	317	309
13	14	209	195	16	18	365	297
15	17	240	222	20	21	305	319
19	23	211	201	22	24	291	281
25		250					

$$\sum X_A = 2878$$
$$\sum X_A^2 = 642{,}716$$
$$\left(\sum X_A\right)^2 = 8{,}282{,}884$$

$$\sum X_B = 3843$$
$$\sum X_B^2 = 1{,}241{,}403$$
$$\left(\sum X_B\right)^2 = 14{,}768{,}649$$

$$\sum x_A^2 = \sum X_A^2 - \frac{\left(\sum X_A\right)^2}{N_A}$$
$$= 642{,}716 - \frac{8{,}282{,}884}{13}$$
$$\sum x_A^2 = 5571$$
$$\overline{X}_A = \frac{\sum X_A}{N_A}$$
$$= \frac{2878}{13}$$
$$= 221.38$$
$$s_A^2 = \frac{\sum x_A}{N_A - 1} = \frac{5571}{12}$$
$$= 464.25$$

$$\sum x_B^2 = \sum X_B^2 - \frac{\left(\sum X_B\right)^2}{N_B}$$
$$= 1{,}241{,}403 - \frac{14{,}768{,}649}{12}$$
$$\sum x_B^2 = 10{,}682$$
$$\overline{X}_B = \frac{\sum X_B}{N_B}$$
$$= \frac{3843}{12}$$
$$= 320.25$$
$$s_B^2 = \frac{\sum x_B}{N_B - 1} = \frac{10{,}682}{11}$$
$$= 971.09$$

s^2 (For combined groups)
$$s^2 = \frac{\sum x_A^2 + \sum x_B^2}{N_A + N_B - 2}$$
$$= \frac{5571.00 + 10{,}682.00}{13 + 12 - 2}$$
$$= \frac{16{,}253.00}{23}$$
$$s^2 = 706.65$$

$$t = \frac{\overline{X}_A - \overline{X}_B}{\sqrt{s^2 \dfrac{N_A + N_B}{N_A N_B}}}$$
$$= \frac{221.38 - 320.25}{\sqrt{706.65 \dfrac{13 + 12}{156}}}$$
$$= \frac{-98.87}{\sqrt{706.65(.1602)}}$$
$$= \frac{-98.87}{\sqrt{113.205}}$$
$$t = \frac{98.87}{10.63} = 9.30$$

2. The Muller-Lyer Illusion: The *t*-Test for Correlated Means (Chapter 7).   One of the standard illusions used in the study of perceptual processes is the Muller-Lyer illusion illustrated in Figure 13–2.

Line segment *A* is equal to line segment *B*. Perceptually, however, *A* appears to be shorter than *B*. It is possible to study the effects of many variables on the magnitude of this illusion. One variable which has been studied is the magnitude of the illusion when a variable arrow "*Y*" is adjusted beginning on some trials from the segment "*B*" as compared to beginning on other trials from the segment "*A*". The following experiment was performed to determine whether the direction from which the variable is adjusted has any effect on the magnitude of the illusion when the subject is instructed to adjust *Y* until the two line segments look equal. Fifteen subjects performed the equality adjustment 16 times: on eight of the trials the variable was moved from the *A* region and on eight of the trials the variable was moved from the *B* region.

Each subject sat five feet from the apparatus and was instructed to adjust the arrow *Y* until Segment *A* was equal to Segment *B*. Figure 13–3 illustrates the nature of the experimental situation. By pulling one of the strings on either side, the arrow can be moved in either direction. *Y* was started in segment *A* half of the time and in segment *B* half of the time according to a random sequence. For each subject a mean score was obtained for the eight trials starting in *A* and for the eight starting in *B*. This score was expressed in terms of the number of millimeters the *Y* arrow was located from objective zero: positive numbers indicate *Y* was located in segment *B* and negative numbers indicate *Y* was located in segment *A*.

The hypothesis to be tested is that the magnitude of the illusion is the same when *Y* is moved starting from Segment *B* as when it is started from Segment *A*. The statistic chosen to test this hypothesis is the *t*-test for correlated means since we have measurements made on each subject in each of the two conditions. The data for each subject in terms of mean number of millimeters from zero in each

Figure 13–2. Muller-Lyer illusion.

Figure 13–3.   Adjustable Muller-Lyer illusion.

of the conditions are listed in Table 13–2 for each subject. Also, the difference score (found by subtracting each subject's mean when starting from *A* from his mean when starting from *B*) is listed as well as the computations necessary to make the *t*-test.

Remember that in a *t*-test for correlated means, the degrees of freedom are equal to the number of pairs minus one. Since we have 15 subjects, the number of degrees of freedom for the differences between *A* and *B* is equal to the number of subjects minus one degree of freedom, or 14.

In Table A–3 the *t* value for 14 degrees of freedom is 2.145 at the .05 level of significance and 2.977 at the .01 level of significance. Since our obtained *t* in Table 13–2 is 4.06 we may safely conclude that the two means are drawn from different underlying populations. Our experimental evidence clearly indicates that the magnitude of the illusion is greater when the adjustable arrow is moved from the *B* line segment than when it is moved from the *A* line segment.

3. The Effect of Associate Strength on Recall: The One–Way Analysis of Variance (Chapter 8). An experimenter wished to study the effect of varying the association value of a list of nonsense syllables on the number of syllables correctly recalled. The association value of a nonsense syllable can be defined in terms of the number of meaningful verbal responses subjects can give to it. In other words, the more things a nonsense syllable reminds people

Table 13–2. Error Scores in Millimeters for the Muller-Lyer Illusion Where Judgment of Equality is Made from Left (Segment A) and Right (Segment B).

Subject #	Adjusted from Segment B	Adjusted from Segment A	Difference B minus A
1	10.9	2.8	8.1
2	1.9	5.1	−3.2
3	8.6	2.7	5.9
4	7.4	2.2	5.2
5	11.9	2.1	9.8
6	7.1	2.9	4.2
7	6.2	2.1	4.1
8	6.0	3.1	2.9
9	8.9	3.8	5.1
10	10.5	2.7	7.8
11	5.4	3.3	2.1
12	1.8	3.6	−1.8
13	10.2	4.0	6.2
14	8.8	2.9	5.9
15	1.9	3.9	−2.0

$$\sum D^2 = 448.35$$

$$(\sum D)^2 = 3636.09$$

$$\sum d^2 = \sum D^2 - \frac{(\sum D)^2}{N}$$

$$= 448.35 - \frac{3636.09}{15}$$

$$= 448.35 = 242.41$$

$$\sum d^2 = 205.94$$

$$s_D^2 = \frac{\sum d^2}{N-1}$$

$$= \frac{205.94}{14}$$

$$= 14.71$$

$$\sum +\text{'s} = 67.3$$
$$\sum -\text{'s} = 7.0$$
$$\sum D = 60.3$$
$$\bar{D} = 4.02$$

$$s_D = \sqrt{14.71}$$
$$= 3.84$$

$$s_{\bar{D}} = \frac{3.84}{3.87}$$
$$= .99$$

$$t = \frac{\bar{D}}{s_{\bar{D}}}$$

$$t = \frac{4.02}{.99}$$

$$= 4.06$$

of, the higher its association value. For example, a syllable with an association value of 21–40% is one to which 21 to 40 per cent of a sample of subjects is reminded of at least one thing. A standard list of association values was used to construct five lists of 20 syllables each. Each list of syllables is presented to each subject in the experiment four times, each time in a different order. After the four presentations of each list the subject is asked to recall all the syllables he can remember. The syllables presented to the different groups have different association values as follows: Group I, 1–20 per cent; Group II, 21–40 per cent; Group III, 51–70 per cent; Group IV, 81–100 per cent. Forty subjects were assigned randomly to each of four groups. Three subjects had to be discarded for

Table 13–3. NUMBER OF NONSENSE SYLLABLES CORRECTLY RECALLED BY EACH EXPERIMENTAL GROUP.

Group I Association Value 1–20%		Group II Association Value 21–40%		Group III Association Value 51–70%		Group IV Association Value 81–100%	
Subject #	Score	Subject #	Score	Subject #	Score	Subject #	Score
1	11	9	13	5	10	2	16
4	6	11	9	7	11	3	19
6	10	13	11	18	14	15	17
8	12	14	14	19	20	16	16
10	15	21	14	24	17	17	20
12	13	23	17	27	19	20	19
25	13	30	12	29	17	26	15
28	10	32	11	36	16	33	19
31	13	35	13			37	19
		38	16			40	17
	—		—		—		—

	$n = 9$	10	8	10
	$\sum X = 103$	130	124	177
	$\overline{X} = 11.44$	13.0	15.5	17.7
	$\sum X^2 = 1233$	1742	2012	3159
	$(\sum X)^2 = 10{,}609$	16,900	15,376	31,329
	$\dfrac{(\sum X)^2}{N} = 1178.7$	1690	1922	3132.9

Total: $N_T = 37$ $\qquad$ $\overline{X}_T = 14.41$ $\qquad$ $(\sum X_T)^2 = 285{,}156$ $\qquad$ $\dfrac{(\sum X_T)^2}{N} = 7706.9$

$\sum X_T = 534$ $\qquad$ $\sum X_T^2 = 8146$ $\qquad$ $\sum \dfrac{(\sum X)^2}{n} = 7923.6$

$$\sum x_T^2 = \sum X_T^2 - \frac{(\sum X_T)^2}{N} = 8146.0 - 7706.9 = 439.1$$

$$\sum x_b^2 = \sum \frac{(\sum X)^2}{n} - \frac{(\sum X_T)^2}{N} = 7923.6 - 7706.9 = 216.7$$

$$\sum x_w^2 = \sum X_T^2 - \sum \frac{(\sum X)^2}{n} = 8146.0 - 7923.6 = 222.4$$

Table 13-4. ANALYSIS OF VARIANCE SUMMARY TABLE.

Source	Sum of Squares	df	Mean Square	F
Between groups	216.7	3	72.23	10.72
Within groups	222.4	33	6.74	
Total	439.1	36		

failure to follow instructions, resulting in an unequal number of subjects in the different groups: Group I, $n = 9$; Group II, $n = 10$; Group III, $n = 8$; Group IV, $n = 10$.

Table 13-3 lists the number of syllables correctly recalled for each group. The computations necessary to construct the analysis of variance table are also included.

Table 13-4 is the summary analysis of variance table constructed from the computations shown in Table 13-3.

From Table A-4 we find that with three degrees of freedom for the numerator and 33 degrees of freedom for the denominator (use 32 df) an F value of 2.90 is required at the .05 level of significance and an F value of 4.46 is required at the .01 level of significance. Since our obtained F value of 10.72 exceeds these tabled values it is concluded that the means for the four samples were not drawn from the same underlying population. Therefore, the number of syllables correctly recalled does differ as a function of the association value of the nonsense syllables. Since the overall test of significance reaches an acceptable level it would be permissible to perform individual tests of significance between the individual groups using a multiple comparison procedure. These procedures are not described in this textbook, but appropriate references are listed in Chapter 8.

4. Position Preferences in Rats: The Chi-Square Test (Chapter 9). An experimenter is interested in studying the ability of rats to detect differences among four stimuli. He constructs an apparatus which has a start box and a Y-shaped choice compartment with four doors at the end, on each of which stimulus cards can be mounted. Each door is four inches from the adjacent door and the two end doors are four inches from the side walls. Prior to starting the experiment it is pointed out to the experimenter that rats might have position preferences since rats tend to run along walls when they can. Therefore, the rats might show a strong preference for the two outside doors; a factor which would have to be taken into account in designing the experiment and interpreting the data. If the rats have no preference in this apparatus they should distribute their choices evenly among the four doors if the doors are all left open. However, if they do have a position preference the distribution of choices would be uneven, probably tending to favor the outside two doors.

To determine whether or not there is any pattern of preference in the apparatus each of the 40 rats to be used in the discrimination experiment is run once through the apparatus.

If there is no position preference then about 25 per cent (ten rats) would be expected to choose each door. If any door is chosen significantly more often than the expected 25 per cent then the experimenter will have to take this factor into account; either he must allow for this in the experimental design or he must redesign the apparatus.

Remember that in a χ^2 test each observation must be independent and the marginal totals for the observed and expected frequencies must be equal. Since our expected frequencies are distributed on the basis of what would be expected by chance, an expected frequency of ten will be entered in each cell. The observed frequencies and the calculations are given in Table 13–5.

Table 13–5. Observed and Expected Frequencies and Chi-Square Calculations for Position Preferences of 40 Rats.

	A	B	C	D	
Observed	18	5	6	11	$\sum O = 40$
Expected	10	10	10	10	$\sum E = 40$

$$\chi^2 = \sum \frac{(O - E)^2}{E}$$

$$= \frac{(18 - 10)^2}{10} + \frac{(5 - 10)^2}{10} + \frac{(6 - 10)^2}{10} + \frac{(11 - 10)^2}{10}$$

$$= \frac{64}{10} + \frac{25}{10} + \frac{16}{10} + \frac{1}{10}$$

$$= 6.4 + 2.5 + 1.6 + .1$$

$$= 10.6$$

From Table A–5 we find that with three degrees of freedom a χ^2 value of 7.82 is required at the .05 level of significance and a χ^2 value of 11.34 is required at the .01 level of significance. Since our obtained χ^2 value exceeds the tabled values for the .05 level of significance it is concluded that the choices are not distributed evenly. Therefore, the experimenter must consider the problem of position preferences.

5. A Retroactive Inhibition Experiment: The Mann-Whitney U Test (Chapter 10). The phenomenon of "retro-active inhibition" is said to occur when material just learned interferes with the memory of material learned at an earlier date. This can be demonstrated by interpolating verbal material between the learning and the recall of a list of nonsense syllables. Each subject in Group A first learns a list of 20 nonsense syllables to a criterion of 18 syllables correct. Ten minutes later each subject learns a second list of 20 nonsense syllables to the same criterion. Ten minutes after learning the second list, the subject is asked to recall the original list. Each subject in Group B also learns the list of 20 nonsense syllables to the criterion of 18 correct syllables. The subjects in this group name colors for the same approximate time period the subjects in Group A take to learn the second, interpolated list. Each subject then recalls the original list. If the subjects in Group A show the effects of retroactive inhibition their recall level will be lower as a function of having learned the interpolated list when compared to the recall level of Group B which performed an irrelevant task during the interpolation interval.

Twenty subjects were assigned randomly between the groups. Two subjects from Group B had to be discarded because of an error on the part of the experimenter. Thus, there are ten subjects in Group A and eight subjects in Group B. The experimenter decides to test the significance of the difference using the Mann-Whitney U statistic.

Table 13–6 contains the original scores in terms of the number of nonsense syllables recalled correctly, the rank order of each, and the computation required to make the test of significance.

From Table A–7 we find that the tabled value of U when $n_1 = 8$ and $n_2 = 10$ is 17 at the .05 level of significance and is 12 at the .01 level of significance. Since our obtained value of U is smaller than the tabled value for the .01 level of significance it is concluded that the two groups are not drawn from the same population of scores:

Table 13–6. ORIGINAL SCORES FOR NUMBER OF NONSENCE SYLLABLES RECALLED CORRECTLY FOR EACH SUBJECT AND EQUIVALENT RANKS FOR THE MANN-WHITNEY U TEST.

| | Group A | | | Group B | |
Subject #	Score	Rank	Subject #	Score	Rank
2	11	4	1	15	9.5
3	15	9.5	4	19	17
5	10	1.5	7	15	9.5
6	11	4	10	12	6.5
8	11	4	11	18	15.5
9	16	12.5	12	17	14
13	12	6.5	14	20	18
16	10	1.5	15	18	15.5
17	15	9.5			
18	16	12.5			
		$R_1 = \overline{65.5}$			$R_2 = \overline{105.5}$

Since Group B has the smaller number of subjects it is n_1, since n_1 is the notation for the smaller sample.

$$U = \left[n_1 n_2 + \frac{n_1(n_1 + 1)}{2} \right] - \sum R_1$$

$$= \left[(8)(10) + \frac{8(9)}{2} \right] - 105.5$$

$$= (80 + 36) - 105.5$$

$$= 116 - 105.5$$

$$= 10.5$$

Group B recalls significantly more syllables than does Group A. This result supports the conclusion that for Group A the original list did suffer from the effects of retroactive inhibition.

6. The Effect of Water Deprivation on Bar Pressing: The Kruskal-Wallis Ranked One-Way Analysis of Variance (Chapter 10). One of the commonly used methods to study motivation in animals is to determine how frequently an animal will perform a given response in order to receive a given reward. If an animal who has learned to press a lever to obtain water is deprived of water for a number of hours and is then allowed to obtain water by pressing the lever, the frequency of lever pressing can be used to indicate the strength of the motivation to obtain water. With this method a number of factors can be varied, such as the amount of effort required to press the bar and the number of times the bar must be pressed to obtain a reward. We know from earlier work that animals (including humans!) will continue to perform a response for a longer period of time when reward is discontinued altogether if they have not been rewarded for every response.

An experimenter wished to study the effect of the number of hours of water deprivation on the number of times a rat would press a heavily weighted lever during a 15 minute period where the response was rewarded an average of one out of every five times the lever pressing response occurred. Each reward consisted of a few drops of water. Four levels of water deprivation were used: 1 hour; 12 hours; 24 hours; and 36 hours. Five animals were assigned randomly to each group. The experimenter decided to rank the data and to test for significance using the Kruskal-Wallis one-way ranked analysis of variance method.

The data in terms of the average number of bar presses per minute are listed for each rat in Table 13–7.

Since we have four groups of five subjects each we can treat our obtained H value as a χ^2 with three degrees of freedom. (See Chapter 10, p. 182 , if this part of the procedure is not clear to you.) From Table A–5 we find a χ^2 value of 7.82 listed at the .05 level of significance and a value of 11.34 listed at the .01 level of significance. Since our obtained H of 15.36 exceeds both of these values we can reject the hypothesis that these four samples were drawn from the same underlying population. Inspection of the data indicates that the animals in the one hour deprived group perform at a much lower level than do the animals in the other group. It also appears that the animals in the 24 hour deprived group perform at a higher level than do the other groups. In order to evaluate the likelihood of these possibilities it is necessary to make individual comparisons among the groups.

7. A Relationship Between Height and Weight: The Pearson Product-Moment Correlation (Chapter 12).

To demonstrate correlation methods a statistics teacher obtains the height in inches and the weight in pounds of each of his students. He is interested in demonstrating that height and weight co-vary. Table 13–8 contains each student's height (X) and weight (Y) and the computations leading to the Pearson r.

Table 13–7. AVERAGE NUMBER OF BAR PRESSES PER MINUTE OVER A 15 MINUTE PERIOD AND EQUIVALENT RANKS FOR FOUR GROUPS OF RATS UNDER DIFFERING AMOUNTS OF WATER DEPRIVATION.

| A | | | B | | | C | | | D | | |
| 1 Hour Deprivation | | | 12 Hours Deprivation | | | 24 Hours Deprivation | | | 36 Hours Deprivation | | |
Sub. #	Score	Rank	Sub. #	Score	Rank	Sub. #	Score	Rank	Sub. #	Score	Rank
3	7	1.0	4	14	9.5	1	16	13.0	2	11	4.5
5	12	6.0	7	19	16.5	12	23	20.0	6	18	14.5
9	11	4.5	11	14	9.5	14	21	18.5	8	18	14.5
13	10	2.5	16	14	9.5	15	21	18.5	10	15	12.0
19	10	2.5	20	14	9.5	18	19	16.5	17	13	7.0

$$\sum R_1 = 16.5 \qquad \sum R_2 = 54.5 \qquad \sum R_3 = 86.5 \qquad \sum R_4 = 52.5$$

$$R_1^2 = 272.25 \qquad R_2^2 = 2970.25 \qquad R_3^2 = 7482.25 \qquad R_4^2 = 2756.25$$

$$\frac{R_1^2}{n_1} = 54.45 \qquad \frac{R_2^2}{n_2} = 594.05 \qquad \frac{R_3^2}{n_3} = 1496.45 \qquad \frac{R_4^2}{n_4} = 551.25$$

$$H = \left[\frac{12}{N(N+1)} \left(\sum \frac{R^2}{n} \right) \right] - 3(N+1)$$

$$= \left[\frac{12}{20(21)} (54.45 + 594.05 + 1496.45 + 551.25) \right] - 3(21)$$

$$= \left[\frac{12}{420} (2696.2) \right] - 63$$

$$= [.029(2696.2)] - 63$$

$$= 78.19 - 63$$

$$= 15.19$$

Applying the correction for ties: $\dfrac{H}{1 - \dfrac{\sum T}{N^3 - N}}$, $t = 2; 2; 2; 2; 2; 4.$

This indicates that there were five instances where two cases were tied and one instance where four cases were tied.

$$\sum T = (t^3 - t)$$

$$= (2^3 - 2) + (2^3 - 2) + (2^3 - 2) + (2^3 - 2) + (2^3 - 2) + (4^3 - 4)$$

$$= 6 + 6 + 6 + 6 + 6 + 60 = 90$$

$$\frac{H}{1 - \dfrac{\sum T}{N^3 - N}} = \frac{15.19}{1 - \dfrac{90}{7980}} = \frac{15.19}{1 - .011} = \frac{15.19}{.989} = 15.36$$

Table 13–8. Height in Inches (X) and Weight in Pounds (Y) for Eleven Subjects.

Subject #	Inches X	Pounds Y
1	63	158
2	68	171
3	65	159
4	73	197
5	59	165
6	69	175
7	74	203
8	70	173
9	61	155
10	58	151
11	65	148

$$\sum X = 725$$
$$\sum X^2 = 48{,}075$$
$$(\sum X)^2 = 525{,}625$$

$$\sum Y = 1855$$
$$\sum Y^2 = 366{,}013$$
$$(\sum Y)^2 = 3{,}441{,}025$$

$$\sum XY = 123{,}073$$

$$r = \frac{N \sum XY - (\sum X)(\sum Y)}{\sqrt{[N \sum X^2 - (\sum X)^2][N \sum Y^2 - (\sum Y)^2]}}$$

$$= \frac{123{,}073 - (725)(1855)}{\sqrt{[(11)(48{,}075) - 525{,}625][(11)(316{,}013) - 3{,}441{,}025]}}$$

$$= \frac{8928}{\sqrt{(3{,}200)(35{,}118)}}$$

$$= \frac{8928}{\sqrt{112{,}366{,}600}}$$

$$= \frac{8928}{10{,}601}$$

$$= .84$$

When Table A–9 is entered with nine degrees of freedom we find that r must equal .602 to be considered to be significantly different from zero at the .05 level of significance and that it must reach .735 to reach significance at the .01 level of significance. The r of .84 calculated between height and weight is larger than either of these values. Therefore, it can be concluded on the basis of this sample that height and weight do co-vary in the population represented by these 11 students.

8. A **Relationship Between Brightness and Pattern Discrimination: The Spearman Rank Difference Correlation (Chapter 12).** An experimenter is studying various aspects of discrimination learning in cats. He has reason to believe that a cat's ability to discriminate pattern is related to its ability to discriminate brightness. To evaluate this proposition he trains eight cats to discriminate black from white in a two-choice discrimination apparatus. He then trains the same eight cats to discriminate between two patterns in the same apparatus.

A problem develops, however. Cat *C* shows no evidence of learning the pattern discrimination in 80 trials. Since the experimenter is only running one trial a day he does not wish to prolong the experiment, especially in the face of results which suggest that

Table 13–9. NUMBER OF CORRECT RESPONSES FOR EIGHT CATS ON BRIGHTNESS AND DISCRIMINATION TRIALS AND EQUIVALENT RANKS FOR CALCULATION OF THE SPEARMAN RANK-DIFFERENCE CORRELATION.

| Cat | Score | | Rank | | d | d^2 |
	Brightness	Pattern	Brightness	Pattern		
A	27	30	1	2	1	1
B	49	57	11	13.5	2.5	6.25
C	65	80+	15	16	1	1
D	37	41	7	9	2	4
E	29	31	4	3	1	1
F	39	42	8	10	2	4
G	57	55	13.5	12	1.5	2.25
H	31	32	5	6	1	1

$$\sum d^2 = \overline{20.5}$$

$$\text{rho} = 1 - \frac{6(\sum d^2)}{N(N^2 - 1)}$$

$$= 1 - \frac{6(20.5)}{8(63)}$$

$$= 1 - \frac{123}{504}$$

$$= 1 - .24$$

$$= .76$$

the cat will not learn the problem for some time to come. The experimenter also does not wish to discard the data for Cat C if he can avoid it. Therefore, he decides to stop the experiment and to assign Cat C a score of $80+$. He then ranks the data (Cat C will, then, have the highest rank) and calculates a Spearman rank difference correlation. The data, in trials to criterion for each cat on each of the discrimination tasks, are presented in Table 13–9.

From Table A–10 we find that, with an N of eight the rank difference correlation coefficient must be .74 to be considered to be significantly different from zero at the .05 level of significance. The obtained coefficient of .76 is larger than this value. Therefore, it can be concluded that there is a significant relationship between the ability of cats to discriminate brightness and pattern given the conditions of this experiment.

EPILOGUE

Hopefully, these eight experiments with their attendant calculations have served to provide a transition from statistics in an abstract sense to statistical method as an integral part of experimental design. All too frequently a research worker becomes concerned with statistical treatment of data to such an extent that he loses sight of the purpose of his experiments.

In any scientific investigation, the experiment must take precedence. Excellent statistical treatment will not save or salvage a poorly designed and executed experiment. Similarly, misapplication of statistics can result in inappropriate or incorrect conclusions from a well designed experiment. Statistics is one of the tools of experimentation and as such should be used with care and precision.

APPENDICES

Appendix I—CODING SCORES FOR HAND
       CALCULATION

Appendix II—STATISTICAL TABLES

Appendix III—ANSWERS TO ODD-NUMBERED
       EXERCISES

Appendix I

CODING SCORES FOR HAND CALCULATION

Anyone who is planning to do any significant amount of statistical work will almost certainly have access to an electric calculator. For large scale statistical calculations an electronic digital computer which can be programmed to carry out hundreds of calculations in a few seconds is often used.

There are still situations in which it is necessary to carry out calculations by hand. Use of raw score formulas in hand calculations often requires the manipulation of rather large numbers. Consequently, it is useful to know ways of simplifying the computations so as to keep the size of the numbers to a minimum. However, a few preliminary steps are necessary in order to use these techniques.

Grouping of Scores

If a statistic is to be calculated directly from the raw scores, there is little advantage to be gained by arranging the scores in order or grouping them in any fashion. If they can be coded in any manner, the work will be greatly simplified if the scores are arranged into a set of *class intervals*. This procedure shortens the number of values it is necessary to work with. Table I–1 contains 30 raw scores and a set of class intervals constructed from these scores.

Table I–1 is constructed from scores taken from our original set of scores (from p. 12) which range from 30 to 77. They are grouped in class intervals of 5, giving us a total of 10 class intervals.

Table I–1. Setting Class Intervals for Raw Scores.

Scores:

34	55	61	39	57	41
51	71	39	76	57	67
31	65	60	33	46	59
70	73	73	77	41	48
66	36	46	69	38	30

Class Intervals	Frequency	
75–79	II	(2)
70–74	IIII	(4)
65–69	IIII	(4)
60–64	II	(2)
55–59	IIII	(4)
50–54	I	(1)
45–49	III	(3)
40–44	II	(2)
35–39	IIII	(4)
30–34	IIII	(4)

$$N = 30$$

What determines the number of class intervals we will choose to use? This is largely arbitrary, since the nature of the scores to be grouped must be taken into consideration. Too fine a grouping defeats the purpose for grouping scores and too coarse a grouping tends to lose information. Usually, 10 to 15 intervals are satisfactory. The usual rule to use to start the class limits is that the lower limit of each class interval must be divisible by the class interval, i. For the example in Table I–1, the class interval, i, is 5. The lowest score 30, is evenly divisible by five, so our lowest class interval can start with 30. If we have had a score of 29, our lowest interval would start with 25 and encompass the range 25–29.

In statistical terminology, the class intervals we have used are in terms of *working limits*. The *theoretical limits* for the lowest interval are 29.5–34.5. This means that the interval *theoretically* encompasses all values within the range 29.5 to 34.5. Keep in mind that these are the limits in the mathematical sense.

How does the grouping change the scores? When using class intervals the midpoint of the class interval represents all the scores in that interval. Thus the class interval 75–79, which contains two scores of 76 and 77 in raw score form, now in effect has two scores of 77—the midpoint of the class interval.

The Coding of Scores

The coding or transformation of scores is basically a very simple process, and will be illustrated by calculating the arithmetic mean. Table I–2 illustrates the sequence of steps.

Table I–2. CALCULATION OF THE MEAN BY CODED SCORES.
(DATA FROM TABLE I–1.)

	Scores	Frequency	x'	fx'
Step I: Set up a column labeled x' next to the column containing the frequencies of the scores. Enter the value of zero in the lowest class interval, the value of 1 in the next interval, and continue, increasing the value of x' by 1 for each interval.	75–79	2	9	18
	70–74	4	8	32
	65–69	4	7	28
	60–64	2	6	12
Step 2: Multiply the values in the x' column by the corresponding row values in the frequency (f_x) column. For interval 75–79, $2 \times 9 = 18$. The value of 18 is entered in the fx' column.	55–59	4	5	20
	50–54	1	4	4
	45–49	3	3	9
	40–44	2	2	4
Step 3: The formula for determining the mean from coded scores is:	35–39	4	1	4
	30–34	4	0	0
$\bar{X} = M + [\sum fx'/N]i,$	$\sum$	30	—	131

$$\bar{X} = M + [\sum fx'/N]i \qquad M = 32$$
$$= 32 + [131/30]5 \qquad i = 5$$
$$= 32 + [4.37]5$$
$$= 32 + 21.85$$
$$= 53.85$$

where M = the midpoint of the interval containing the 0 value,

$\sum fx'$ = the sum of the fx' column,

i = the size of the class interval,

N = the number of observations.

The column headed x' contains the values 0 through 9, beginning with 0 in the first class interval and progressing by steps of 1 up to the highest class interval. The column headed fx' is the result of multiplying the x' values by the values in the frequency (f_x) column. The sum of this column is then taken and substituted into the formula for obtaining the mean from coded scores.

It is important to keep in mind that the formulas for obtaining the mean from raw scores and from coded scores are the same formula. The only difference in the coded score version lies in the necessity to specify the point of origin for the coding and in correcting for the class interval size. Note that scores can be coded using a class interval of 1, just as if they were raw scores under which circumstances the multiplication by i has no effect on the value of the mean.

The point of origin for coding does not need to be placed at the lowest score interval—it can be placed in the center of the class intervals, for example. This method is advantageous in that numbers are kept even smaller than in the calculations of Table I–2. However, one disadvantage lies in the fact that the signs of numbers must be noted.

To illustrate this, Table I–3 repeats the calculation of the mean placing the point of origin at interval 50–54. The calculation is identical with the calculation of Table I–2, with the difference that the algebraic sum of fx' must be obtained.

Table I–3. CALCULATION OF THE MEAN FROM A POINT OF ORIGIN IN THE CENTER OF THE DISTRIBUTION.

Scores	f_x Frequency	x'	fx'
75–79	2	5	10
70–74	4	4	16
65–69	4	3	12
60–64	2	2	4
55–59	4	1	4
50–54	1	0	0
45–49	3	-1	-3
40–44	2	-2	-4
35–39	4	-3	-12
30–34	4	-4	-16
Σ	30		11

$$\bar{X} = M + [\textstyle\sum fx'/N]i$$
$$= 52 + [11/30]5$$
$$= 52 + [.37]5$$
$$= 52 + 1.85$$
$$= 53.85$$

Calculation of the Variance

To calculate the variance in terms of coded scores an additional column is necessary. Table I–4 repeats the calculations of Table I–2, with the additional calculations required to obtain the variance.

Note that the formula for the sum of squares from coded scores is identical to the raw score form, the only difference being the difference in symbols.

Table I–4. Calculation of the Variance.

Scores	f_x	x'	fx'	fx'^2
75–79	2	9	18	162
70–74	4	8	32	256
65–69	4	7	28	196
60–64	2	6	12	72
55–59	4	5	20	100
50–54	1	4	4	16
45–49	3	3	9	27
40–44	2	2	4	8
35–39	4	1	4	4
30–34	4	0	0	0
Σ	30	—	131	841

The only change from the calculations of Table I–2 is in the calculation of the values in the column labeled fx'^2. These values are obtained by multiplying each value in the fx' column by its corresponding x' value. For interval 60–64 $x' = 6$ and $fx' = 12$, resulting in an fx'^2 value of 72.

$$\Sigma \chi^2 = [\Sigma fx'^2 - \{(\Sigma fx')^2/N\}]i^2 \qquad s^2 = \Sigma \chi^2/(N - 1)$$

$$= [841 - \{(131^2)/30\}]5^2 \qquad = 6724.25/29$$

$$= [841 - \{(17161)/30\}]25 \qquad = 231.87$$

$$= [841 - 572.03]25$$

$$= [268.97]25$$

$$= 6724.25$$

$$s = \sqrt{s^2} \qquad\qquad s = \sqrt{s^2}$$

$$= \sqrt{185.7} \qquad\qquad s = \sqrt{231.87}$$

$$= 13.7 \qquad\qquad s = 15.22$$

Hand Calculation of the Correlation Coefficient

The example given in Chapter 11 will be used to illustrate the procedures used in the hand calculation of the Pearson correlation coefficient. Table I–5 illustrates the computation.

The scores are coded in exactly the same manner as for a single array of scores (cf. Table I–1). However, for the correlation, the coding is done on two sides of the bivariate frequency distribution to allow for the simultaneous coding of X and Y. The coding is arranged so that the values of the coded scores increase with increases in the value of the observations. The first row at the bottom of the bivariate frequency distribution labeled f_x contains the frequencies for the values of the variable X. The first column to the right of the frequency distribution labeled f_y lists the frequencies for variable Y. The second row is labeled x' and contains the coding values for X. The corresponding column for Y contains the coding for Y and is labeled y'. The remaining columns and rows, fx', fy', fx'^2, and fy'^2, are all calculated in the same manner as for the mean and standard deviation.

The first new calculation is in the row labeled $fy' \cdot x'$, which can be translated as "the sum of the fy' coding on the corresponding fx' coding."

To illustrate what is meant by this rather cumbersome definition, look at the first entry in the x' row. There is one score tallied for that entry and the x' code is 0. Now we look over to the y' column and see that the y' code is also 0. Since there is only one score, the value of 0 is entered at the beginning of the $fy' \cdot x'$ row. For the next entry, where the x' code is 1, there is also only one score, and its y' code is 2, so the value of 2 is entered in the next position in the $fy' \cdot x'$ row. For the third position, there are 3 scores which have y' scores of 2, 3, and 5, respectively, and the entry in the $fy' \cdot x'$ column will be the sum of these, which is 10. The sum of this row, when completed, should be identical to the sum of the fy' column. If it does not agree exactly, an error has been made. When this process is completed, the final row, labeled $fx'y'$, can be calculated. This is done by multiplying the $fy' \cdot x'$ values by the x' values in the same column. For the first entry 0×0, for the second entry $1 \times 2 = 2$, for the third entry $2 \times 10 = 20$, and so forth.

We are now ready to calculate r. We will need the sums of the fx', fy', fx'^2, fy'^2, $fy' \cdot x'$, and $fx'y'$. The remaining calculations are

Table I–5. HAND CALCULATION OF THE CORRELATION COEFFICIENT.

		Score on X							f_y	y'	fy'	fy'^2	
		1	2	3	4	5	6	7					
Score on Y	8							1	1	7	7	49	
	7								0	6	0	0	
	6			1					1	5	5	25	
	5				11		1		3	4	12	48	
	4			1	1				2	3	6	18	
	3		1	1	1				2	2	4	8	
	2								0	1	0	0	
	1	1							1	0	0	0	
f_x		1	1	3	3	0	1	1	10			34	148
x'		0	1	2	3	4	5	6					
fx'		0	1	6	9	0	5	6	27				
fx'^2		0	1	12	27	0	25	36	101				
$fy' \cdot x'$		0	2	10	11	0	4	7	34	← CHECK			
$fx'y'$		0	2	20	33	0	20	42	117				

$$\sum xy = \left[\sum fx'y' - \frac{(\sum fx')(\sum fy')}{N} \right] i_x i_y \qquad \sum y^2 = \left[\sum fy'^2 - \frac{(\sum fy')^2}{N} \right] i_y^2$$

$$= \left[117 - \frac{(27)(34)}{10} \right] 1 \cdot 1 \qquad\qquad = \left[148 - \frac{(34)^2}{10} \right] 1$$

$$= \left[117 - \frac{918}{10} \right] 1 \cdot 1 \qquad\qquad = \left[148 - \frac{1156}{10} \right] 1$$

$$= [117 - 91.8] 1 \cdot 1 \qquad\qquad = [148 - 115.6] 1$$

$$= 25.2 \qquad\qquad = 32.4$$

$$\sum x^2 = \left[\sum fx'^2 - \frac{(\sum fx')^2}{N} \right] i_x^2$$

$$= \left[101 - \frac{(27)^2}{10} \right] 1$$

$$= [101 - 72.9]$$

$$= 28.1$$

$$r = \frac{\sum xy}{\sqrt{\sum x^2 \sum y^2}} = \frac{25.2}{\sqrt{(28.1)(32.4)}} = \frac{25.2}{\sqrt{910.44}} = \frac{25.2}{30.17} = .83$$

Chapter 4. To find the covariance, we substitute into the formula:

$$\Sigma\, xy = \left[\Sigma\, fx'y' - \frac{(\Sigma\, fx')(\Sigma\, fy')}{N} \right] i_x i_y,$$

and for the sums of squares for X and Y:

$$\Sigma\, x^2 = \left[\Sigma\, fx' - \frac{(\Sigma\, fx')^2}{N} \right] i_x^{\,2}, \quad \Sigma\, y^2 = \left[\Sigma\, fy' - \frac{(\Sigma\, fy')^2}{N} \right] i_y^{\,2}.$$

When these calculations are completed, r may be found by substituting into

$$r = \frac{\Sigma\, xy}{\sqrt{\Sigma\, x^2 y^2}}.$$

Appendix II

STATISTICAL TABLES

Table A–1. Random Numbers

    This table may be entered at any point and read in any direction. For example, to randomly select a sample of ten observations from a total of 100, begin in the upper left hand corner and read two-digit groups until the sample is selected. In this example, observation No. 10 would be the first to be selected, followed by No. 9, then No. 73 and so forth until the entire sample has been selected. The point of origin is unimportant— you may begin anywhere and read in any direction.

Table A-1. Random Numbers*

10097	32533	76520	13586	34673	54876	80959	09117	39292	74945
37542	04805	64894	74296	24805	24037	20636	10402	00822	91665
08422	68953	19645	09303	23209	02560	15953	34764	35080	33606
99019	02529	09376	70715	38311	31165	88676	74397	04436	27659
12807	99970	80157	36147	64032	36653	98951	16877	12171	76833
66065	74717	34072	76850	36697	36170	65813	39885	11199	29170
31060	10805	45571	82406	35303	42614	86799	07439	23403	09732
85269	77602	02051	65692	68665	74818	73053	85247	18623	88579
63573	32135	05325	47048	90553	57548	28468	28709	83491	25624
73796	45753	03529	64778	35808	34282	60935	20344	35273	88435
98520	17767	14905	68607	22109	40558	60970	93433	50500	73998
11805	05431	39808	27732	50725	68248	29405	24201	52775	67851
83452	99634	06288	98083	13746	70078	18475	40610	68711	77817
88685	40200	86507	58401	36766	67951	90364	76493	29609	11062
99594	67348	87517	64969	91826	08928	93785	61368	23478	34113
65481	17674	17468	50950	58047	76974	73039	57186	40218	16544
80124	35635	17727	08015	45318	22374	21115	78253	14385	53763
74350	99817	77402	77214	43236	00210	45521	64237	96286	02655
69916	26803	66252	29148	36936	87203	76621	13990	94400	56418
09893	20505	14225	68514	46427	56788	96297	78822	54382	14598
91499	14523	68479	27686	46162	83554	94750	89923	37089	20048
80336	94598	26940	36858	70297	34135	53140	33340	42050	82341
44104	81949	85157	47954	32979	26575	57600	40881	22222	06413
12550	73742	11100	02040	12860	74697	96644	89439	28707	25815
63606	49329	16505	34484	40219	52563	43651	77082	07207	31790
61196	90446	26457	47774	51924	33729	65394	59593	42582	60527
15474	45266	95270	79953	59367	83848	82396	10118	33211	59466
94557	28573	67897	54387	54622	44431	91190	42592	92927	45973
42481	16213	97344	08721	16868	48767	03071	12059	25701	46670
23523	78317	73208	89837	68935	91416	26252	29663	05522	82562
04493	52494	75246	33824	45862	51025	61962	79335	65337	12472
00549	97654	64051	88159	96119	63896	54692	82391	23287	29529
35963	15307	26898	09354	33351	35462	77974	50024	90103	39333
59808	08391	45427	26842	83609	49700	13021	24892	78565	20106
46058	85236	01390	92286	77281	44077	93910	83647	70617	42941
32179	00597	87379	25241	05567	07007	86743	17157	85394	11838
69234	61406	20117	45204	15956	60000	18743	92423	97118	96338
19565	41430	01758	75379	40419	21585	66674	36806	84962	85207
45155	14938	19476	07246	43667	94543	59047	90033	20826	69541
94864	31994	36168	10851	34888	81553	01540	35456	05014	51176
98086	24826	45240	28404	44999	08896	39094	73407	35441	31880
33185	16232	41941	50949	89435	48581	88695	41994	37548	73043
80951	00406	96382	70774	20151	23387	25016	25298	94624	61171
79752	49140	71961	28296	69861	02591	74852	20539	00387	59579
18633	32537	98145	06571	31010	24674	05455	61427	77938	91936
74029	43902	77557	32270	97790	17119	52527	58021	80814	51748
54178	45611	80993	37143	05335	12969	56127	19255	36040	90324
11664	49883	52079	84827	59381	71539	09973	33440	88461	23356
48324	77928	31249	64710	02295	36870	32307	57546	15020	09994
69074	94138	87637	91976	35584	04401	10518	21615	01848	76938

* This table is reproduced with permission from the RAND Corporation: *A Million Random Digits*, 1955.

Table A-1. *Continued*

03991	10461	93716	16894	66083	24653	84609	58232	88618	19161
38555	95554	32886	59780	08355	60860	29735	47762	71299	23853
17546	73704	92052	46215	55121	29281	59076	07936	27954	58909
32643	52861	95819	06831	00911	98936	76355	93779	80863	00514
69572	68777	39510	35905	14060	40619	29549	69616	33564	60780
24122	66591	27699	06494	14845	46672	61958	77100	90899	75754
61196	30231	92962	61773	41839	55382	17267	70943	78038	70267
30532	21704	10274	12202	39685	23309	10061	68829	55986	66485
03788	97599	75867	20717	74416	53166	35208	33374	87539	08823
48228	63379	85783	47619	53152	67433	35663	52972	16818	60311
60365	94653	35075	33949	42614	29297	01918	28316	98953	73231
83799	42402	56623	34442	34994	41374	70071	14736	09958	18065
32960	07405	36409	83232	99385	41600	11133	07586	15917	06253
19322	53845	57620	52606	66497	68646	78138	66559	19640	99413
11220	94747	07399	37408	48509	23929	27482	45476	85244	35159
31751	57260	68980	05339	15470	48355	88651	22596	03152	19121
88492	99382	14454	04504	20094	98977	74843	93413	22109	78508
30934	47744	07481	83828	73788	06533	28597	20405	94205	20380
22888	48893	27499	98748	60530	45128	74022	84617	82037	10268
78212	16993	35902	91386	44372	15486	65741	14014	87481	37220
41849	84547	46850	52326	34677	58300	74910	64345	19325	81549
46352	33049	69248	93460	45305	07521	61318	31855	14413	70951
11087	96294	14013	31792	59747	67277	76503	34513	39663	77544
52701	08337	56303	87315	16520	69676	11654	99893	02181	68161
57275	36898	81304	48585	68652	27376	92852	55866	88448	03584
20857	73156	70284	24326	79375	95220	01159	63267	10622	48391
15633	84924	90415	93614	33521	26665	55823	47641	86225	31704
92694	48297	39904	02115	59589	49067	66821	41575	49767	04037
77613	19019	88152	00080	20554	91409	96277	48257	50816	97616
38688	32486	45134	63545	59404	72059	43947	51680	43852	59693
25163	01889	70014	15021	41290	67312	71857	15957	68971	11403
65251	07629	37239	33295	05870	01119	92784	26340	18477	65622
36815	43625	18637	37509	82444	99005	04921	73701	14707	93997
64397	11692	05327	82162	20247	81759	45197	25332	83745	22567
04515	25624	95096	67946	48460	85558	15191	18782	16930	33361
83761	60873	43253	84145	60833	25983	01291	41349	20368	07126
14387	06345	80854	09279	43529	06318	38384	74761	41196	37480
51321	92246	80088	77074	88722	56736	66164	49431	66919	31678
72472	00008	80890	18002	94813	31900	54155	83436	35352	54131
05466	55306	93128	18464	74457	90561	72848	11834	79982	68416
39528	72484	82474	25593	48545	35247	18619	13674	18611	19241
81616	18711	53342	44276	75122	11724	74627	73707	58319	15997
07586	16120	82641	22820	92904	13141	32392	19763	61199	67940
90767	04235	13574	17200	69902	63742	78464	22501	18627	90872
40188	28193	29593	88627	94972	11598	62095	36787	00441	58997
34414	82157	86887	55087	19152	00023	12302	80783	32624	68691
63439	75363	44989	16822	36024	00867	76378	41605	65961	73488
67049	09070	93399	45547	94458	74284	05041	49807	20288	34060
79495	04146	52162	90286	54158	34243	46978	35482	59362	95938
91704	30552	04737	21031	75051	93029	47665	64382	99782	93478

Table A–1. *Continued*

```
19612 78430   11661 94770   77603 65669   86868 12665   30012 75989
39141 77400   28000 64238   73258 71794   31340 26256   66453 37016
64756 80457   08747 12836   03469 50678   03274 43423   66677 82556
92901 51878   56441 22998   29718 38447   06453 25311   07565 53771
03551 90070   09483 94050   45938 18135   36908 43321   11073 51803

98884 66209   06830 53656   14663 56346   71430 04909   19818 05707
27369 86882   53473 07541   53633 70863   03748 12822   19360 49088
59066 75974   63335 20483   43514 37481   58278 26967   49325 43951
91647 93783   64169 49022   98588 09495   49829 59068   38831 04838
83605 92419   39542 07772   71568 75673   35185 89759   44901 74291

24895 88530   70774 35439   46758 70472   70207 92675   91623 61275
35720 26556   95596 20094   73750 85788   34264 01703   46833 65248
14141 53410   38649 06343   57256 61342   72709 75318   90379 37562
27416 75670   92176 72535   93119 56077   06886 18244   92344 31374
82071 07429   81007 47749   40744 56974   23336 88821   53841 10536

21445 82793   24831 93241   14199 76268   70883 68002   03829 17443
72513 76400   52225 92348   62308 98481   29744 33165   33141 61020
71479 45027   76160 57411   13780 13632   52308 77762   88874 33697
83210 51466   09088 50395   26743 05306   21706 70001   99439 80767
68749 95148   94897 78636   96750 09024   94538 91143   96693 61886

05184 75763   47075 88158   05313 53439   14908 08830   60096 21551
13651 62546   96892 25240   47511 58483   87342 78818   07855 39269
00566 21220   00292 24069   25072 29519   52548 54091   21282 21296
50958 17695   58072 68990   60329 95955   71586 63417   35947 67807
57621 64547   46850 37981   38527 09037   64756 03324   04986 83666

09282 25844   79139 78435   35428 43561   69799 63314   12991 93516
23394 94206   93432 37836   94919 26846   02555 74410   94915 48199
05280 37470   93622 04345   15092 19510   18094 16613   78234 50001
95491 97976   38306 32192   82639 54624   72434 92606   23191 74693
78521 00104   18248 75583   90326 50785   54034 66251   35774 14692

96345 44579   85932 44053   75704 20840   86583 83944   52456 73766
77963 31151   32364 91691   47357 40338   23435 24065   08458 95366
07520 11294   23238 01748   41690 67328   54814 37777   10057 42332
38423 02309   70703 85736   46148 14258   29236 12152   05088 65825
02463 65533   21199 60555   33928 01817   07396 89215   30722 22102

15880 92261   17292 88190   61781 48898   92525 21283   88581 60098
71926 00819   59144 00224   30570 90194   18329 06999   26857 19238
64425 28108   16554 16016   00042 83229   10333 36168   65617 94834
79782 23924   49440 30432   81077 31543   95216 64865   13658 51081
35337 74538   44553 64672   90960 41849   93865 44608   93176 34851

05249 29329   19715 94082   14738 86667   43708 66354   93692 25527
56463 99380   38793 85774   19056 13939   46062 27647   66146 63210
96296 33121   54196 34108   75814 85986   71171 15102   28992 63165
98380 36269   60014 07201   62448 46385   42175 88350   46182 49126
52567 64350   16315 53969   80395 81114   54358 64578   47269 15747

78498 90830   25955 99236   43286 91064   99969 95144   64424 77377
49553 24241   08150 89535   08703 91041   77323 81079   45127 93686
32151 07075   83155 10252   73100 88618   23891 87418   45417 20268
11314 50363   26860 27799   49416 83534   19187 08059   76677 02110
12364 71210   87052 50241   90785 97889   81399 58130   64439 05614
```

Table A–1. *Continued*

94015	46874	32444	48277	59820	96163	64654	25843	41145	42820
74108	88222	88570	74015	25704	91035	01755	14750	48968	38603
62880	87873	95160	59221	22304	90314	72877	17334	39283	04149
11748	12102	80580	41867	17710	59621	06554	07850	73950	79552
17944	05600	60478	03343	25852	58905	57216	39618	49856	99326
66067	42792	95043	52680	46780	56487	09971	59481	37006	22186
54244	91030	45547	70818	59849	96169	61459	21647	87417	17198
30945	57589	31732	57260	47670	07654	46376	25366	94746	49580
69170	37403	86995	90307	94304	71803	26825	05511	12459	91314
08345	88975	35841	85771	08105	59987	87112	21476	14713	71181
27767	43584	85301	88977	29490	69714	73035	41207	74699	09310
13025	14338	54066	15243	47724	66733	47431	43905	31048	56699
80217	36292	98525	24335	24432	24896	43277	58874	11466	16082
10875	62004	90391	61105	57411	06368	53856	30743	08670	84741
54127	57326	26629	19087	24472	88779	30540	27886	61732	75454
60311	42824	37301	42678	45990	43242	17374	52003	70707	70214
49739	71484	92003	98086	76668	73209	59202	11973	02902	33250
78626	51594	16453	94614	39014	97066	83012	09832	25571	77628
66692	13986	99837	00582	81232	44987	09504	96412	90193	79568
44071	28091	07362	97703	76447	42537	98524	97831	65704	09514
41468	85149	49554	17994	14924	39650	95294	00556	70481	06905
94559	37559	49678	53119	70312	05682	66986	34099	74474	20740
41615	70360	64114	58660	90850	64618	80620	51790	11436	38072
50273	93113	41794	86861	24781	89683	55411	85667	77535	99892
41396	80504	90670	08289	40902	05069	95083	06783	28102	57816
25807	24260	71529	78920	72682	07385	90726	57166	98884	08583
06170	97965	88302	98041	21443	41808	68984	83620	89747	98882
60808	54444	74412	81105	01176	28838	36421	16489	18059	51061
80940	44893	10408	36222	80582	71944	92638	40333	67054	16067
19516	90120	46759	71643	13177	55292	21036	82808	77501	97427
49386	54480	23604	23554	21785	41101	91178	10174	29420	90438
06312	88940	15995	69321	47458	64809	98189	81851	29651	84215
60942	00307	11897	92674	40405	68032	96717	54244	10701	41393
92329	98932	78284	46347	71209	92061	39448	93136	25722	08564
77936	63574	31384	51924	85561	29671	58137	17820	22751	36518
38101	77756	11657	13897	95889	57067	47648	13885	70669	93406
39641	69457	91339	22502	92613	89719	11947	56203	19324	20504
84054	40455	99396	63680	67667	60631	69181	96845	38525	11600
47468	03577	57649	63266	24700	71594	14004	23153	69249	05747
43321	31370	28977	23896	76479	68562	62342	07589	08899	05985
64281	61826	18555	64937	13173	33365	78851	16499	87064	13075
66847	70495	32350	02985	86716	38746	26313	77463	55387	72681
72461	33230	21529	53424	92581	02262	78438	66276	18396	73538
21032	91050	13058	16218	12470	56500	15292	76139	59526	52113
95362	67011	06651	16136	01016	00857	55018	56374	35824	71708
49712	97380	10404	55452	34030	60726	75211	10271	36633	68424
58275	61764	97586	54716	50259	46345	87195	46092	26787	60939
89514	11788	68224	23417	73959	76145	30342	40277	11049	72049
15472	50669	48139	36732	46874	37088	73465	09819	58869	35220
12120	86124	51247	44302	60883	52109	21437	36786	49226	77837

Table A-1. *Continued*

09188 20097	32825 39527	04220 86304	83389 87374	64278 58044
90045 85497	51981 50654	94938 81997	91870 76150	68476 64659
73189 50207	47677 26269	62290 64464	27124 67018	41361 82760
75768 76490	20971 87749	90429 12272	95375 05871	93823 43178
54016 44056	66281 31003	00682 27398	20714 53295	07706 17813
08358 69910	78542 42785	13661 58873	04618 97553	31223 08420
28306 03264	81333 10591	40510 07893	32604 60475	94119 01840
53840 86233	81594 13628	51215 90290	28466 68795	77762 20791
91757 53741	61613 62269	50263 90212	55781 76514	83483 47055
89415 92694	00397 58391	12607 17646	48949 72306	94541 37408
77513 03820	86864 29901	68414 82774	51908 13980	72893 55507
19502 37174	69979 20288	55210 29773	74287 75251	65344 67415
21818 59313	93278 81757	05686 73156	07082 85046	31853 38452
51474 66499	68107 23621	94049 91345	42836 09191	08007 45449
99559 68331	62535 24170	69777 12830	74819 78142	43860 72834
33713 48007	93584 72869	51926 64721	58303 29822	93174 93972
85274 86893	11303 22970	28834 34137	73515 90400	71148 43643
84133 89640	44035 52166	73852 70091	61222 60561	62327 18423
56732 16234	17395 96131	10123 91622	85496 57560	81604 18880
65138 56806	87648 85261	34313 65861	45875 21069	85644 47277
38001 02176	81719 11711	71602 92937	74219 64049	65584 49698
37402 96397	01304 77586	56271 10086	47324 62605	40030 37438
97125 40348	87083 31417	21815 39250	75237 62047	15501 29578
21826 41134	47143 34072	64638 85902	49139 06441	03856 54552
73135 42742	95719 09035	85794 74296	08789 88156	64691 19202
07638 77929	03061 18072	96207 44156	23821 99538	04713 66994
60528 83441	07954 19814	59175 20695	05533 52139	61212 06455
83596 35655	06958 92983	05128 09719	77433 53783	92301 50498
10850 62746	99599 10507	13499 06319	53075 71839	06410 19362
39820 98952	43622 63147	64421 80814	43800 09351	31024 73167
59580 06478	75569 78800	88835 54486	23768 06156	04111 08408
38508 07341	23793 48763	90822 97022	17719 04207	95954 49953
30692 70668	94688 16127	56196 80091	82067 63400	05462 69200
65443 95659	18288 27437	49632 24041	08337 65676	96299 90836
27267 50264	13192 72294	07477 44606	17985 48911	97341 30358
91307 06991	19072 24210	36699 53728	28825 35793	28976 66252
68434 94688	84473 13622	62126 98408	12843 82590	09815 93146
48908 15877	54745 24591	35700 04754	83824 52692	54130 55160
06913 45197	42672 78601	11883 09528	63011 98901	14974 40344
10455 16019	14210 33712	91342 37821	88325 80851	43667 70883
12883 97343	65027 61184	04285 01392	17974 15077	90712 26769
21778 30976	38807 36961	31649 42096	63281 02023	08816 47449
19523 59515	65122 59659	86283 68258	69572 13798	16435 91529
67245 52670	35583 16563	79246 86686	76463 34222	26655 90802
60584 47377	07500 37992	45134 26529	26760 83637	41326 44344
53853 41377	36066 94850	58838 73859	49364 73331	96240 43642
24637 38736	74384 89342	52623 07992	12369 18601	03742 83873
83080 12451	38992 22815	07759 51777	97377 27585	51972 37867
16444 24334	36151 99073	27493 70939	85130 32552	54846 54759
60790 18157	57178 65762	11161 78576	45819 52979	65130 04860

Table A-2. Areas of a Standard Normal Distribution*

Standard score values are listed in the column headed "z." To find the proportion of the total area occurring between the mean and any given z-score, locate the entry indicated by the z-score. For example, a z-score of $+1.96$ is located by reading across to column 6 from the value of 1.9 in the "z" column. The value in the body of the table is .4750. Since the total area above the mean is equal to .5000, this means that only .0250 of the area is beyond the z-score of $+1.96$. Similarly, a z-score of -2.58 has a value of .4951, indicating that only .0049 of the area lies beyond the z-score of -2.58.·

z	.00	.01	.02	.03	.04	.05	.06	.07	.08	.09
0.0	.0000	.0040	.0080	.0120	.0160	.0199	.0239	.0279	.0319	.0359
0.1	.0398	.0438	.0478	.0517	.0557	.0596	.0636	.0675	.0714	.0753
0.2	.0793	.0832	.0871	.0910	.0948	.0987	.1026	.1064	.1103	.1141
0.3	.1179	.1217	.1255	.1293	.1331	.1368	.1406	.1443	.1480	.1517
0.4	.1554	.1591	.1628	.1664	.1700	.1736	.1772	.1808	.1844	.1879
0.5	.1915	.1950	.1985	.2019	.2054	.2088	.2123	.2157	.2190	.2224
0.6	.2257	.2291	.2324	.2357	.2389	.2422	.2454	.2486	.2517	.2549
0.7	.2580	.2611	.2642	.2673	.2703	.2734	.2764	.2794	.2823	.2852
0.8	.2881	.2910	.2939	.2967	.2995	.3023	.3051	.3078	.3106	.3133
0.9	.3159	.3186	.3212	.3238	.3264	.3289	.3315	.3340	.3365	.3389
1.0	.3413	.3438	.3461	.3485	.3508	.3531	.3554	.3577	.3599	.3621
1.1	.3643	.3665	.3686	.3708	.3729	.3749	.3770	.3790	.3810	.3830
1.2	.3849	.3869	.3888	.3907	.3925	.3944	.3962	.3980	.3997	.4015
1.3	.4032	.4049	.4066	.4082	.4099	.4115	.4131	.4147	.4162	.4177
1.4	.4192	.4207	.4222	.4236	.4251	.4265	.4279	.4292	.4306	.4319
1.5	.4332	.4345	.4357	.4370	.4382	.4394	.4406	.4418	.4429	.4441
1.6	.4452	.4463	.4474	.4484	.4495	.4505	.4515	.4525	.4535	.4545
1.7	.4554	.4564	.4573	.4582	.4591	.4599	.4608	.4616	.4625	.4633
1.8	.4641	.4649	.4656	.4664	.4671	.4678	.4686	.4693	.4699	.4706
1.9	.4713	.4719	.4726	.4732	.4738	.4744	.4750	.4756	.4761	.4767
2.0	.4772	.4778	.4783	.4788	.4793	.4798	.4803	.4808	.4812	.4817
2.1	.4821	.4826	.4830	.4834	.4838	.4842	.4846	4850	.4854	.4857
2.2	.4861	.4864	.4868	.4871	.4875	.4878	.4881	.4884	.4887	.4890
2.3	.4893	.4896	.4898	.4901	.4904	.4906	.4909	.4911	.4913	.4916
2.4	.4918	.4920	.4922	.4925	.4927	.4929	.4931	.4932	.4934	.4936
2.5	.4938	.4940	.4941	.4943	.4945	.4946	.4948	.4949	.4951	.4952
2.6	.4953	.4955	.4956	.4957	.4959	.4960	.4961	.4962	.4963	.4964
2.7	.4965	.4966	.4967	.4968	.4969	.4970	.4971	.4972	.4973	.4974
2.8	.4974	.4975	.4976	.4977	.4977	.4978	.4979	.4979	.4980	.4981
2.9	.4981	.4982	.4982	.4983	.4984	.4984	.4985	.4985	.4986	.4986
3.0	.4987	.4987	.4987	.4988	.4988	.4989	.4989	.4989	.4990	.4990

* Reproduced with permission from Hoel, P. G.: *Elementary Statistics*, 2nd Ed. New York: John Wiley and Sons, Inc., 1966.

Table A-3. STUDENT'S t DISTRIBUTION*

The first column contains the number of degrees of freedom (df). The values in the body of the table are the values of t that must be exceeded to attain a certain probability value. For example, a t value of 3.63 with 9 degrees of freedom will occur less than 0.01 of the time since it exceeds the tabled value of 3.2498 shown for the probability of .01 and 9 df.

df \ P	0.50	0.25	0.10	0.05	0.025	0.01	0.005
1	1.00000	2.4142	6.3138	12.706	25.452	63.657	127.32
2	0.81650	1.6036	2.9200	4.3027	6.2053	9.9248	14.089
3	0.76489	1.4226	2.3534	3.1825	4.1765	5.8409	7.4533
4	0.74070	1.3444	2.1318	2.7764	3.4954	4.6041	5.5976
5	0.72669	1.3009	2.0150	2.5706	3.1634	4.0321	4.7733
6	0.71756	1.2733	1.9432	2.4469	2.9687	3.7074	4.3168
7	0.71114	1.2543	1.8946	2.3646	2.8412	3.4995	4.0293
8	0.70639	1.2403	1.8595	2.3060	2.7515	3.3554	3.8325
9	0.70272	1.2297	1.8331	2.2622	2.6850	3.2498	3.6897
10	0.69981	1.2213	1.8125	2.2281	2.6338	3.1693	3.5814
11	0.69745	1.2145	1.7959	2.2010	2.5931	3.1058	3.4966
12	0.69548	1.2089	1.7823	2.1788	2.5600	3.0545	3.4284
13	0.69384	1.2041	1.7709	2.1604	2.5326	3.0123	3.3725
14	0.69242	1.2001	1.7613	2.1448	2.5096	2.9768	3.3257
15	0.69120	1.1967	1.7530	2.1315	2.4899	2.9467	3.2860
16	0.69013	1.1937	1.7459	2.1199	2.4729	2.9208	3.2520
17	0.68919	1.1910	1.7396	2.1098	2.4581	2.8982	3.2225
18	0.68837	1.1887	1.7341	2.1009	2.4450	2.8784	3.1966
19	0.68763	1.1866	1.7291	2.0930	2.4334	2.8609	3.1737
20	0.68696	1.1848	1.7247	2.0860	2.4231	2.8453	3.1534
21	0.68635	1.1831	1.7207	2.0796	2.4138	2.8314	3.1352
22	0.68580	1.1816	1.7171	2.0739	2.4055	2.8188	3.1188
23	0.68531	1.1802	1.7139	2.0687	2.3979	2.8073	3.1040
24	0.68485	1.1789	1.7109	2.0639	2.3910	2.7969	3.0905
25	0.68443	1.1777	1.7081	2.0595	2.3846	2.7874	3.0782
26	0.68405	1.1766	1.7056	2.0555	2.3788	2.7787	3.0669
27	0.68370	1.1757	1.7033	2.0518	2.3734	2.7707	3.0565
28	0.68335	1.1748	1.7011	2.0484	2.3685	2.7633	3.0469
29	0.68304	1.1739	1.6991	2.0452	2.3638	2.7564	3.0380
30	0.68276	1.1731	1.6973	2.0423	2.3596	2.7500	3.0298
40	0.68066	1.1673	1.6839	2.0211	2.3289	2.7045	2.9712
60	0.67862	1.1616	1.6707	2.0003	2.2991	2.6603	2.9146
120	0.67656	1.1559	1.6577	1.9799	2.2699	2.6174	2.8599
∞	0.67449	1.1503	1.6449	1.9600	2.2414	2.5758	2.8070

* Reproduced with permission from Hoel, P. G.: *Elementary Statistics*, 2nd Ed. New York: John Wiley and Sons, Inc., 1966.

263

Table A–4. F Distribution*

5% (Roman Type) and 1% (Bold Face Type) Points for the Distribution of F

Find the column containing the number of degrees of freedom for the numerator (f_1) and the row containing the number of degrees of freedom for the denominator (f_2). If the value in the body of the table is exceeded by the obtained F value, the 5 per cent significance level has been reached. For example, an F of 5.02 with df for the numerator equal to 3 and df for the denominator equal to 10 exceeds the table value of 4.96 at the 5 per cent level and would be judged significant at that level.

f_1 Degrees of Freedom (for greater mean square)

f_2	1	2	3	4	5	6	7	8	9	10	11	12	14	16	20	24	30	40	50	75	100	200	500	∞	f_2
1	161 **4,052**	200 **4,999**	216 **5,403**	225 **5,625**	230 **5,764**	234 **5,859**	237 **5,928**	239 **5,981**	241 **6,022**	242 **6,056**	243 **6,082**	244 **6,106**	245 **6,142**	246 **6,169**	248 **6,208**	249 **6,234**	250 **6,261**	251 **6,286**	252 **6,302**	253 **6,323**	253 **6,334**	254 **6,352**	254 **6,361**	254 **6,366**	1
2	18.51 **98.49**	19.00 **99.00**	19.16 **99.17**	19.25 **99.25**	19.30 **99.30**	19.33 **99.33**	19.36 **99.36**	19.37 **99.37**	19.38 **99.39**	19.39 **99.40**	19.40 **99.41**	19.41 **99.42**	19.42 **99.43**	19.43 **99.44**	19.44 **99.45**	19.45 **99.46**	19.46 **99.47**	19.47 **99.48**	19.47 **99.48**	19.48 **99.49**	19.49 **99.49**	19.49 **99.49**	19.50 **99.50**	19.50 **99.50**	2
3	10.13 **34.12**	9.55 **30.82**	9.28 **29.46**	9.12 **28.71**	9.01 **28.24**	8.94 **27.91**	8.88 **27.67**	8.84 **27.49**	8.81 **27.34**	8.78 **27.23**	8.76 **27.13**	8.74 **27.05**	8.71 **26.92**	8.69 **26.83**	8.66 **26.69**	8.64 **26.60**	8.62 **26.50**	8.60 **26.41**	8.58 **26.35**	8.57 **26.27**	8.56 **26.23**	8.54 **26.18**	8.54 **26.14**	8.53 **26.12**	3
4	7.71 **21.20**	6.94 **18.00**	6.59 **16.69**	6.39 **15.98**	6.26 **15.52**	6.16 **15.21**	6.09 **14.98**	6.04 **14.80**	6.00 **14.66**	5.96 **14.54**	5.93 **14.45**	5.91 **14.37**	5.87 **14.24**	5.84 **14.15**	5.80 **14.02**	5.77 **13.93**	5.74 **13.83**	5.71 **13.74**	5.70 **13.69**	5.68 **13.61**	5.66 **13.57**	5.65 **13.52**	5.64 **13.48**	5.63 **13.46**	4
5	6.61 **16.26**	5.79 **13.27**	5.41 **12.06**	5.19 **11.39**	5.05 **10.97**	4.95 **10.67**	4.88 **10.45**	4.82 **10.29**	4.78 **10.15**	4.74 **10.05**	4.70 **9.96**	4.68 **9.89**	4.64 **9.77**	4.60 **9.68**	4.56 **9.55**	4.53 **9.47**	4.50 **9.38**	4.46 **9.29**	4.44 **9.24**	4.42 **9.17**	4.40 **9.13**	4.38 **9.07**	4.37 **9.04**	4.36 **9.02**	5
6	5.99 **13.74**	5.14 **10.92**	4.76 **9.78**	4.53 **9.15**	4.39 **8.75**	4.28 **8.47**	4.21 **8.26**	4.15 **8.10**	4.10 **7.98**	4.06 **7.87**	4.03 **7.79**	4.00 **7.72**	3.96 **7.60**	3.92 **7.52**	3.87 **7.39**	3.84 **7.31**	3.81 **7.23**	3.77 **7.14**	3.75 **7.09**	3.72 **7.02**	3.71 **6.99**	3.69 **6.94**	3.68 **6.90**	3.67 **6.88**	6
7	5.59 **12.25**	4.74 **9.55**	4.35 **8.45**	4.12 **7.85**	3.97 **7.46**	3.87 **7.19**	3.79 **7.00**	3.73 **6.84**	3.68 **6.71**	3.63 **6.62**	3.60 **6.54**	3.57 **6.47**	3.52 **6.35**	3.49 **6.27**	3.44 **6.15**	3.41 **6.07**	3.38 **5.98**	3.34 **5.90**	3.32 **5.85**	3.29 **5.78**	3.28 **5.75**	3.25 **5.70**	3.24 **5.67**	3.23 **5.65**	7
8	5.32 **11.26**	4.46 **8.65**	4.07 **7.59**	3.84 **7.01**	3.69 **6.63**	3.58 **6.37**	3.50 **6.19**	3.44 **6.03**	3.39 **5.91**	3.34 **5.82**	3.31 **5.74**	3.28 **5.67**	3.23 **5.56**	3.20 **5.48**	3.15 **5.36**	3.12 **5.28**	3.08 **5.20**	3.05 **5.11**	3.03 **5.06**	3.00 **5.00**	2.98 **4.96**	2.96 **4.91**	2.94 **4.88**	2.93 **4.86**	8
9	5.12 **10.56**	4.26 **8.02**	3.86 **6.99**	3.63 **6.42**	3.48 **6.06**	3.37 **5.80**	3.29 **5.62**	3.23 **5.47**	3.18 **5.35**	3.13 **5.26**	3.10 **5.18**	3.07 **5.11**	3.02 **5.00**	2.98 **4.92**	2.93 **4.80**	2.90 **4.73**	2.86 **4.64**	2.82 **4.56**	2.80 **4.51**	2.77 **4.45**	2.76 **4.41**	2.73 **4.36**	2.72 **4.33**	2.71 **4.31**	9
10	4.96 **10.04**	4.10 **7.56**	3.71 **6.55**	3.48 **5.99**	3.33 **5.64**	3.22 **5.39**	3.14 **5.21**	3.07 **5.06**	3.02 **4.95**	2.97 **4.85**	2.94 **4.78**	2.91 **4.71**	2.86 **4.60**	2.82 **4.52**	2.77 **4.41**	2.74 **4.33**	2.70 **4.25**	2.67 **4.17**	2.64 **4.12**	2.61 **4.05**	2.59 **4.01**	2.56 **3.96**	2.55 **3.93**	2.54 **3.91**	10

* Reproduced with permission from Hoel, P. G.: *Elementary Statistics*, 2nd Ed. New York: John Wiley and Sons, Inc., 1966.

Table A-4. *Continued*

f_1, Degrees of Freedom (for greater mean square)

Each cell gives two values: the upper (5%) and lower (1%) critical values of F.

f_2	1	2	3	4	5	6	7	8	9	10	11	12	14	16	20	24	30	40	50	75	100	200	500	∞
11	4.84 9.65	3.98 7.20	3.59 6.22	3.36 5.67	3.20 5.32	3.09 5.07	3.01 4.88	2.95 4.74	2.90 4.63	2.86 4.54	2.82 4.46	2.79 4.40	2.74 4.29	2.70 4.21	2.65 4.10	2.61 4.02	2.57 3.94	2.53 3.86	2.50 3.80	2.47 3.74	2.45 3.70	2.42 3.66	2.41 3.62	2.40 3.60
12	4.75 9.33	3.88 6.93	3.49 5.95	3.26 5.41	3.11 5.06	3.00 4.82	2.92 4.65	2.85 4.50	2.80 4.39	2.76 4.30	2.72 4.22	2.69 4.16	2.64 4.05	2.60 3.98	2.54 3.86	2.50 3.78	2.46 3.70	2.42 3.61	2.40 3.56	2.36 3.49	2.35 3.46	2.32 3.41	2.31 3.38	2.30 3.36
13	4.67 9.07	3.80 6.70	3.41 5.74	3.18 5.20	3.02 4.86	2.92 4.62	2.84 4.44	2.77 4.30	2.72 4.19	2.67 4.10	2.63 4.02	2.60 3.96	2.55 3.85	2.51 3.78	2.46 3.67	2.42 3.59	2.38 3.51	2.34 3.42	2.32 3.37	2.28 3.30	2.26 3.27	2.24 3.21	2.22 3.18	2.21 3.16
14	4.60 8.86	3.74 6.51	3.34 5.56	3.11 5.03	2.96 4.69	2.85 4.46	2.77 4.28	2.70 4.14	2.65 4.03	2.60 3.94	2.56 3.86	2.53 3.80	2.48 3.70	2.44 3.62	2.39 3.51	2.35 3.43	2.31 3.34	2.27 3.26	2.24 3.21	2.21 3.14	2.19 3.11	2.16 3.06	2.14 3.02	2.13 3.00
15	4.54 8.68	3.68 6.36	3.29 5.42	3.06 4.89	2.90 4.56	2.79 4.32	2.70 4.14	2.64 4.00	2.59 3.89	2.55 3.80	2.51 3.73	2.48 3.67	2.43 3.56	2.39 3.48	2.33 3.36	2.29 3.29	2.25 3.20	2.21 3.12	2.18 3.07	2.15 3.00	2.12 2.97	2.10 2.92	2.08 2.89	2.07 2.87
16	4.49 8.53	3.63 6.23	3.24 5.29	3.01 4.77	2.85 4.44	2.74 4.20	2.66 4.03	2.59 3.89	2.54 3.78	2.49 3.69	2.45 3.61	2.42 3.55	2.37 3.45	2.33 3.37	2.28 3.25	2.24 3.18	2.20 3.10	2.16 3.01	2.13 2.96	2.09 2.91	2.07 2.86	2.04 2.80	2.02 2.77	2.01 2.75
17	4.45 8.40	3.59 6.11	3.20 5.18	2.96 4.67	2.81 4.34	2.70 4.10	2.62 3.93	2.55 3.79	2.50 3.68	2.45 3.59	2.41 3.52	2.38 3.45	2.33 3.35	2.29 3.27	2.23 3.16	2.19 3.08	2.15 3.00	2.11 2.92	2.08 2.86	2.04 2.79	2.02 2.76	1.99 2.70	1.97 2.67	1.96 2.65
18	4.41 8.28	3.55 6.01	3.16 5.09	2.93 4.58	2.77 4.25	2.66 4.01	2.58 3.85	2.51 3.71	2.46 3.60	2.41 3.51	2.37 3.44	2.34 3.37	2.29 3.27	2.25 3.19	2.19 3.07	2.15 3.00	2.11 2.91	2.07 2.83	2.04 2.78	2.00 2.71	1.98 2.68	1.95 2.62	1.93 2.59	1.92 2.57
19	4.38 8.18	3.52 5.93	3.13 5.01	2.90 4.50	2.74 4.17	2.63 3.94	2.55 3.77	2.48 3.63	2.43 3.52	2.38 3.43	2.34 3.36	2.31 3.30	2.26 3.19	2.21 3.12	2.15 3.00	2.11 2.92	2.07 2.84	2.02 2.76	2.00 2.70	1.96 2.63	1.94 2.60	1.91 2.54	1.90 2.51	1.88 2.49
20	4.35 8.10	3.49 5.85	3.10 4.94	2.87 4.43	2.71 4.10	2.60 3.87	2.52 3.71	2.45 3.56	2.40 3.45	2.35 3.37	2.31 3.30	2.28 3.23	2.23 3.13	2.18 3.05	2.12 2.94	2.08 2.86	2.04 2.77	1.99 2.69	1.96 2.63	1.92 2.56	1.90 2.53	1.87 2.47	1.85 2.44	1.84 2.42
21	4.32 8.02	3.47 5.78	3.07 4.87	2.84 4.37	2.68 4.04	2.57 3.81	2.49 3.65	2.42 3.51	2.37 3.40	2.32 3.31	2.28 3.24	2.25 3.17	2.20 3.07	2.15 2.99	2.09 2.88	2.05 2.80	2.00 2.72	1.96 2.63	1.93 2.58	1.89 2.51	1.87 2.47	1.84 2.42	1.82 2.38	1.81 2.36
22	4.30 7.94	3.44 5.72	3.05 4.82	2.82 4.31	2.66 3.99	2.55 3.76	2.47 3.59	2.40 3.45	2.35 3.35	2.30 3.26	2.26 3.18	2.23 3.12	2.18 3.02	2.13 2.94	2.07 2.83	2.03 2.75	1.98 2.67	1.93 2.58	1.91 2.53	1.87 2.46	1.84 2.42	1.81 2.37	1.80 2.33	1.78 2.31
23	4.28 7.88	3.42 5.66	3.03 4.76	2.80 4.26	2.64 3.94	2.53 3.71	2.45 3.54	2.38 3.41	2.32 3.30	2.28 3.21	2.24 3.14	2.20 3.07	2.14 2.97	2.10 2.89	2.04 2.78	2.00 2.70	1.96 2.62	1.91 2.53	1.88 2.48	1.84 2.41	1.82 2.37	1.79 2.32	1.77 2.28	1.76 2.26
24	4.26 7.82	3.40 5.61	3.01 4.72	2.78 4.22	2.62 3.90	2.51 3.67	2.43 3.50	2.36 3.36	2.30 3.25	2.26 3.17	2.22 3.09	2.18 3.03	2.13 2.93	2.09 2.85	2.02 2.74	1.98 2.66	1.94 2.58	1.89 2.49	1.86 2.44	1.82 2.36	1.80 2.33	1.76 2.27	1.74 2.23	1.73 2.21
25	4.24 7.77	3.38 5.57	2.99 4.68	2.76 4.18	2.60 3.86	2.49 3.63	2.41 3.46	2.34 3.32	2.28 3.21	2.24 3.13	2.20 3.05	2.16 2.99	2.11 2.89	2.06 2.81	2.00 2.70	1.96 2.62	1.92 2.54	1.87 2.45	1.84 2.40	1.80 2.32	1.77 2.29	1.74 2.23	1.72 2.19	1.71 2.17

The function, $F = e$ with exponent $2z$, is computed in part from Fisher's table VI (7). Additional entries are by interpolation, mostly graphical.

Table A–4. *Continued*

f_1 Degrees of Freedom (for greater mean square)

f_2	1	2	3	4	5	6	7	8	9	10	11	12	14	16	20	24	30	40	50	75	100	200	500	∞	f_2
26	4.22 7.72	3.37 5.53	2.98 4.64	2.74 4.14	2.59 3.82	2.47 3.59	2.39 3.42	2.32 3.29	2.27 3.17	2.22 3.09	2.18 3.02	2.15 2.96	2.10 2.86	2.05 2.77	1.99 2.66	1.95 2.58	1.90 2.50	1.85 2.41	1.82 2.36	1.78 2.28	1.76 2.25	1.72 2.19	1.70 2.15	1.69 2.13	26
27	4.21 7.68	3.35 5.49	2.96 4.60	2.73 4.11	2.57 3.79	2.46 3.56	2.37 3.39	2.30 3.26	2.25 3.14	2.20 3.06	2.16 2.98	2.13 2.93	2.08 2.83	2.03 2.74	1.97 2.63	1.93 2.55	1.88 2.47	1.84 2.38	1.80 2.33	1.76 2.25	1.74 2.21	1.71 2.16	1.68 2.12	1.67 2.10	27
28	4.20 7.64	3.34 5.45	2.95 4.57	2.71 4.07	2.56 3.76	2.44 3.53	2.36 3.36	2.29 3.23	2.24 3.11	2.19 3.03	2.15 2.95	2.12 2.90	2.06 2.80	2.02 2.71	1.96 2.60	1.91 2.52	1.87 2.44	1.81 2.35	1.78 2.30	1.75 2.22	1.72 2.18	1.69 2.13	1.67 2.09	1.65 2.06	28
29	4.18 7.60	3.33 5.42	2.93 4.54	2.70 4.04	2.54 3.73	2.43 3.50	2.35 3.33	2.28 3.20	2.22 3.08	2.18 3.00	2.14 2.92	2.10 2.87	2.05 2.77	2.00 2.68	1.94 2.57	1.90 2.49	1.85 2.41	1.80 2.32	1.77 2.27	1.73 2.19	1.71 2.15	1.68 2.10	1.65 2.06	1.64 2.03	29
30	4.17 7.56	3.32 5.39	2.92 4.51	2.69 4.02	2.53 3.70	2.42 3.47	2.34 3.30	2.27 3.17	2.21 3.06	2.16 2.98	2.12 2.90	2.09 2.84	2.04 2.74	1.99 2.66	1.93 2.55	1.89 2.47	1.84 2.38	1.79 2.29	1.76 2.24	1.72 2.16	1.69 2.13	1.66 2.07	1.64 2.03	1.62 2.01	30
32	4.15 7.50	3.30 5.34	2.90 4.46	2.67 3.97	2.51 3.66	2.40 3.42	2.32 3.25	2.25 3.12	2.19 3.01	2.14 2.94	2.10 2.86	2.07 2.80	2.02 2.70	1.97 2.62	1.91 2.51	1.86 2.42	1.82 2.34	1.76 2.25	1.74 2.20	1.69 2.12	1.67 2.08	1.64 2.02	1.61 1.98	1.59 1.96	32
34	4.13 7.44	3.28 5.29	2.88 4.42	2.65 3.93	2.49 3.61	2.38 3.38	2.30 3.21	2.23 3.08	2.17 2.97	2.12 2.89	2.08 2.82	2.05 2.76	2.00 2.66	1.95 2.58	1.89 2.47	1.84 2.38	1.80 2.30	1.74 2.21	1.71 2.15	1.67 2.08	1.64 2.04	1.61 1.98	1.59 1.94	1.57 1.91	34
36	4.11 7.39	3.26 5.25	2.86 4.38	2.63 3.89	2.48 3.58	2.36 3.35	2.28 3.18	2.21 3.04	2.15 2.94	2.10 2.86	2.06 2.78	2.03 2.72	1.98 2.62	1.93 2.54	1.87 2.43	1.82 2.35	1.78 2.26	1.72 2.17	1.69 2.12	1.65 2.04	1.62 2.00	1.59 1.94	1.56 1.90	1.55 1.87	36
38	4.10 7.35	3.25 5.21	2.85 4.34	2.62 3.86	2.46 3.54	2.35 3.32	2.26 3.15	2.19 3.02	2.14 2.91	2.09 2.82	2.05 2.75	2.02 2.69	1.96 2.59	1.92 2.51	1.85 2.40	1.80 2.32	1.76 2.22	1.71 2.14	1.67 2.08	1.63 2.00	1.60 1.97	1.57 1.90	1.54 1.86	1.53 1.84	38
40	4.08 7.31	3.23 5.18	2.84 4.31	2.61 3.83	2.45 3.51	2.34 3.29	2.25 3.12	2.18 2.99	2.12 2.88	2.07 2.80	2.04 2.73	2.00 2.66	1.95 2.56	1.90 2.49	1.84 2.37	1.79 2.29	1.74 2.20	1.69 2.11	1.66 2.05	1.61 1.97	1.59 1.94	1.55 1.88	1.53 1.84	1.51 1.81	40
42	4.07 7.27	3.22 5.15	2.83 4.29	2.59 3.80	2.44 3.49	2.32 3.26	2.24 3.10	2.17 2.96	2.11 2.86	2.06 2.77	2.02 2.70	1.99 2.64	1.94 2.54	1.89 2.46	1.82 2.35	1.78 2.26	1.73 2.17	1.68 2.08	1.64 2.02	1.60 1.94	1.57 1.91	1.54 1.85	1.51 1.80	1.49 1.78	42
44	4.06 7.24	3.21 5.12	2.82 4.26	2.58 3.78	2.43 3.46	2.31 3.24	2.23 3.07	2.16 2.94	2.10 2.84	2.05 2.75	2.01 2.68	1.98 2.62	1.92 2.52	1.88 2.44	1.81 2.32	1.76 2.24	1.72 2.15	1.66 2.06	1.63 2.00	1.58 1.92	1.56 1.88	1.52 1.82	1.50 1.78	1.48 1.75	44
46	4.05 7.21	3.20 5.10	2.81 4.24	2.57 3.76	2.42 3.44	2.30 3.22	2.22 3.05	2.14 2.92	2.09 2.82	2.04 2.73	2.00 2.66	1.97 2.60	1.91 2.50	1.87 2.42	1.80 2.30	1.75 2.22	1.71 2.13	1.65 2.04	1.62 1.98	1.57 1.90	1.54 1.86	1.51 1.80	1.48 1.76	1.46 1.72	46
48	4.04 7.19	3.19 5.08	2.80 4.22	2.56 3.74	2.41 3.42	2.30 3.20	2.21 3.04	2.14 2.90	2.08 2.80	2.03 2.71	1.99 2.64	1.96 2.58	1.90 2.48	1.86 2.40	1.79 2.28	1.74 2.20	1.70 2.11	1.64 2.02	1.61 1.96	1.56 1.88	1.53 1.84	1.50 1.78	1.47 1.73	1.45 1.70	48

Table A-4. Continued

f_1 Degrees of Freedom (for greater mean square)

f_2	1	2	3	4	5	6	7	8	9	10	11	12	14	16	20	24	30	40	50	75	100	200	500	∞	f_2
50	4.03/7.17	3.18/5.06	2.79/4.20	2.56/3.72	2.40/3.41	2.29/3.18	2.20/3.02	2.13/2.88	2.07/2.78	2.02/2.70	1.98/2.62	1.95/2.56	1.90/2.46	1.85/2.39	1.78/2.26	1.74/2.18	1.69/2.10	1.63/2.00	1.60/1.94	1.55/1.86	1.52/1.82	1.48/1.76	1.46/1.71	1.44/1.68	50
55	4.02/7.12	3.17/5.01	2.78/4.16	2.54/3.68	2.38/3.37	2.27/3.15	2.18/2.98	2.11/2.85	2.05/2.75	2.00/2.66	1.97/2.59	1.93/2.53	1.88/2.43	1.83/2.35	1.76/2.23	1.72/2.15	1.67/2.06	1.61/1.96	1.58/1.90	1.52/1.82	1.50/1.78	1.46/1.71	1.43/1.66	1.41/1.64	55
60	4.00/7.08	3.15/4.98	2.76/4.13	2.52/3.65	2.37/3.34	2.25/3.12	2.17/2.95	2.10/2.82	2.04/2.72	1.99/2.63	1.95/2.56	1.92/2.50	1.86/2.40	1.81/2.32	1.75/2.20	1.70/2.12	1.65/2.03	1.59/1.93	1.56/1.87	1.50/1.79	1.48/1.74	1.44/1.68	1.41/1.63	1.39/1.60	60
65	3.99/7.04	3.14/4.95	2.75/4.10	2.51/3.62	2.36/3.31	2.24/3.09	2.15/2.93	2.08/2.79	2.02/2.70	1.98/2.61	1.94/2.54	1.90/2.47	1.85/2.37	1.80/2.30	1.73/2.18	1.68/2.09	1.63/2.00	1.57/1.90	1.54/1.84	1.49/1.76	1.45/1.71	1.42/1.64	1.39/1.60	1.37/1.56	65
70	3.98/7.01	3.13/4.92	2.74/4.08	2.50/3.60	2.35/3.29	2.23/3.07	2.14/2.91	2.07/2.77	2.01/2.67	1.97/2.59	1.93/2.51	1.89/2.45	1.84/2.35	1.79/2.28	1.72/2.15	1.67/2.07	1.62/1.98	1.56/1.88	1.53/1.82	1.47/1.74	1.45/1.69	1.40/1.62	1.37/1.56	1.35/1.53	70
80	3.96/6.96	3.11/4.88	2.72/4.04	2.48/3.56	2.33/3.25	2.21/3.04	2.12/2.87	2.05/2.74	1.99/2.64	1.95/2.55	1.91/2.48	1.88/2.41	1.82/2.32	1.77/2.24	1.70/2.11	1.65/2.03	1.60/1.94	1.54/1.84	1.51/1.78	1.45/1.70	1.42/1.65	1.38/1.57	1.35/1.52	1.32/1.49	80
100	3.94/6.90	3.09/4.82	2.70/3.98	2.46/3.51	2.30/3.20	2.19/2.99	2.10/2.82	2.03/2.69	1.97/2.59	1.92/2.51	1.88/2.43	1.85/2.36	1.79/2.26	1.75/2.19	1.68/2.06	1.63/1.98	1.57/1.89	1.51/1.79	1.48/1.73	1.42/1.64	1.39/1.59	1.34/1.51	1.30/1.46	1.28/1.43	100
125	3.92/6.84	3.07/4.78	2.68/3.94	2.44/3.47	2.29/3.17	2.17/2.95	2.08/2.79	2.01/2.65	1.95/2.56	1.90/2.47	1.86/2.40	1.83/2.33	1.77/2.23	1.72/2.15	1.65/2.03	1.60/1.94	1.55/1.85	1.49/1.75	1.45/1.68	1.39/1.59	1.36/1.54	1.31/1.46	1.27/1.40	1.25/1.37	125
150	3.91/6.81	3.06/4.75	2.67/3.91	2.43/3.44	2.27/3.14	2.16/2.92	2.07/2.76	2.00/2.62	1.94/2.53	1.89/2.44	1.85/2.37	1.82/2.30	1.76/2.20	1.71/2.12	1.64/2.00	1.59/1.91	1.54/1.83	1.47/1.72	1.44/1.66	1.37/1.56	1.34/1.51	1.29/1.43	1.25/1.37	1.22/1.33	150
200	3.89/6.76	3.04/4.71	2.65/3.88	2.41/3.41	2.26/3.11	2.14/2.90	2.05/2.73	1.98/2.60	1.92/2.50	1.87/2.41	1.83/2.34	1.80/2.28	1.74/2.17	1.69/2.09	1.62/1.97	1.57/1.88	1.52/1.79	1.45/1.69	1.42/1.62	1.35/1.53	1.32/1.48	1.26/1.39	1.22/1.33	1.19/1.28	200
400	3.86/6.70	3.02/4.66	2.62/3.83	2.39/3.36	2.23/3.06	2.12/2.85	2.03/2.69	1.96/2.55	1.90/2.46	1.85/2.37	1.81/2.29	1.78/2.23	1.72/2.12	1.67/2.04	1.60/1.92	1.54/1.84	1.49/1.74	1.42/1.64	1.38/1.57	1.32/1.47	1.28/1.42	1.22/1.32	1.16/1.24	1.13/1.19	400
1000	3.85/6.66	3.00/4.62	2.61/3.80	2.38/3.34	2.22/3.04	2.10/2.82	2.02/2.66	1.95/2.53	1.89/2.43	1.84/2.34	1.80/2.26	1.76/2.20	1.70/2.09	1.65/2.01	1.58/1.89	1.53/1.81	1.47/1.71	1.41/1.61	1.36/1.54	1.30/1.44	1.26/1.38	1.19/1.28	1.13/1.19	1.08/1.11	1000
∞	3.84/6.64	2.99/4.60	2.60/3.78	2.37/3.32	2.21/3.02	2.09/2.80	2.01/2.64	1.94/2.51	1.88/2.41	1.83/2.32	1.79/2.24	1.75/2.18	1.69/2.07	1.64/1.99	1.57/1.87	1.52/1.79	1.46/1.69	1.40/1.59	1.35/1.52	1.28/1.41	1.24/1.36	1.17/1.25	1.11/1.15	1.00/1.00	∞

Table A–5. DISTRIBUTION OF χ^2 *

The first column contains the number of degrees of freedom (see page 157). The values in the body of the table are the values of χ^2 required for the listed probability levels. For example, a χ^2 of 4.22 with 1 *df* exceeds the tabled value of 3.84 for 1 *df* at the .05 level and would be judged significant at that level.

df	P = .99	.98	.95	.90	.80	.70	.50
1	.00016	.00063	.0039	.016	.064	.15	.46
2	.02	.04	.10	.21	.45	.71	1.39
3	.12	.18	.35	.58	1.00	1.42	2.37
4	.30	.43	.71	1.06	1.65	2.20	3.36
5	.55	.75	1.14	1.61	2.34	3.00	4.35
6	.87	1.13	1.64	2.20	3.07	3.83	5.35
7	1.24	1.56	2.17	2.83	3.82	4.67	6.35
8	1.65	2.03	2.73	3.49	4.59	5.53	7.34
9	2.09	2.53	3.32	4.17	5.38	6.39	8.34
10	2.56	3.06	3.94	4.86	6.18	7.27	9.34
11	3.05	3.61	4.58	5.58	6.99	8.15	10.34
12	3.57	4.18	5.23	6.30	7.81	9.03	11.34
13	4.11	4.76	5.89	7.04	8.63	9.93	12.34
14	4.66	5.37	6.57	7.79	9.47	10.82	13.34
15	5.23	5.98	7.26	8.55	10.31	11.72	14.34
16	5.81	6.61	7.96	9.31	11.15	12.62	15.34
17	6.41	7.26	8.67	10.08	12.00	13.53	16.34
18	7.02	7.91	9.39	10.86	12.86	14.44	17.34
19	7.63	8.57	10.12	11.65	13.72	15.35	18.34
20	8.26	9.24	10.85	12.44	14.58	16.27	19.34
21	8.90	9.92	11.59	13.24	15.44	17.18	20.34
22	9.54	10.60	12.34	14.04	16.31	18.10	21.34
23	10.20	11.29	13.09	14.85	17.19	19.02	22.34
24	10.86	11.99	13.85	15.66	18.06	19.94	23.34
25	11.52	12.70	14.61	16.47	18.94	20.87	24.34
26	12.20	13.41	15.38	17.29	19.82	21.79	25.34
27	12.88	14.12	16.15	18.11	20.70	22.72	26.34
28	13.56	14.85	16.93	18.94	21.59	23.65	27.34
29	14.26	15.57	17.71	19.77	22.48	24.58	28.34
30	14.95	16.31	18.49	20.60	23.36	25.51	29.34

* Reproduced with permission from McNemar, Q.: *Psychological Statistics*, 3rd Ed. New York: John Wiley and Sons, Inc. 1962.

Table A–5. *Continued*

df	.30	.20	.10	.05	.02	.01	.001
1	1.07	1.64	2.71	3.84	5.41	6.64	10.83
2	2.41	3.22	4.60	5.99	7.82	9.21	13.82
3	3.66	4.64	6.25	7.82	9.84	11.34	16.27
4	4.88	5.99	7.78	9.49	11.67	13.28	18.46
5	6.06	7.29	9.24	11.07	13.39	15.09	20.52
6	7.23	8.56	10.64	12.59	15.03	16.81	22.46
7	8.38	9.80	12.02	14.07	16.62	18.48	24.32
8	9.52	11.03	13.36	15.51	18.17	20.09	26.12
9	10.66	12.24	14.68	16.92	19.68	21.67	27.88
10	11.78	13.44	15.99	18.31	21.16	23.21	29.59
11	12.90	14.63	17.28	19.68	22.62	24.72	31.26
12	14.01	15.81	18.55	21.03	24.05	26.22	32.91
13	15.12	16.98	19.81	22.36	25.47	27.69	34.53
14	16.22	18.15	21.06	23.68	26.87	29.14	36.12
15	17.32	19.31	22.31	25.00	28.26	30.58	37.70
16	18.42	20.46	23.54	26.30	29.63	32.00	39.25
17	19.51	21.62	24.77	27.59	31.00	33.41	40.79
18	20.60	22.76	25.99	28.87	32.35	34.80	42.31
19	21.69	23.90	27.20	30.14	33.69	36.19	43.82
20	22.78	25.04	28.41	31.41	35.02	37.57	45.32
21	23.86	26.17	29.62	32.67	36.34	38.93	46.80
22	24.94	27.30	30.81	33.92	37.66	40.29	48.27
23	26.02	28.43	32.01	35.17	38.97	41.64	49.73
24	27.10	29.55	33.20	36.42	40.27	42.98	51.18
25	28.17	30.68	34.38	37.65	41.57	44.31	52.62
26	29.25	31.80	35.56	38.88	42.86	45.64	54.05
27	30.32	32.91	36.74	40.11	44.14	46.96	55.48
28	31.39	34.03	37.92	41.34	45.42	48.28	56.89
29	32.46	35.14	39.09	42.56	46.69	49.59	58.30
30	33.53	36.25	40.26	43.77	47.96	50.89	59.70

Table A–6. CRITICAL VALUES OF r FOR THE SIGN TEST

The number of signs with the smaller number of occurrences is counted (ignoring zero differences), and this number is called r. Values of r are contained in the body of the table. The column headed "N" indicates the total number of observations disregarding the zero differences. For 12 observations with two zero differences, the value of N used would be 10 and r may be no larger than 1 for a difference to be judged significant at the .05 level.

Table A–6. Critical Values of r for the Sign Test*

N	1%	5%	10%	25%	N	1%	5%	10%	25%
1					46	13	15	16	18
2					47	14	16	17	19
3				0	48	14	16	17	19
4				0	49	15	17	18	19
5			0	0	50	15	17	18	20
6		0	0	1	51	15	18	19	20
7		0	0	1	52	16	18	19	21
8	0	0	1	1	53	16	18	20	21
9	0	1	1	2	54	17	19	20	22
10	0	1	1	2	55	17	19	20	22
11	0	1	2	3	56	17	20	21	23
12	1	2	2	3	57	18	20	21	23
13	1	2	3	3	58	18	21	22	24
14	1	2	3	4	59	19	21	22	24
15	2	3	3	4	60	19	21	23	25
16	2	3	4	5	61	20	22	23	25
17	2	4	4	5	62	20	22	24	25
18	3	4	5	6	63	20	23	24	26
19	3	4	5	6	64	21	23	24	26
20	3	5	5	6	65	21	24	25	27
21	4	5	6	7	66	22	24	25	27
22	4	5	6	7	67	22	25	26	28
23	4	6	7	8	68	22	25	26	28
24	5	6	7	8	69	23	25	27	29
25	5	7	7	9	70	23	26	27	29
26	6	7	8	9	71	24	26	28	30
27	6	7	8	10	72	24	27	28	30
28	6	8	9	10	73	25	27	28	31
29	7	8	9	10	74	25	28	29	31
30	7	9	10	11	75	25	28	29	32
31	7	9	10	11	76	26	28	30	32
32	8	9	10	12	77	26	29	30	32
33	8	10	11	12	78	27	29	31	33
34	9	10	11	13	79	27	30	31	33
35	9	11	12	13	80	28	30	32	34
36	9	11	12	14	81	28	31	32	34
37	10	12	13	14	82	28	31	33	35
38	10	12	13	14	83	29	32	33	35
39	11	12	13	15	84	29	32	33	36
40	11	13	14	15	85	30	32	34	36
41	11	13	14	16	86	30	33	34	37
42	12	14	15	16	87	31	33	35	37
43	12	14	15	17	88	31	34	35	38
44	13	15	16	17	89	31	34	36	38
45	13	15	16	18	90	32	35	36	39

For values of N larger than 90, approximate values of r may be found by taking the nearest integer less than $(N - 1)/2 - k \sqrt{N + 1}$, where k is 1.2879, 0.9800, 0.8224, 0.5752 for the 1, 5, 10, 25% values, respectively.

* Reproduced with permission from Dixon, W. J., and Massey, F. J., Jr.: *Introduction to Statistical Analysis*, 2nd Ed. New York: McGraw-Hill, 1957.

Table A–7. Significant Values of U

The value at the top of each column is the number of observations in the larger sample (N_2). The value along the left hand column is the number of observations in the smaller sample. The body of the table contains values of U. For example a U of 4 with $N_1 = 4$ and $N_2 = 11$ is smaller than the tabled value of $U(6)$ at the .05 level and is judged to be significant at the .05 level.

Table A-7. Significant Values of U.*

Two-Tailed Test, $\alpha = .05$

							N_2											
N_1	3	4	5	6	7	8	9	10	11	12	13	14	15	16	17	18	19	20
1	–	–	–	–	–	–	–	–	–	–	–	–	–	–	–	–	–	–
2	–	–	–	–	–	0	0	0	0	1	1	1	1	1	2	2	2	2
3	–	–	0	1	1	2	2	3	3	4	4	5	5	6	6	7	7	8
4		0	1	2	3	4	4	5	6	7	8	9	10	11	11	12	13	13
5			2	3	5	6	7	8	9	11	12	13	14	15	17	18	19	20
6				5	6	8	10	11	13	14	16	17	19	21	22	24	25	27
7					8	10	12	14	16	18	20	22	24	26	28	30	32	34
8						13	15	17	19	22	24	26	29	31	34	36	38	41
9							17	20	23	26	28	31	34	37	39	42	45	48
10								23	26	29	33	36	39	42	45	48	52	55
11									30	33	37	40	44	47	51	55	58	62
12										37	41	45	49	53	57	61	65	69
13											45	50	54	59	63	67	72	76
14												55	59	64	67	74	78	83
15													64	70	75	80	85	90
16														75	81	86	92	98
17															87	93	99	105
18																99	106	112
19																	113	119
20																		127

$z = 1.960$

Two-Tailed Test, $\alpha = .01$

							N_2											
N_1	3	4	5	6	7	8	9	10	11	12	13	14	15	16	17	18	19	20
1	–	–	–	–	–	–	–	–	–	–	–	–	–	–	–	–	–	–
2	–	–	–	–	–	–	–	–	–	–	–	–	–	–	–	–	0	0
3	–	–	–	–	–	–	0	0	0	1	1	1	2	2	2	2	3	3
4		–	–	0	0	1	1	2	2	3	4	4	5	5	6	6	7	8
5			0	1	1	2	3	4	5	6	7	7	8	9	10	11	12	13
6				2	3	4	5	6	7	9	10	11	12	13	15	16	17	18
7					4	6	7	9	10	12	13	15	16	18	19	21	22	24
8						8	10	12	14	16	18	19	21	23	25	27	29	31
9							11	13	16	18	20	22	24	27	29	31	33	36
10								16	18	21	24	26	29	31	34	37	39	42
11									21	24	27	30	33	36	39	42	45	48
12										27	31	34	37	41	44	47	51	54
13											34	38	42	45	49	53	56	60
14												42	46	50	54	58	63	67
15													51	55	60	64	69	73
16														60	65	70	74	79
17															70	75	81	86
18																81	87	92
19																	93	99
20																		105

$z = 2.576$

* Reproduced with permission from Freeman, L. C.: Elementary Applied Statistics. New York, Wiley, 1965.

Table A–8.   VALUES OF H FOR THREE SAMPLES SIGNIFICANT AT THE 10, 5, AND 1 PER CENT SIGNIFICANCE LEVELS

Locate the combination of sample sizes in the left hand columns. The values of H are in the body of the table. To be significant, a value of H must be equal to or larger than the tabled value. For example, with sample sizes of 5, 2, and 1 the value of H must be equal to or greater than the tabled value of 5.00 to be judged significant at the .05 level.

Table A–8. VALUES OF H FOR THREE SAMPLES SIGNIFICANT AT THE 10, 5, AND 1 PER CENT SIGNIFICANCE LEVELS*

	Sample Sizes			Significance Level	
N_1	N_2	N_3	.10	.05	.01
2	2	2	4.57		
3	2	1	4.29		
3	2	2	4.50	4.71	
3	3	1	4.57	5.14	
3	3	2	4.56	5.36	6.25
3	3	3	4.62	5.60	6.49
4	2	1	4.50		
4	2	2	4.46	5.33	
4	3	1	4.06	5.21	
4	3	2	4.51	5.44	6.30
4	3	3	4.70	5.73	6.75
4	4	1	4.17	4.97	6.67
4	4	2	4.55	5.45	6.87
4	4	3	4.55	5.60	7.14
4	4	4	4.65	5.69	7.54
5	2	1	4.20	5.00	
5	2	2	4.37	5.16	6.53
5	3	1	4.02	4.96	
5	3	2	4.49	5.25	6.82
5	3	3	4.53	5.44	6.98
5	4	1	3.99	4.99	6.84
5	4	2	4.52	5.27	7.12
5	4	3	4.55	5.63	7.40
5	4	4	4.62	5.62	7.74
5	5	1	4.11	5.13	6.84
5	5	2	4.51	5.25	7.27
5	5	3	4.55	5.63	7.54
5	5	4	4.52	5.64	7.79
5	5	5	4.56	5.66	7.98

* Reproduced with permission from Tate, M. W., and Clelland, R. C.: *Nonparametric and Shortcut Statistics*. Danville, Ill.: Interstate, 1957.

Table A-9. CRITICAL VALUES OF THE CORRELATION COEFFICIENT*

The number of degrees of freedom are given in the left-hand column. An obtained correlation coefficient must be as large as or larger than the value in the body of the table to be significant at the level of significance stated for the column. For example, an obtained r with $N = 2$ would have a df of 18 and must exceed the tabled value of .444 to be judged significant at the .05 level.

CRITICAL VALUES OF THE CORRELATION COEFFICIENT*

df	Level of significance for two-tailed test			
	.10	.05	.02	.01
1	.988	.997	.9995	.9999
2	.900	.950	.980	.990
3	.805	.878	.934	.959
4	.729	.811	.882	.917
5	.669	.754	.833	.874
6	.622	.707	.789	.834
7	.582	.666	.750	.798
8	.549	.632	.716	.765
9	.521	.602	.685	.735
10	.497	.576	.658	.708
11	.476	.553	.634	.684
12	.458	.532	.612	.661
13	.441	.514	.592	.641
14	.426	.497	.574	.623
15	.412	.482	.558	.606
16	.400	.468	.542	.590
17	.389	.456	.528	.575
18	.378	.444	.516	.561
19	.369	.433	.503	.549
20	.360	.423	.492	.537
21	.352	.413	.482	.526
22	.344	.404	.472	.515
23	.337	.396	.462	.505
24	.330	.388	.453	.496
25	.323	.381	.445	.487
26	.317	.374	.437	.479
27	.311	.367	.430	.471
28	.306	.361	.423	.463
29	.301	.355	.416	.456
30	.296	.349	.409	.449
35	.275	.325	.381	.418
40	.257	.304	.358	.393
45	.243	.288	.338	.372
50	.231	.273	.322	.354
60	.211	.250	.295	.325
70	.195	.232	.274	.303
80	.183	.217	.256	.283
90	.173	.205	.242	.267
100	.164	.195	.230	.254

* Abridged from Fisher, R. A., and Yates, F.: *Statistical Tables for Biological, Agricultural, and Medical Research*, Oliver & Boyd, Ltd., Edinburgh, by pemission of the authors and publisher. Reproduced with permission from Ferguson, G. A.: *Statistical Analysis in Psychology and Education*. New York: McGraw-Hill, 1959.

Table A–11. *Continued*

N	N²	√N̄	√10N̄	N	N²	√N̄	√10N̄
3.00	9.0000	1.73205	5.47723	**3.50**	12.2500	1.87083	5.91608
3.01	9.0601	1.73494	5.48635	3.51	12.3201	1.87350	5.92453
3.02	9.1204	1.73781	5.49545	3.52	12.3904	1.87617	5.93296
3.03	9.1809	1.74069	5.50454	3.53	12.4609	1.87883	5.94138
3.04	9.2416	1.74356	5.51362	3.54	12.5316	1.88149	5.94979
3.05	9.3025	1.74642	5.52268	3.55	12.6025	1.88414	5.95819
3.06	9.3636	1.74929	5.53173	3.56	12.6736	1.88680	5.96657
3.07	9.4249	1.75214	5.54076	3.57	12.7449	1.88944	5.97495
3.08	9.4864	1.75499	5.54977	3.58	12.8164	1.89209	5.98331
3.09	9.5481	1.75784	5.55878	3.59	12.8881	1.89473	5.99166
3.10	9.6100	1.76068	5.56776	**3.60**	12.9600	1.89737	6.00000
3.11	9.6721	1.76352	5.57674	3.61	13.0321	1.90000	6.00833
3.12	9.7344	1.76636	5.58570	3.62	13.1044	1.90263	6.01664
3.13	9.7969	1.76918	5.59464	3.63	13.1769	1.90526	6.02495
3.14	9.8596	1.77200	5.60357	3.64	13.2496	1.90788	6.03324
3.15	9.9225	1.77482	5.61249	3.65	13.3225	1.91050	6.04152
3.16	9.9856	1.77764	5.62139	3.66	13.3956	1.91311	6.04979
3.17	10.0489	1.78045	5.63028	3.67	13.4689	1.91572	6.05805
3.18	10.1124	1.78326	5.63915	3.68	13.5424	1.91833	6.06630
3.19	10.1761	1.78606	5.64801	3.69	13.6161	1.92094	6.07454
3.20	10.2400	1.78885	5.65685	**3.70**	13.6900	1.92354	6.08276
3.21	10.3041	1.79165	5.66569	3.71	13.7641	1.92614	6.09098
3.22	10.3684	1.79444	5.67450	3.72	13.8384	1.92873	6.09918
3.23	10.4329	1.79722	5.68331	3.73	13.9129	1.93132	6.10737
3.24	10.4976	1.80000	5.69210	3.74	13.9876	1.93391	6.11555
3.25	10.5625	1.80278	5.70088	3.75	14.0625	1.93649	6.12372
3.26	10.6276	1.80555	5.70964	3.76	14.1376	1.93907	6.13188
3.27	10.6929	1.80831	5.71839	3.77	14.2129	1.94165	6.14003
3.28	10.7584	1.81108	5.72713	3.78	14.2884	1.94422	6.14817
3.29	10.8241	1.81384	5.73585	3.79	14.3641	1.94679	6.15630
3.30	10.8900	1.81659	5.74456	**3.80**	14.4400	1.94936	6.16441
3.31	10.9561	1.81934	5.75326	3.81	14.5161	1.95192	6.17252
3.32	11.0224	1.82209	5.76194	3.82	14.5924	1.95448	6.18061
3.33	11.0889	1.82483	5.77062	3.83	14.6689	1.95704	6.18870
3.34	11.1556	1.82757	5.77927	3.84	14.7456	1.95959	6.19677
3.35	11.2225	1.83030	5.78792	3.85	14.8225	1.96214	6.20484
3.36	11.2896	1.83303	5.79655	3.86	14.8996	1.96469	6.21289
3.37	11.3569	1.83576	5.80517	3.87	14.9769	1.96723	6.22093
3.38	11.4244	1.83848	5.81378	3.88	15.0544	1.96977	6.22896
3.39	11.4921	1.84120	5.82237	3.89	15.1321	1.97231	6.23699
3.40	11.5600	1.84391	5.83095	**3.90**	15.2100	1.97484	6.24500
3.41	11.6281	1.84662	5.83952	3.91	15.2881	1.97737	6.25300
3.42	11.6964	1.84932	5.84808	3.92	15.3664	1.97990	6.26099
3.43	11.7649	1.85203	5.85662	3.93	15.4449	1.98242	6.26897
3.44	11.8336	1.85472	5.86515	3.94	15.5236	1.98494	6.27694
3.45	11.9025	1.85742	5.87367	3.95	15.6025	1.98746	6.28490
3.46	11.9716	1.86011	5.88218	3.96	15.6816	1.98997	6.29285
3.47	12.0409	1.86279	5.89067	3.97	15.7609	1.99249	6.30079
3.48	12.1104	1.86548	5.89915	3.98	15.8404	1.99499	6.30872
3.49	12.1801	1.86815	5.90762	3.99	15.9201	1.99750	6.31664
3.50	12.2500	1.87083	5.91608	**4.00**	16.0000	2.00000	6.32456
N	N²	√N̄	√10N̄	N	N²	√N̄	√10N̄

Table A–11. *Continued*

N	N²	√N	√10N	N	N²	√N	√10N
4.00	16.0000	2.00000	6.32456	**4.50**	20.2500	2.12132	6.70820
4.01	16.0801	2.00250	6.33246	4.51	20.3401	2.12368	6.71565
4.02	16.1604	2.00499	6.34035	4.52	20.4304	2.12603	6.72309
4.03	16.2409	2.00749	6.34823	4.53	20.5209	2.12838	6.73053
4.04	16.3216	2.00998	6.35610	4.54	20.6116	2.13073	6.73795
4.05	16.4025	2.01246	6.36396	4.55	20.7025	2.13307	6.74537
4.06	16.4836	2.01494	6.37181	4.56	20.7936	2.13542	6.75278
4.07	16.5649	2.01742	6.37966	4.57	20.8849	2.13776	6.76018
4.08	16.6464	2.01990	6.38749	4.58	20.9764	2.14009	6.76757
4.09	16.7281	2.02237	6.39531	4.59	21.0681	2.14243	6.77495
4.10	16.8100	2.02485	6.40312	**4.60**	21.1600	2.14476	6.78233
4.11	16.8921	2.02731	6.41093	4.61	21.2521	2.14709	6.78970
4.12	16.9744	2.02978	6.41872	4.62	21.3444	2.14942	6.79706
4.13	17.0569	2.03224	6.42651	4.63	21.4369	2.15174	6.80441
4.14	17.1396	2.03470	6.43428	4.64	21.5296	2.15407	6.81175
4.15	17.2225	2.03715	6.44205	4.65·	21.6225	2.15639	6.81909
4.16	17.3056	2.03961	6.44981	4.66	21.7156	2.15870	6.82642
4.17	17.3889	2.04206	6.45755	4.67	21.8089	2.16102	6.83374
4.18	17.4724	2.04450	6.46529	4.68	21.9024	2.16333	5.84105
4.19	17.5561	2.04695	6.47302	4.69	21.9961	2.16564	6.84836
4.20	17.6400	2.04939	6.48074	**4.70**	22.0900	2.16795	6.85565
4.21	17.7241	2.05183	6.48845	4.71	22.1841	2.17025	6.86294
4.22	17.8084	2.05426	6.49615	4.72	22.2784	2.17256	6.87023
4.23	17.8929	2.05670	6.50384	4.73	22.3729	2.17486	6.87750
4.24	17.9776	2.05913	6.51153	4.74	22.4676	2.17715	6.88477
4.25	18.0625	2.06155	6.51920	4.75	22.5625	2.17945	6.89202
4.26	18.1476	2.06398	6.52687	4.76	22.6576	2.18174	6.89928
4.27	18.2329	2.06640	6.53452	4.77	22.7529	2.18403	6.90652
4.28	18.3184	2.06882	6.54217	4.78	22.8484	2.18632	6.91375
4.29	18.4041	2.07123	6.54981	4.79	22.9441	2.18861	6.92098
4.30	18.4900	2.07364	6.55744	**4.80**	23.0400	2.19089	6.92820
4.31	18.5761	2.07605	6.56506	4.81	23.1361	2.19317	6.93542
4.32	18.6624	2.07846	6.57267	4.82	23.2324	2.19545	6.94262
4.33	18.7489	2.08087	6.58027	4.83	23.3289	2.19773	6.94982
4.34	18.8356	2.08327	6.58787	4.84	23.4256	2.20000	6.95701
4.35	18.9225	2.08567	6.59545	4.85	23.5225	2.20227	6.96419
4.36	19.0096	2.08806	6.60303	4.86	23.6196	2.20454	6.97137
4.37	19.0969	2.09045	6.61060	4.87	23.7169	2.20681	6.97854
4.38	19.1844	2.09284	6.61816	4.88	23.8144	2.20907	6.98570
4.39	19.2721	2.09523	6.62571	4.89	23.9121	2.21133	6.99285
4.40	19.3600	2.09762	6.63325	**4.90**	24.0100	2.21359	7.00000
4.41	19.4481	2.10000	6.64078	4.91	24.1081	2.21585	7.00714
4.42	19.5364	2.10238	6.64831	4.92	24.2064	2.21811	7.01427
4.43	19.6249	2.10476	6.65582	4.93	24.3049	2.22036	7.02140
4.44	19.7136	2.10713	6.66333	4.94	24.4036	2.22261	7.02851
4.45	19.8025	2.10950	6.67083	4.95	24.5025	2.22486	7.03562
4.46	19.8916	2.11187	6.67832	4.96	24.6016	2.22711	7.04273
4.47	19.9809	2.11424	6.68581	4.97	24.7009	2.22935	7.04982
4.48	20.0704	2.11660	6.69328	4.98	24.8004	2.23159	7.05691
4.49	20.1601	2.11896	6.70075	4.99	24.9001	2.23383	7.06399
4.50	20.2500	2.12132	6.70820	**5.00**	25.0000	2.23607	7.07107
N	N²	√N	√10N	N	N²	√N	√10N

Table A–11. *Continued*

N	N²	√N	√10N	N	N²	√N	√10N
5.00	25.0000	2.23607	7.07107	**5.50**	30.2500	2.34521	7.41620
5.01	25.1001	2.23830	7.07814	5.51	30.3601	2.34734	7.42294
5.02	25.2004	2.24054	7.08520	5.52	30.4704	2.34947	7.42967
5.03	25.3009	2.24277	7.09225	5.53	30.5809	2.35160	7.43640
5.04	25.4016	2.24499	7.09930	5.54	30.6916	2.35372	7.44312
5.05	25.5025	2.24722	7.10634	5.55	30.8025	2.35584	7.44983
5.06	25.6036	2.24944	7.11337	5.56	30.9136	2.35797	7.45654
5.07	25.7049	2.25167	7.12039	5.57	31.0249	2.36008	7.46324
5.08	25.8064	2.25389	7.12741	5.58	31.1364	2.36220	7.46994
5.09	25.9081	2.25610	7.13442	5.59	31.2481	2.36432	7.47663
5.10	26.0100	2.25832	7.14143	**5.60**	31.3600	2.36643	7.48331
5.11	26.1121	2.26053	7.14843	5.61	31.4721	2.36854	7.48999
5.12	26.2144	2.26274	7.15542	5.62	31.5844	2.37065	7.49667
5.13	26.3169	2.26495	7.16240	5.63	31.6969	2.37276	7.50333
5.14	26.4196	2.26716	7.16938	5.64	31.8096	2.37487	7.50999
5.15	26.5225	2.26936	7.17635	5.65	31.9225	2.37697	7.51665
5.16	26.6256	2.27156	7.18331	5.66	32.0356	2.37908	7.52330
5.17	26.7289	2.27376	7.19027	5.67	32.1489	2.38118	7.52994
5.18	26.8324	2.27596	7.19722	5.68	32.2624	2.38328	7.53658
5.19	26.9361	2.27816	7.20417	5.69	32.3761	2.38537	7.54321
5.20	27.0400	2.28035	7.21110	**5.70**	32.4900	2.38747	7.54983
5.21	27.1441	2.28254	7.21803	5.71	32.6041	2.38956	7.55645
5.22	27.2484	2.28473	7.22496	5.72	32.7184	2.39165	7.56307
5.23	27.3529	2.28692	7.23187	5.73	32.8329	2.39374	7.56968
5.24	27.4576	2.28910	7.23878	5.74	32.9476	2.39583	7.57628
5.25	27.5625	2.29129	7.24569	5.75	33.0625	2.39792	7.58288
5.26	27.6676	2.29347	7.25259	5.76	33.1776	2.40000	7.58947
5.27	27.7729	2.29565	7.25948	5.77	33.2929	2.40208	7.59605
5.28	27.8784	2.29783	7.26636	5.78	33.4084	2.40416	7.60263
5.29	27.9841	2.30000	7.27324	5.79	33.5241	2.40624	7.60920
5.30	28.0900	2.30217	7.28011	**5.80**	33.6400	2.40832	7.61577
5.31	28.1961	2.30434	7.28697	5.81	33.7561	2.41039	7.62234
5.32	28.3024	2.30651	7.29383	5.82	33.8724	2.41247	7.62889
5.33	28.4089	2.30868	7.30068	5.83	33.9889	2.41454	7.63544
5.34	28.5156	2.31084	7.30753	5.84	34.1056	2.41661	7.64199
5.35	28.6225	2.31301	7.31437	5.85	34.2225	2.41868	7.64853
5.36	28.7296	2.31517	7.32120	5.86	34.3396	2.42074	7.65506
5.37	28.8369	2.31733	7.32803	5.87	34.4569	2.42281	7.66159
5.38	28.9444	2.31948	7.33485	5.88	34.5744	2.42487	7.66812
5.39	29.0521	2.32164	7.34166	5.89	34.6921	2.42693	7.67463
5.40	29.1600	2.32379	7.34847	**5.90**	34.8100	2.42899	7.68115
5.41	29.2681	2.32594	7.35527	5.91	34.9281	2.43105	7.68765
5.42	29.3764	2.32809	7.36206	5.92	35.0464	2.43311	7.69415
5.43	29.4849	2.33024	7.36885	5.93	35.1649	2.43516	7.70065
5.44	29.5936	2.33238	7.37564	5.94	35.2836	2.43721	7.70714
5.45	29.7025	2.33452	7.38241	5.95	35.4025	2.43926	7.71362
5.46	29.8116	2.33666	7.38918	5.96	35.5216	2.44131	7.72010
5.47	29.9209	2.33880	7.39594	5.97	35.6409	2.44336	7.72658
5.48	30.0304	2.34094	7.40270	5.98	35.7604	2.44540	7.73305
5.49	30.1401	2.34307	7.40945	5.99	35.8801	2.44745	7.73951
5.50	30.2500	2.34521	7.41620	**6.00**	36.0000	2.44949	7.74597
N	N²	√N	√10N	N	N²	√N	√10N

Table A-11. *Continued*

N	N²	√N	√10N	N	N²	√N	√10N
6.00	36.0000	2.44949	7.74597	**6.50**	42.2500	2.54951	8.06226
6.01	36.1201	2.45153	7.75242	6.51	42.3801	2.55147	8.06846
6.02	36.2404	2.45357	7.75887	6.52	42.5104	2.55343	8.07465
6.03	36.3609	2.45561	7.76531	6.53	42.6409	2.55539	8.08084
6.04	36.4816	2.45764	7.77174	6.54	42.7716	2.55734	8.08703
6.05	36.6025	2.45967	7.77817	6.55	42.9025	2.55930	8.09321
6.06	36.7236	2.46171	7.78460	6.56	43.0336	2.56125	8.09938
6.07	36.8449	2.46374	7.79102	6.57	43.1649	2.56320	8.10555
6.08	36.9664	2.46577	7.79744	6.58	43.2964	2.56515	8.11172
6.09	37.0881	2.46779	7.80385	6.59	43.4281	2.56710	8.11788
6.10	37.2100	2.46982	7.81025	**6.60**	43.5600	2.56905	8.12404
6.11	37.3321	2.47184	7.81665	6.61	43.6921	2.57099	8.13019
6.12	37.4544	2.47386	7.82304	6.62	43.8244	2.57294	8.13634
6.13	37.5769	2.47588	7.82943	6.63	43.9569	2.57488	8.14248
6.14	37.6996	2.47790	7.83582	6.64	44.0896	2.57682	8.14862
6.15	37.8225	2.47992	7.84219	6.65	44.2225	2.57876	8.15475
6.16	37.9456	2.48193	7.84857	6.66	44.3556	2.58070	8.16088
6.17	38.0689	2.48395	7.85493	6.67	44.4889	2.58263	8.16701
6.18	38.1924	2.48596	7.86130	6.68	44.6224	2.58457	8.17313
6.19	38.3161	2.48797	7.86766	6.69	44.7561	2.58650	8.17924
6.20	38.4400	2.48998	7.87401	**6.70**	44.8900	2.58844	8.18535
6.21	38.5641	2.49199	7.88036	6.71	45.0241	2.59037	8.19146
6.22	38.6884	2.49399	7.88670	6.72	45.1584	2.59230	8.19756
6.23	38.8129	2.49600	7.89303	6.73	45.2929	2.59422	8.20366
6.24	38.9376	2.49800	7.89937	6.74	45.4276	2.59615	8.20975
6.25	39.0625	2.50000	7.90569	6.75	45.5625	2.59808	8.21584
6.26	39.1876	2.50200	7.91202	6.76	45.6976	2.60000	8.22192
6.27	39.3129	2.50400	7.91833	6.77	45.8329	2.60192	8.22800
6.28	39.4384	2.50599	7.92465	6.78	45.9684	2.60384	8.23408
6.29	39.5641	2.50799	7.93095	6.79	46.1041	2.60576	8.24015
6.30	39.6900	2.50998	7.93725	**6.80**	46.2400	2.60768	8.24621
6.31	39.8161	2.51197	7.94355	6.81	46.3761	2.60960	8.25227
6.32	39.9424	2.51396	7.94984	6.82	46.5124	2.61151	8.25833
6.33	40.0689	2.51595	7.95613	6.83	46.6489	2.61343	8.26438
6.34	40.1956	2.51794	7.96241	6.84	46.7856	2.61534	8.27043
6.35	40.3225	2.51992	7.96869	6.85	46.9225	2.61725	8.27647
6.36	40.4496	2.52190	7.97496	6.86	47.0596	2.61916	8.28251
6.37	40.5769	2.52389	7.98123	6.87	47.1969	2.62107	8.28855
6.38	40.7044	2.52587	7.98749	6.88	47.3344	2.62298	8.29458
6.39	40.8321	2.52784	7.99375	6.89	47.4721	2.62488	8.30060
6.40	40.9600	2.52982	8.00000	**6.90**	47.6100	2.62679	8.30662
6.41	41.0881	2.53180	8.00625	6.91	47.7481	2.62869	8.31264
6.42	41.2164	2.53377	8.01249	6.92	47.8864	2.63059	8.31865
6.43	41.3449	2.53574	8.01873	6.93	48.0249	2.63249	8.32466
6.44	41.4736	2.53772	8.02496	6.94	48.1636	2.63439	8.33067
6.45	41.6025	2.53969	8.03119	6.95	48.3025	2.63629	8.33667
6.46	41.7316	2.54165	8.03741	6.96	48.4416	2.63818	8.34266
6.47	41.8609	2.54362	8.04363	6.97	48.5809	2.64008	8.34865
6.48	41.9904	2.54558	8.04984	6.98	48.7204	2.64197	8.35464
6.49	42.1201	2.54755	8.05605	6.99	48.8601	2.64386	8.36062
6.50	42.2500	2.54951	8.06226	**7.00**	49.0000	2.64575	8.36660
N	**N²**	**√N**	**√10N**	**N**	**N²**	**√N**	**√10N**

Table A-11. *Continued*

N	N²	√N	√10N	N	N²	√N	√10N
7.00	49.0000	2.64575	8.36660	**7.50**	56.2500	2.73861	8.66025
7.01	49.1401	2.64764	8.37257	7.51	56.4001	2.74044	8.66603
7.02	49.2804	2.64953	8.37854	7.52	56.5504	2.74226	8.67179
7.03	49.4209	2.65141	8.38451	7.53	56.7009	2.74408	8.67756
7.04	49.5616	2.65330	8.39047	7.54	56.8516	2.74591	8.68332
7.05	49.7025	2.65518	8.39643	7.55	57.0025	2.74773	8.68907
7.06	49.8436	2.65707	8.40238	7.56	57.1536	2.74955	8.69483
7.07	49.9849	2.65895	8.40833	7.57	57.3049	2.75136	8.70057
7.08	50.1264	2.66083	8.41427	7.58	57.4564	2.75318	8.70632
7.09	50.2681	2.66271	8.42021	7.59	57.6081	2.75500	8.71206
7.10	50.4100	2.66458	8.42615	**7.60**	57.7600	2.75681	8.71780
7.11	50.5521	2.66646	8.43208	7.61	57.9121	2.75862	8.72353
7.12	50.6944	2.66833	8.43801	7.62	58.0644	2.76043	8.72926
7.13	50.8369	2.67021	8.44393	7.63	58.2169	2.76225	8.73499
7.14	50.9796	2.67208	8.44985	7.64	58.3696	2.76405	8.74071
7.15	51.1225	2.67395	8.45577	7.65	58.5225	2.76586	8.74643
7.16	51.2656	2.67582	8.46168	7.66	58.6756	2.76767	8.75214
7.17	51.4089	2.67769	8.46759	7.67	58.8289	2.76948	8.75785
7.18	51.5524	2.67955	8.47349	7.68	58.9824	2.77128	8.76356
7.19	51.6961	2.68142	8.47939	7.69	59.1361	2.77308	8.76926
7.20	51.8400	2.68328	8.48528	**7.70**	59.2900	2.77489	8.77496
7.21	51.9841	2.68514	8.49117	7.71	59.4441	2.77669	8.78066
7.22	52.1284	2.68701	8.49706	7.72	59.5984	2.77849	8.78635
7.23	52.2729	2.68887	8.50294	7.73	59.7529	2.78029	8.79204
7.24	52.4176	2.69072	8.50882	7.74	59.9076	2.78209	8.79773
7.25	52.5625	2.69258	8.51469	7.75	60.0625	2.78388	8.80341
7.26	52.7076	2.69444	8.52056	7.76	60.2176	2.78568	8.80909
7.27	52.8529	2.69629	8.52643	7.77	60.3729	2.78747	8.81476
7.28	52.9984	2.69815	8.53229	7.78	60.5284	2.78927	8.82043
7.29	53.1441	2.70000	8.53815	7.79	60.6841	2.79106	8.82610
7.30	53.2900	2.70185	8.54400	**7.80**	60.8400	2.79285	8.83176
7.31	53.4361	2.70370	8.54985	7.81	60.9961	2.79464	8.83742
7.32	53.5824	2.70555	8.55570	7.82	61.1524	2.79643	8.84308
7.33	53.7289	2.70740	8.56154	7.83	61.3089	2.79821	8.84873
7.34	53.8756	2.70924	8.56738	7.84	61.4656	2.80000	8.85438
7.35	54.0225	2.71109	8.57321	7.85	61.6225	2.80179	8.86002
7.36	54.1696	2.71293	8.57904	7.86	61.7796	2.80357	8.86566
7.37	54.3169	2.71477	8.58487	7.87	61.9369	2.80535	8.87130
7.38	54.4644	2.71662	8.59069	7.88	62.0944	2.80713	8.87694
7.39	54.6121	2.71846	8.59651	7.89	62.2521	2.80891	8.88257
7.40	54.7600	2.72029	8.60233	**7.90**	62.4100	2.81069	8.88819
7.41	54.9081	2.72213	8.60814	7.91	62.5681	2.81247	8.89382
7.42	55.0564	2.72397	8.61394	7.92	62.7264	2.81425	8.89944
7.43	55.2049	2.72580	8.61974	7.93	62.8849	2.81603	8.90505
7.44	55.3536	2.72764	8.62554	7.94	63.0436	2.81780	8.91067
7.45	55.5025	2.72947	8.63134	7.95	63.2025	2.81957	8.91628
7.46	55.6516	2.73130	8.63713	7.96	63.3616	2.82135	8.92188
7.47	55.8009	2.73313	8.64292	7.97	63.5209	2.82312	8.92749
7.48	55.9504	2.73496	8.64870	7.98	63.6804	2.82489	8.93308
7.49	56.1001	2.73679	8.65448	7.99	63.8401	2.82666	8.93868
7.50	56.2500	2.73861	8.66025	**8.00**	64.0000	2.82843	8.94427
N	N²	√N	√10N	N	N²	√N	√10N

Table A–11. *Continued*

N	N²	√N	√10N	N	N²	√N	√10N
8.00	64.0000	2.82843	8.94427	**8.50**	72.2500	2.91548	9.21954
8.01	64.1601	2.83019	8.94986	8.51	72.4201	2.91719	9.22497
8.02	64.3204	2.83196	8.95545	8.52	72.5904	2.91890	9.23038
8.03	64.4809	2.83373	8.96103	8.53	72.7609	2.92062	9.23580
8.04	64.6416	2.83549	8.96660	8.54	72.9316	2.92233	9.24121
8.05	64.8025	2.83725	8.97218	8.55	73.1025	2.92404	9.24662
8.06	64.9636	2.83901	8.97775	8.56	73.2736	2.92575	9.25203
8.07	65.1249	2.84077	8.98332	8.57	73.4449	2.92746	9.25743
8.08	65.2864	2.84253	8.98888	8.58	73.6164	2.92916	9.26283
8.09	65.4481	2.84429	8.99444	8.59	73.7881	2.93087	9.26823
8.10	65.6100	2.84605	9.00000	**8.60**	73.9600	2.93258	9.27362
8.11	65.7721	2.84781	9.00555	8.61	74.1321	2.93428	9.27901
8.12	65.9344	2.84956	9.01110	8.62	74.3044	2.93598	9.28440
8.13	66.0969	2.85132	9.01665	8.63	74.4769	2.93769	9.28978
8.14	66.2596	2.85307	9.02219	8.64	74.6496	2.93939	9.29516
8.15	66.4225	2.85482	9.02774	8.65	74.8225	2.94109	9.30054
8.16	66.5856	2.85657	9.03327	8.66	74.9956	2.94279	9.30591
8.17	66.7489	2.85832	9.03881	8.67	75.1689	2.94449	9.31128
8.18	66.9124	2.86007	9.04434	8.68	75.3424	2.94618	9.31665
8.19	67.0761	2.86182	9.04986	8.69	75.5161	2.94788	9.32202
8.20	67.2400	2.86356	9.05539	**8.70**	75.6900	2.94958	9.32738
8.21	67.4041	2.86531	9.06091	8.71	75.8641	2.95127	9.33274
8.22	67.5684	2.86705	9.06642	8.72	76.0384	2.95296	9.33809
8.23	67.7329	2.86880	9.07193	8.73	76.2129	2.95466	9.34345
8.24	67.8976	2.87054	9.07744	8.74	76.3876	2.95635	9.34880
8.25	68.0625	2.87228	9.08295	8.75	76.5625	2.95804	9.35414
8.26	68.2276	2.87402	9.08845	8.76	76.7376	2.95973	9.35949
8.27	68.3929	2.87576	9.09395	8.77	76.9129	2.96142	9.36483
8.28	68.5584	2.87750	9.09945	8.78	77.0884	2.96311	9.37017
8.29	68.7241	2.87924	9.10494	8.79	77.2641	2.96479	9.37550
8.30	68.8900	2.88097	9.11043	**8.80**	77.4400	2.96648	9.38083
8.31	69.0561	2.88271	9.11592	8.81	77.6161	2.96816	9.38616
8.32	69.2224	2.88444	9.12140	8.82	77.7924	2.96985	9.39149
8.33	69.3889	2.88617	9.12688	8.83	77.9689	2.97153	9.39681
8.34	69.5556	2.88791	9.13236	8.84	78.1456	2.97321	9.40213
8.35	69.7225	2.88964	9.13783	8.85	78.3225	2.97489	9.40744
8.36	69.8896	2.89137	9.14330	8.86	78.4996	2.97658	9.41276
8.37	70.0569	2.89310	9.14877	8.87	78.6769	2.97825	9.41807
8.38	70.2244	2.89482	9.15423	8.88	78.8544	2.97993	9.42338
8.39	70.3921	2.89655	9.15969	8.89	79.0321	2.98161	9.42868
8.40	70.5600	2.89828	9.16515	**8.90**	79.2100	2.98329	9.43398
8.41	70.7281	2.90000	9.17061	8.91	79.3881	2.98496	9.43928
8.42	70.8964	2.90172	9.17606	8.92	79.5664	2.98664	9.44458
8.43	71.0649	2.90345	9.18150	8.93	79.7449	2.98831	9.44987
8.44	71.2336	2.90517	9.18695	8.94	79.9236	2.98998	9.45516
8.45	71.4025	2.90689	9.19239	8.95	80.1025	2.99166	9.46044
8.46	71.5716	2.90861	9.19783	8.96	80.2816	2.99333	9.46573
8.47	71.7409	2.91033	9.20326	8.97	80.4609	2.99500	9.47101
8.48	71.9104	2.91204	9.20869	8.98	80.6404	2.99666	9.47629
8.49	72.0801	2.91376	9.21412	8.99	80.8201	2.99833	9.48156
8.50	72.2500	2.91548	9.21954	**9.00**	81.0000	3.00000	9.48683
N	N²	√N	√10N	N	N²	√N	√10N

Table A–11. *Continued*

N	N²	√N	√10N	N	N²	√N	√10N
9.00	81.0000	3.00000	9.48683	**9.50**	90.2500	3.08221	9.74679
9.01	81.1801	3.00167	9.49210	9.51	90.4401	3.08383	9.75192
9.02	81.3604	3.00333	9.49737	9.52	90.6304	3.08545	9.75705
9.03	81.5409	3.00500	9.50263	9.53	90.8209	3.08707	9.76217
9.04	81.7216	3.00666	9.50789	9.54	91.0116	3.08869	9.76729
9.05	81.9025	3.00832	9.51315	9.55	91.2025	3.09031	9.77241
9.06	82.0836	3.00998	9.51840	9.56	91.3936	3.09192	9.77753
9.07	82.2649	3.01164	9.52365	9.57	91.5849	3.09354	9.78264
9.08	82.4464	3.01330	9.52890	9.58	91.7764	3.09516	9.78775
9.09	82.6281	3.01496	9.53415	9.59	91.9681	3.09677	9.79285
9.10	82.8100	3.01662	9.53939	**9.60**	92.1600	3.09839	9.79796
9.11	82.9921	3.01828	9.54463	9.61	92.3521	3.10000	9.80306
9.12	83.1744	3.01993	9.54987	9.62	92.5444	3.10161	9.80816
9.13	83.3569	3.02159	9.55510	9.63	92.7369	3.10322	9.81326
9.14	83.5396	3.02324	9.56033	9.64	92.9296	3.10483	9.81835
9.15	83.7225	3.02490	9.56556	9.65	93.1225	3.10644	9.82344
9.16	83.9056	3.02655	9.57079	9.66	93.3156	3.10805	9.82853
9.17	84.0889	3.02820	9.57601	9.67	93.5089	3.10966	9.83362
9.18	84.2724	3.02985	9.58123	9.68	93.7024	3.11127	9.83870
9.19	84.4561	3.03150	9.58645	9.69	93.8961	3.11288	9.84378
9.20	84.6400	3.03315	9.59166	**9.70**	94.0900	3.11448	9.84886
9.21	84.8241	3.03480	9.59687	9.71	94.2841	3.11609	9.85393
9.22	85.0084	3.03645	9.60208	9.72	94.4784	3.11769	9.85901
9.23	85.1929	3.03809	9.60729	9.73	94.6729	3.11929	9.86408
9.24	85.3776	3.03974	9.61249	9.74	94.8676	3.12090	9.86914
9.25	85.5625	3.04138	9.61769	9.75	95.0625	3.12250	9.87421
9.26	85.7476	3.04302	9.62289	9.76	95.2576	3.12410	9.87927
9.27	85.9329	3.04467	9.62808	9.77	95.4529	3.12570	9.88433
9.28	86.1184	3.04631	9.63328	9.78	95.6484	3.12730	9.88939
9.29	86.3041	3.04795	9.63846	9.79	95.8441	3.12890	9.89444
9.30	86.4900	3.04959	9.64365	**9.80**	96.0400	3.13050	9.89949
9.31	86.6761	3.05123	9.64883	9.81	96.2361	3.13209	9.90454
9.32	86.8624	3.05287	9.65401	9.82	96.4324	3.13369	9.90959
9.33	87.0489	3.05450	9.65919	9.83	96.6289	3.13528	9.91464
9.34	87.2356	3.05614	9.66437	9.84	96.8256	3.13688	9.91968
9.35	87.4225	3.05778	9.66954	9.85	97.0225	3.13847	9.92472
9.36	87.6096	3.05941	9.67471	9.86	97.2196	3.14006	9.92975
9.37	87.7969	3.06105	9.67988	9.87	97.4169	3.14166	9.93479
9.38	87.9844	3.06268	9.68504	9.88	97.6144	3.14325	9.93982
9.39	88.1721	3.06431	9.69020	9.89	97.8121	3.14484	9.94485
9.40	88.3600	3.06594	9.69536	**9.90**	98.0100	3.14643	9.94987
9.41	88.5481	3.06757	9.70052	9.91	98.2081	3.14802	9.95490
9.42	88.7364	3.06920	9.70567	9.92	98.4064	3.14960	9.95992
9.43	88.9249	3.07083	9.71082	9.93	98.6049	3.15119	9.96494
9.44	89.1136	3.07246	9.71597	9.94	98.8036	3.15278	9.96995
9.45	89.3025	3.07409	9.72111	9.95	99.0025	3.15436	9.97497
9.46	89.4916	3.07571	9.72625	9.96	99.2016	3.15595	9.97998
9.47	89.6809	3.07734	9.73139	9.97	99.4009	3.15753	9.98499
9.48	89.8704	3.07896	9.73653	9.98	99.6004	3.15911	9.98999
9.49	90.0601	3.08058	9.74166	9.99	99.8001	3.16070	9.99500
9.50	90.2500	3.08221	9.74679	**10.00**	100.000	3.16228	10.0000
N	**N²**	**√N**	**√10N**	**N**	**N²**	**√N**	**√10N**

Table A–12. RECIPROCALS

The reciprocal of any number between 1.00 and 9.99 may be found in the table. For larger and smaller numbers use the following guide to determine placement of the decimal point.

N	$Reciprocal\ \dfrac{1}{N}$
3160	.00031646
316	.0031646
31.6	.031646
3.16	.31646
.316	3.1646

Table A-12. RECIPROCALS*

	0	1	2	3	4	5	6	7	8	9
1.00	1.00000	.99900	.99800	.99701	.99602	.99502	.99404	.99305	.99206	.99108
1.01	.99010	.98912	.98814	.98717	.98619	.98522	.98425	.98328	.98232	.98135
1.02	.98039	.97943	.97847	.97752	.97656	.97561	.97466	.97371	.97276	.97182
1.03	.97087	.96993	.96899	.96805	.96712	.96618	.96525	.96432	.96339	.96246
1.04	.96154	.96061	.95969	.95877	.95785	.95694	.95602	.95511	.95420	.95329
1.05	.95238	.95147	.95057	.94967	.94877	.94787	.94697	.94607	.94518	.94429
1.06	.94340	.94251	.94162	.94073	.93985	.93897	.93809	.93721	.93633	.93545
1.07	.93458	.93371	.93284	.93197	.93110	.93023	.92937	.92851	.92764	.92678
1.08	.92593	.92507	.92421	.92336	.92251	.92166	.92081	.91996	.91912	.91827
1.09	.91743	.91659	.91575	.91491	.91408	.91324	.91241	.91158	.91075	.90992
1.1	.90909	.90090	.89286	.88496	.87719	.86957	.86207	.85470	.84746	.84034
1.2	.83333	.82645	.81967	.81301	.80645	.80000	.79365	.78740	.78125	.77519
1.3	.76923	.76336	.75758	.75188	.74627	.74074	.73529	.72993	.72464	.71942
1.4	.71429	.70922	.70423	.69930	.69444	.68966	.68493	.68027	.67568	.67114
1.5	.66667	.66225	.65789	.65359	.64935	.64516	.64103	.63694	.63291	.62893
1.6	.62500	.62112	.61728	.61350	.60976	.60606	.60241	.59880	.59524	.59172
1.7	.58824	.58480	.58140	.57803	.57471	.57143	.56818	.56497	.56180	.55866
1.8	.55556	.55249	.54945	.54645	.54348	.54054	.53763	.53476	.53191	.52910
1.9	.52632	.52356	.52083	.51813	.51546	.51282	.51020	.50761	.50505	.50251
2.0	.50000	.49751	.49505	.49261	.49020	.48780	.48544	.48309	.48077	.47847
2.1	.47619	.47393	.47170	.46948	.46729	.46512	.46296	.46083	.45872	.45662
2.2	.45455	.45249	.45045	.44843	.44643	.44444	.44248	.44053	.43860	.43668
2.3	.43478	.43290	.43103	.42918	.42735	.42553	.42373	.42194	.42017	.41841
2.4	.41667	.41494	.41322	.41152	.40984	.40816	.40650	.40486	.40323	.40161
2.5	.40000	.39841	.39683	.39526	.39370	.39216	.39063	.38911	.38760	.38610
2.6	.38462	.38314	.38168	.38023	.37879	.37736	.37594	.37453	.37313	.37175
2.7	.37037	.36900	.36765	.36630	.36496	.36364	.36232	.36101	.35971	.35842
2.8	.35714	.35587	.35461	.35336	.35211	.35088	.34965	.34843	.34722	.34602
2.9	.34483	.34364	.34247	.34130	.34014	.33898	.33784	.33670	.33557	.33445
3.0	.33333	.33223	.33113	.33003	.32895	.32787	.32680	.32573	.32468	.32362
3.1	.32258	.32154	.32051	.31949	.31847	.31746	.31646	.31546	.31447	.31348
3.2	.31250	.31153	.31056	.30960	.30864	.30769	.30675	.30581	.30488	.30395
3.3	.30303	.30211	.30120	.30030	.29940	.29851	.29762	.29674	.29586	.29499
3.4	.29412	.29326	.29240	.29155	.29070	.28986	.28902	.28818	.28736	.28653
3.5	.28571	.28490	.28409	.28329	.28249	.28169	.28090	.28011	.27933	.27855
3.6	.27778	.27701	.27624	.27548	.27473	.27397	.27322	.27248	.27174	.27100
3.7	.27027	.26954	.26882	.26810	.26738	.26667	.26596	.26525	.26455	.26385
3.8	.26316	.26247	.26178	.26110	.26042	.25974	.25907	.25840	.25773	.25707
3.9	.25641	.25575	.25510	.25445	.25381	.25316	.25253	.25189	.25126	.25063
4.0	.25000	.24938	.24876	.24814	.24752	.24691	.24631	.24570	.24510	.24450
4.1	.24390	.24331	.24272	.24213	.24155	.24096	.24038	.23981	.23923	.23866
4.2	.23810	.23753	.23697	.23641	.23585	.23529	.23474	.23419	.23364	.23310
4.3	.23256	.23202	.23148	.23095	.23041	.22989	.22936	.22883	.22831	.22779
4.4	.22727	.22676	.22624	.22573	.22523	.22472	.22422	.22371	.22321	.22272
4.5	.22222	.22173	.22124	.22075	.22026	.21978	.21930	.21882	.21834	.21786
4.6	.21739	.21692	.21645	.21598	.21552	.21505	.21459	.21413	.21368	.21322
4.7	.21277	.21231	.21186	.21142	.21097	.21053	.21008	.20964	.20921	.20877
4.8	.20833	.20790	.20747	.20704	.20661	.20619	.20576	.20534	.20492	.20450
4.9	.20408	.20367	.20325	.20284	.20243	.20202	.20161	.20121	.20080	.20040

* Reproduced with permission from Dixon, W. J., and Massey, F. J., Jr.: *Introduction to Statistical Analysis*, 2nd Ed. New York: McGraw-Hill, 1957.

Table A–12. *Continued*

	0	1	2	3	4	5	6	7	8	9
5.0	.20000	.19960	.19920	.19881	.19841	.19802	.19763	.19724	.19685	.19646
5.1	.19608	.19569	.19531	.19493	.19455	.19417	.19380	.19342	.19305	.19268
5.2	.19231	.19194	.19157	.19120	.19084	.19048	.19011	.18975	.18939	.18904
5.3	.18868	.18832	.18797	.18762	.18727	.18692	.18657	.18622	.18587	.18553
5.4	.18519	.18484	.18450	.18416	.18382	.18349	.18315	.18282	.18248	.18215
5.5	.18182	.18149	.18116	.18083	.18051	.18018	.17986	.17953	.17921	.17889
5.6	.17857	.17825	.17794	.17762	.17731	.17699	.17668	.17637	.17606	.17575
5.7	.17544	.17513	.17483	.17452	.17422	.17391	.17361	.17331	.17301	.17271
5.8	.17241	.17212	.17182	.17153	.17123	.17094	.17065	.17036	.17007	.16978
5.9	.16949	.16920	.16892	.16863	.16835	.16807	.16779	.16750	.16722	.16694
6.0	.16667	.16639	.16611	.16584	.16556	.16529	.16502	.16474	.16447	.16420
6.1	.16393	.16367	.16340	.16313	.16287	.16260	.16234	.16207	.16181	.16155
6.2	.16129	.16103	.16077	.16051	.16026	.16000	.15974	.15949	.15924	.15898
6.3	.15873	.15848	.15823	.15798	.15773	.15748	.15723	.15699	.15674	.15649
6.4	.15625	.15601	.15576	.15552	.15528	.15504	.15480	.15456	.15432	.15408
6.5	.15385	.15361	.15337	.15314	.15291	.15267	.15244	.15221	.15198	.15175
6.6	.15152	.15129	.15106	.15083	.15060	.15038	.15015	.14993	.14970	.14948
6.7	.14925	.14903	.14881	.14859	.14837	.14815	.14793	.14771	.14749	.14728
6.8	.14706	.14684	.14663	.14641	.14620	.14599	.14577	.14556	.14535	.14514
6.9	.14493	.14472	.14451	.14430	.14409	.14388	.14368	.14347	.14327	.14306
7.0	.14286	.14265	.14245	.14225	.14205	.14184	.14164	.14144	.14124	.14104
7.1	.14085	.14065	.14045	.14025	.14006	.13986	.13966	.13947	.13928	.13908
7.2	.13889	.13870	.13850	.13831	.13812	.13793	.13774	.13755	.13736	.13717
7.3	.13699	.13680	.13661	.13643	.13624	.13605	.13587	.13569	.13550	.13532
7.4	.13514	.13495	.13477	.13459	.13441	.13423	.13405	.13387	.13369	.13351
7.5	.13333	.13316	.13298	.13280	.13263	.13245	.13228	.13210	.13193	.13175
7.6	.13158	.13141	.13123	.13106	.13089	.13072	.13055	.13038	.13021	.13004
7.7	.12987	.12970	.12953	.12937	.12920	.12903	.12887	.12870	.12853	.12837
7.8	.12821	.12804	.12788	.12771	.12755	.12739	.12723	.12706	.12690	.12674
7.9	.12658	.12642	.12626	.12610	.12594	.12579	.12563	.12547	.12531	.12516
8.0	.12500	.12484	.12469	.12453	.12438	.12422	.12407	.12392	.12376	.12361
8.1	.12346	.12330	.12315	.12300	.12285	.12270	.12255	.12240	.12225	.12210
8.2	.12195	.12180	.12165	.12151	.12136	.12121	.12107	.12092	.12077	.12063
8.3	.12048	.12034	.12019	.12005	.11990	.11976	.11962	.11947	.11933	.11919
8.4	.11905	.11891	.11876	.11862	.11848	.11834	.11820	.11806	.11792	.11779
8.5	.11765	.11751	.11737	.11723	.11710	.11696	.11682	.11669	.11655	.11641
8.6	.11628	.11614	.11601	.11587	.11574	.11561	.11547	.11534	.11521	.11507
8.7	.11494	.11481	.11468	.11455	.11442	.11429	.11416	.11403	.11390	.11377
8.8	.11364	.11351	.11338	.11325	.11312	.11299	.11287	.11274	.11261	.11249
8.9	.11236	.11223	.11211	.11198	.11186	.11173	.11161	.11148	.11136	.11123
9.0	.11111	.11099	.11086	.11074	.11062	.11050	.11038	.11025	.11013	.11001
9.1	.10989	.10977	.10965	.10953	.10941	.10929	.10917	.10905	.10893	.10881
9.2	.10870	.10858	.10846	.10834	.10823	.10811	.10799	.10787	.10776	.10764
9.3	.10753	.10741	.10730	.10718	.10707	.10695	.10684	.10672	.10661	.10650
9.4	.10638	.10627	.10616	.10604	.10593	.10582	.10571	.10560	.10549	.10537
9.5	.10526	.10515	.10504	.10493	.10482	.10471	.10460	.10449	.10438	.10428
9.6	.10417	.10406	.10395	.10384	.10373	.10363	.10352	.10341	.10331	.10320
9.7	.10309	.10299	.10288	.10277	.10267	.10256	.10246	.10235	.10225	.10215
9.8	.10204	.10194	.10183	.10173	.10163	.10152	.10142	.10132	.10121	.10111
9.9	.10101	.10091	.10081	.10070	.10060	.10050	.10040	.10030	.10020	.10010

Appendix III

ANSWERS TO ODD-NUMBERED EXERCISES

Chapter 3

1. 18.0.
3. (a) $\bar{X} = 17.4$; Median $= 13.5$.
   (b) Median. The distribution is positively skewed. As a result the mean is located considerably above the center of the distribution.
5. Zero. $\sum x = 0$.
7. Mean; Median; Mode.
9. 22.5.

Chapter 4

1. (a) 51.33.
   (b) $\sum x^2 = 458.9$; $s^2 = 65.56$; $s = 8.10$.
3. 61.
5. A.D. $= 6.2$.
7. 83.2.
9. 70.24 and 49.76.

Chapter 5

1. .0156.
3. 252.
5. About 7.

7. (a) 44.52.
   (b) 52.68.

Chapter 6

1. 71.66 and 78.34.
3. (a) 0.2.
   (b) 90.8 and 93.2.
   (c) 91.8 and 92.2.
5. (a) .40.
   (b) 20.32 and 21.88.
   (c) 20.07 and 22.13.
7. .678.
9. 77.4 and 116.6.

Chapter 7

1. $t = 1.87$; 8 df; $p > .05$; No.
3. $t = 4.22$.
5. $t = 2.98$; 9 df; $p > .05$; No.
7. (a) No.
   (b) That $\mu = 50$.
   (c) .05
   (d) .9004.
   (e) .0996.

Chapter 8

1.

Source	$\sum x^2$	df	Mean Sq.	F	p
Between groups	103.9	2	51.95	13.32	$<.01$
Within groups	39.0	10	3.90		
Total	142.9	12			

Yes

3.

Source	$\sum x^2$	df	M	F	p
Between groups	662.2	4	165.6	15.6	$<.01$
Within groups	275.7	26	10.6		
Total	837.9	30			

Yes

Chapter 9

1. $\chi^2 = 4.90$; 5 df; $p > .05$; Yes.
3. $\chi^2 = 4.70$; 1 df; $p < .05$; No.

5. $z = 2.17$; $p < .05$; No.

7. $\chi^2 = 3.95$; 1 df; $p < .05$; No.

Chapter 10

1. $N = 9$; $p = .25$; No.

3. $\chi^2 = .44$; 1 df; $p > .05$; No.

5. $U = 4$; $p > .05$; No.

7. $H = 6.97$; $p < .05$; Yes.

Chapter 11

1. $b = \dfrac{[(35)(846.97)] - [(193)(144)]}{[(35)(1119)] - 33489}$

   $= .579$;

   $a = 4.114 - (.579)(5.228)$

   $= 1.087$;

   $Y' = 1.087 + .579X.$

3. $Y'' = 1.087 + .579(-1.877)$;

   $Y' = 0.$

5. $Y = 1.39 + (.713)(3.48)$

   $= 3.87.$

7. $Sy \cdot x \sqrt{\dfrac{\dfrac{1}{35}\left\{(35)(962) - 20736 - \dfrac{[(35)(846.97) - (183)(144)]^2}{(35)(1119) - 33489}\right\}}{35 - 2}}$

   $= 3.09.$

9. $2.58\, Sy \cdot y = 2.58(3.09) = 7.97$

   (since $Y' = 0$).

11. $Sy \cdot x(1.96) = (5.43)(1.96) = 10.642$

   $\therefore\ -6.772 > X > 14.512.$

Chapter 12

1. $r = 19.71/54 = .365.$

3. $r = \dfrac{846.97 - \dfrac{(183)(144)}{35}}{\sqrt{\left[1119 - \dfrac{33489}{35}\right]\left[962 - \dfrac{2037}{35}\right]}}$

   $= .245.$

5.

	X rank	Y rank	d	d^2
A	10	8	2	4
B	9	10	1	1
C	8	7	1	1
D	7	3	4	16
E	6	5	1	1
F	5	9	−4	16
G	4	4	0	0
H	3	6	−3	9
I	2	1	1	1
J	1	2	−1	1

7. $r = \dfrac{897 \dfrac{(80)(90)}{10}}{\sqrt{\left[880 - \dfrac{6400}{10}\right]\left[1050 - \dfrac{8100}{10}\right]}}$

$= .73.$

9. $\sum x = 1553 \qquad\qquad \sum Y = 1559$

$\sum x^2 = 166913 \qquad\qquad \sum Y^2 = 167657$

$(\sum x)^2 = 2411809 \qquad (\sum Y)^2 = 2430481$

$N = 15 \qquad\qquad \sum XY = 167140$

$r = \dfrac{167140 - \dfrac{(1553)(1559)}{15}}{\sqrt{\left[166913 - \dfrac{2411809}{15}\right]\left[167657 - \dfrac{243048}{15}\right]}}$

$= \dfrac{5731.6}{5870}$

$= .976.$

SUMMARY OF
ARITHMETICAL RULES

A. Signed numbers

1. *Addition:* To add numbers with different signs, add all the numbers with the same signs, find the difference of the sums, and assign the difference to the sign of the larger sum.

$$
\begin{array}{r}
-4 \\
-8 \\
-3 \\
\hline
-15
\end{array}
\qquad
\begin{array}{r}
+2 \\
+6 \\
+1 \\
\hline
+9
\end{array}
$$

Difference = 6 and the larger sum has a minus sign, so the total is −6.

2. *Multiplication:* The multiplication of numbers with the same sign results in a positive product; multiplying numbers with different signs results in a negative product.

$$
\begin{array}{r}
-2 \\
-3 \\
\hline
+6
\end{array}
\qquad
\begin{array}{r}
-2 \\
+3 \\
\hline
-6
\end{array}
$$

3. *Division:* A signed number divided by another with the same sign results in a positive number; a signed number divided by another with an unlike sign results in a negative number.

$$
-2\overline{)\,{-6}\,}^{\,3}
\qquad
-2\overline{)\,{6}\,}^{\,-3}
$$

B. Decimals

1. *Addition and subtraction:* To add or subtract numbers with

295

decimals, keep the decimal points in line. The decimal point in the result should be in line with the figures being added or subtracted.

$$
\begin{array}{r}
1.34 \\
+2.07 \\
\hline
3.41
\end{array}
\qquad
\begin{array}{r}
1.47049 \\
-0.00032 \\
\hline
1.47017
\end{array}
$$

2. *Multiplication:* The number of decimal places in the product of the two numbers multiplied together is equal to sum of the decimal places in the two numbers.

$$
\begin{array}{r}
1.20 \\
1.14 \\
\hline
480 \\
120 \\
120 \\
\hline
1.3680
\end{array}
$$

3. *Division:* The number of decimal places in the result of a number divided by another is equal to the number of decimal places in the dividend minus the number of places in the divisor.

$$
.2\overline{)\,.04}^{\,.2}
$$

C. Proportions

1. *Finding a proportion of a number:* To find the proportion of a total for a number, divide the number by the total.

Example: Find what proportion 27 is of 60.

$$
60\overline{)\,27}^{\,.4500}
$$

2. *Changing a proportion to a number:* To find the number for a proportion of a total, multiply the total by the proportion.

$$
.45 \times 75 = 33.75
$$

D. Reciprocals

1. The reciprocal of a number is the value obtained by dividing one by that number.

2. Multiplication of a number (A) by the reciprocal of another number (B) is equivalent to dividing A by B.

Example:

A ÷ B	A = 8	8
		.25000
B = 4	1/B = .2500	40000
		16
		2.00000

E. Operations

1. In any sequence of operations involving addition, subtraction, multiplication, and division, multiplication and division are performed first.

Example: $2 \times 4 + 3 - 1 + 8/2 = 8 + 3 - 1 + 4 = 14$

2. Terms inside parentheses, brackets, or square root signs are treated as single terms.

Example: $(3 + 1) - [(6 + 2) - (3 + 1) + \sqrt{3 + 6}]$
$= (4) - [(8) - (4) + \sqrt{9}]$
$= (4) - [(8) - (4) + 3]$
$= (4) - [7]$
$= -3$

INDEX

Page numbers in *italic* refer to figures and tables.

Abscissa, 8
α, 124
Analysis of variance. See *Variance, analysis of.*
Answers to exercises, 291-294
Arithmetic mean, 9, 13-15, 26, 27. See also *Mean.*
  algebraic properties of, 31-32
  of sample, 50
  of population, 50
Attenuation, 212
Average deviation, 45-46, 62

Bar diagram, 77
"Best fit" line, 193
β, 125
Bivariate data, 193

C^N_K, 72
Calculation, hand, coding scores for, 247-254
Causation, correlation and, 204-205
Central tendency, estimation of, 25-42
  measures of, comparison of, 38-40
χ^2, 155-167
  restrictions on use of, 166
χ^2 distribution, 162-163, *162*
  table of, 157-159, *268-269*
χ^2 test, application of, 235-237
Chi-square. See χ^2.
Class interval, 8, 247
Coefficient, reliability, 219
  validity, 220
Coefficient of correlation. See *Correlation, coefficient of.*
Coefficient of determination, 217
Combinations, 70-75
Conditional distribution, 197

Confidence intervals, 96-98
Contingency table, four-fold, 163-164
Continuity, Yates' correction for, 164-166
Correlated scores, 122
Correlation, 203-226
  and causation, 204-205
  coefficient of, 205-208. See also *Pearson r.*
    calculation of, 252-254
    critical values of, *276*
    product moment, 206
    size of, 212-213
  negative, 203
  positive, 203
  rank difference, 221
  Spearman's rank order, 221-223
  zero, 204
Covariance, 208
Curve, normal. See *Normal curve.*

Data, bivariate, 193
Degree of relationship, 203
Degrees of freedom, 101-103, 118, 123, 142, 146-149, 157, 161
Determination, coefficient of, 217
Deviation, average, 45-46, 62
  standard. See *Standard deviation.*
df, 101, 119, 123, 146, 157, 161
Differences between means, sampling distribution of, 112-114
  standard error of, 114-116
Differences between two groups, 107-134
Dispersion. See *Variance.*
Distribution, 9
  bimodal, 35, *36*
  χ^2, 162-163, *162*
    table of, 157-159, *268-269*
  conditional, 197
  F, table of, 149, *264-267*
  normal, 19, 77
    standard, areas of, *262*

299

Distribution (*Continued*)
  sampling, 91-93
    of difference between means, 112-114
  skewed, 35-37, *37*
  t. See *t* distribution.
  unimodal, 35, *36*
Distribution-free methods, 173-187

Error of estimate, 197
Expected frequency, 160

F and *t*, relationship of, 151
F distribution, table of, 149, *264-267*
Factorial, 71, *72*
Factorial designs, 152
Fiftieth percentile, 35
Four-fold contingency table, 163-164
F-ratio, 142-151
  interpretation of, 147-149
Frequency, expected, 160
Frequency polygon, 8

Geometric mean, 207
Gossett, W. S., 100
Graphical methods, 8

H, values of, 274, *275*
Histogram, 8, 77
Homoscedasticity, 207

Inference, probability and, 68-70
  statistical, 15-16
Interval, class, 8, 247
  confidence, 96-98

Kruskal-Wallis *H* test, 179-182
  correction for ties with, 181
Kruskal-Wallis ranked one-way analysis
  of variance, application of, 238-239

Line, "best fit," 193
Luck, runs of, determination of, 68

Mann-Whitney *U* test, 177-179
  application of, 237-238

Mean (s), arithmetic. See *Arithmetic
  mean.*
  differences between, sampling distribu-
    tion of, 112-114
    standard error of, 114-116
  geometric, 207
  population, sample means as estimates
    of, 27-32
  sample, 27-32
  standard error of, 92
    calculation of, 93-96
Mean Square, 142
Mean square between groups, 142
Mean square within groups, 142
Measurement (s), and observations, 5-7
  reliability of, 218
  validity of, 220
Median, 32-35
Median test, 176-177
Mode, 35
μ, 50

Negative correlation, 203
Non-parametric methods, 173
  advantages and disadvantages of, 183
Normal curve, 9, 16-21, *17*, 75-85
  probability and, 67-87
  uses of, 19
Normal curve methods, sample size for,
  79
Normal curve models, precision estimate
  with, 89-105
Normal curve table, use of, 79
Normal distribution, 19, 77
  standard, areas of, *262*
Notation, statistical, 25-27

Observations, and measurements, 5-7
One-tailed test, 120
One-way analysis of variance, application
  of, 232-235
One-way classification problem, 156-157
Ordinate, 8

P, 68
P^N_K, 71
Parameter, population, 16
Pascal's triangle, 74, *74*
Pearson, Karl, 206
Pearson product-moment correlation, application of, 239-241
Pearson *r*. See also *Correlation, coefficient of.*
  calculation of, 211
  computing formula for, 211

Pearson *r* (*Continued*)
  definitional formula for, 207
  inferences regarding, 213-216
  interpretation of, 217-220
  relation to regression line, 209-211
  significance of, 217
  standard error of, 215
  table of significant values of, 216, 270, *271*
Percentile, fiftieth, 35
Permutations, 70-75
Polygon, frequency, 8
Population (s), 7-9
Population mean, sample means as estimates of, 27-32
Population parameter (s), 16
  formulas for, 49-52
  sample-based estimates for, 49
Population statistics, formulas for, 49-52
Positive correlation, 203
Power curves, 129, *130*
Power of test, 125-131
Prediction, 189-190
Probability, 21-22
  and inference, 68-70
  and normal curve, 67-87
  rules of, 69-70
  of Type I and Type II errors, 124-125
Product-moment correlation coefficient, 206
Proportions, 167-169
  corrections for continuity in, 169
Psychology, experimental, statistical applications to, 227-243

Quartile, 62

Random numbers, table of, 256, *257-261*
Random sampling, with replacement, 11
  without replacement, 12
Range, 63
  semi-interquartile, 62
Rank difference correlation, 221
Rank-correlation coefficient, absolute values of, *277*
Ranking methods, 177-182
Raw score, 26
Reciprocals, table of, 288, *289-290*
Regression, 189-201
  linear, 190-192
  linearity of, 212
Regression line, relation of Pearson *r* to, 209-211
Relationship, degree of, 203

Reliability, split-half, 219
Reliability coefficient, 219
rho, 221

s, 54
s^2, 49
$s_{x \cdot y}$, 197
Sample (s), 9-10
  random selection of, 10-13
  size of, 29
Sample means, 27-32
Sample size, and t distribution, 119
Sampling, random, with replacement, 11
  without replacement, 12
Sampling distributions (s), 91-93
  of differences between means, 112-114
Scatter diagram, 192-196, *205*
Score (s), coding of, 249-250
  raw, 26
Semi-interquartile range, 62
σ, 54
σ^2, 46
σ_x, 92
$\sigma_{x_1 - x_2}$, 114
Σ, 26
Sign test, 175-176
Slope constant, 196
Spearman rank difference correlation, 242-243
Spearman's rank order correlation, 221-223
Spearman-Brown prophecy formula, 219
Split-half reliability, 219
Squares and square roots, table of, 278, *279-287*
Standard error, 93
Standard error of differences between means, 114-116
Standard error of estimate, 197
Standard error of mean, 92
  calculation of, 93-96
Standard error of Pearson *r*, 215
Standard error of sample mean, 95
Standard deviation, 16, 53-56, 62
  estimate of, 93
Standard scores, 56-61
  calculation of, *57, 59*
  transformations of, 58
  use of, 61
Statistical inference, 15-16
Statistical notation, 25-27
Statistical tables, 256-290
Statistics, fundamental concepts of, 5-24
  in behavioral sciences, 2
  in everyday life, 1-2

Statistics (*Continued*)
  methods of teaching, 2-3
Student's t distribution. See t *distribution.*
Sum of squares, 46-47
  between groups, 139
  source of, 141
  total, components of, 138

t and F, relationship of, 151
t distribution, 99-103
  sample size and, 119
  significance criteria of, 119
  table of, *263*
Tendency, central. See *Central tendency.*
Test, Kruskal-Wallis H, 179-182
  correction for ties with, 181
  Mann-Whitney U, 177-179
  median, 176-177
  power of, 125-131
  sign, 175-176
Tests of hypotheses, 120
Total sum of squares, components of, 138
Total variance, 137-142
t-ratio, unequal sample in, 119
t-ratio for independent groups, 116-118
t-test for correlated means, application of, 231-232
t-test for independent groups, application of, 228-230
t-test for non-independent groups, 121-123
Two-tailed test, 120
Two-way classification problem, 159-161
Type I and Type II errors, 123-125

U, values of, 272, *273*

Validity coefficient, 220
Variability, estimation of, 43-66
  index of, 16
  measure of, 44
Variance, 46
  analysis of, 135-154
    calculation of, 143-147
      errors in, 144-145
    complex, 151-152
    one-way, application of, 232-235
  calculation of, 251
  population, 46, 50
    estimate of for t-ratio, 117
  sample, 47, 49, 50
    calculation of, 52-53
  total, 137-142

X, 26

Y intercept, 196
Yates' correction for continuity, 164-166

Zero correlation, 204
z-scores, 56
Z-scores, 58